No. 624
$8.95

How To Solve Solid-State Circuit Troubles

By Wayne Lemons

FIRST EDITION

FIRST PRINTING—OCTOBER 1972

Printed in the United States
of America

Hardbound Edition: International Standard Book No. 0-8306-2624-7

Paperbound Edition: International Standard Book No. 0-8306-1624-1

Library of Congress Card Number: 72-87453

PREFACE

The purpose of this book is to present a wide variety of representative solid-state circuits with a "nuts and bolts" approach to troubleshooting them. To help in troubleshooting there is a description for each circuit that tells how it works and what can be expected of it. This is followed with information which provides a logical, step-by-step procedure for checking the circuit and pinpointing defective components.

Of course, in a book of this size, it is not possible to include this much data on every circuit variation, but I think you will find representative circuits in this book which relate to more than 90 percent of the circuits found in radios, television sets, tape recorders, record players, and other home entertainment units.

To aid you in finding any particular circuit, they have been grouped into individual sections such as RF amplifiers, IF amplifiers, oscillators, audio circuits, etc. No attempt was made to avoid repetition in troubleshooting procedures, so that when you look up a circuit or a group of similar circuits, all the information for troubleshooting that circuit will be close by.

At the beginning of each section is a general observation which applies for the most part to all circuits in the group. In some cases these observations are repeated in different words when talking about a particular circuit, especially when the information is of particular importance.

I sincerely hope and fully believe that you will find this book very helpful if you regularly or occasionally troubleshoot solid-state circuits. The color photograph on the cover has been provided by courtesy of Radio-Electronics Magazine.

Wayne Lemons

CONTENTS

GENERAL SERVICING PROCEDURES

Know how the circuit should work...if it isn't working right, find out why...pinpoint the bad part(s)...fix it. That's the overall troubleshooting method every good technician follows. Even with unfamiliar solid-state circuits, you can do the job easier, and faster, and with greater confidence that the repair will be permanent, if you first understand what the circuit does and how it does it. That's why I start with a very general review of transistor theory.

Bipolar transistors are of two main types, germanium or silicon. And each of these types has two main divisions, PNP and NPN. Germanium transistors were once the only kind commercially available, and they are used in millions of radios, tape recorders, amplifiers, etc., still in operation. The germanium transistor has one major drawback; its leakage current increases rather drastically with heat increase. Just touching an operating germanium transistor causes current through it to increase, especially if a "hard" bias (low resistance) is not used. Because of leakage, the germanium transistor generally is more noisy than its silicon counterpart. Also, because of its serious thermal deficiency, a germanium transistor generally requires more circuit components, such as an emitter protective resistor, which necessitates a capacitor bypass. Of course, silicons also use emitter resistors in many circuit designs, but often for a different reason. Germanium types always require a base bleeder resistor in any complex circuit or any circuit where there are any critical factors, so that the effect of the collector to base leakage (ICBO) will be minimal. (See Fig. 1-1.) Making R1 a low value to reduce the effects of leakage means the value of R2 must be lowered to provide ample bias so the transistor will conduct. A lower R2 value means more current will be required from a DC power supply because of the lowered resistance across it.

By far the most popular type of germanium transistor is the PNP. A PNP transistor requires a negative collector voltage with respect to the emitter. The PNP also requires

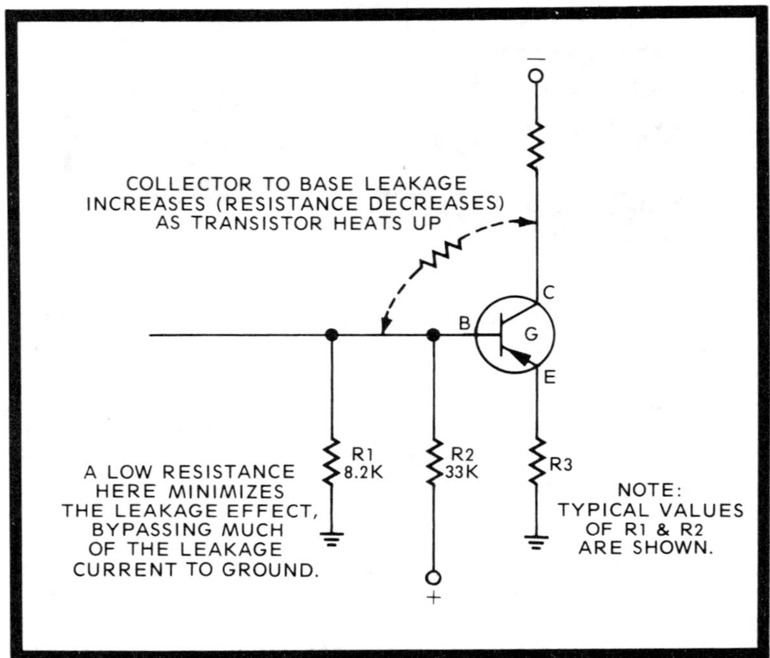

Fig. 1-1. Stabilizing a germanium PNP transistor.

about a 0.1 to 0.2 volt negative bias between base and emitter. It is because the base is biased negative and the collector has a negative supply that the leakage current between collector and base is such a factor. In effect, because of the amplification of the stage, any collector to base leakage is amplified by the transistor itself.

For several years, most bipolar transistors used in new equipment have been silicons. The silicon transistor also comes in PNPs and NPNs but the NPN is much more popular. Silicon transistors require more base bias than the germanium, usually from about 0.4 to 0.6 volt. But the silicon has one great advantage over germanium—its minimal leakage current. And because the leakage is small and stable, interchangeability is much higher with silicon than with germanium types, and circuits can be simplified.

The silicon type, because it is thermally stable, also makes an ideal transistor for use in direct-coupled circuits.

Silicon transistors also generally have a much wider frequency response range due both to lowered leakage and lowered internal capacity.

Throughout this book, I recommend that voltages be measured during troubleshooting, not to ground but with respect to the emitter. Fig. 1-2 shows why. The same NPN silicon transistor circuit is shown in all drawings of Fig. 1-2. Note, though, that in Fig. 1-2A, where the voltages are shown measured to ground, there is a considerable difference in the **apparent** voltages on the transistor. Obviously, after looking at the circuits a bit, you see there is no difference in the circuit operation and the apparent DC difference results because circuit (a) uses a positive voltage on the collector circuit with respect to ground while circuit (b) uses a negative voltage on the emitter with respect to ground.

A careful look at Fig. 1-2 (a) and (b) shows that the bias on both stages is the same. In (a) there is +1.4 volts on the base and 0.9 volt on the emitter, meaning the base is 0.5 volt more positive than the emitter, in other words, a base bias of 0.5 volt. In Fig. 1-2(b), the base voltage to ground is —7.6 volts and the emitter is —8.1 volts, meaning again that the base is 0.5 volt more positive (less negative, which is the same thing) than the emitter.

Fig. 1-2 (c) and (d) shows that if you measure in either of the circuits from base to emitter, you will get a 0.5 volt base bias reading. The collector-to-emitter voltage reads the same, 4.1 volts.

Reading the voltage drop across the emitter resistor, you obtain the same 0.9 volts in both circuits, but note carefully that in Fig. 1-2(c) measuring across the emitter resistor is the same as measuring from emitter to ground, while in Fig. 1-2(d), measuring across the emitter resistor is the same as measuring from the emitter to the negative supply line.

How transistor internal resistance changes as bias changes, and therefore the voltage drop across it also changes, is illustrated in Fig. 1-3.

TESTING BY COMPARISON

Especially in audio circuits it is often practical to check by comparison. If, for example, you are working on a stereo set, there will be two nearly identical amplifiers. If you have trouble in one side, for instance, the left side, then check DC voltage readings with those obtained for the right side amplifier, and the discrepancy will quickly show. Or for a non-DC trouble, that is, perhaps an open electrolytic bypass, use an oscilloscope to follow the signal and see where the left and right amplifier signals differ. It's at this point that trouble is indicated in the defective amplifier.

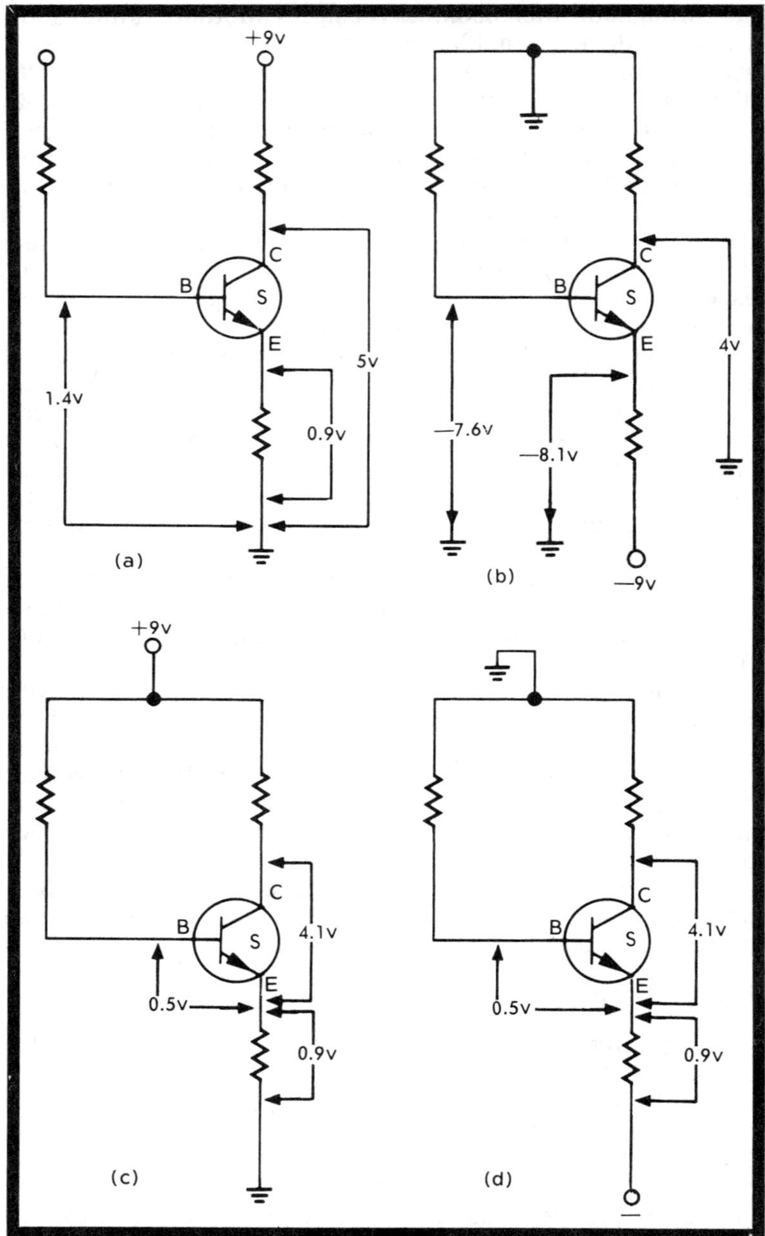

Fig. 1-2. Comparative voltage measurement methods (NPN silicon transistor).

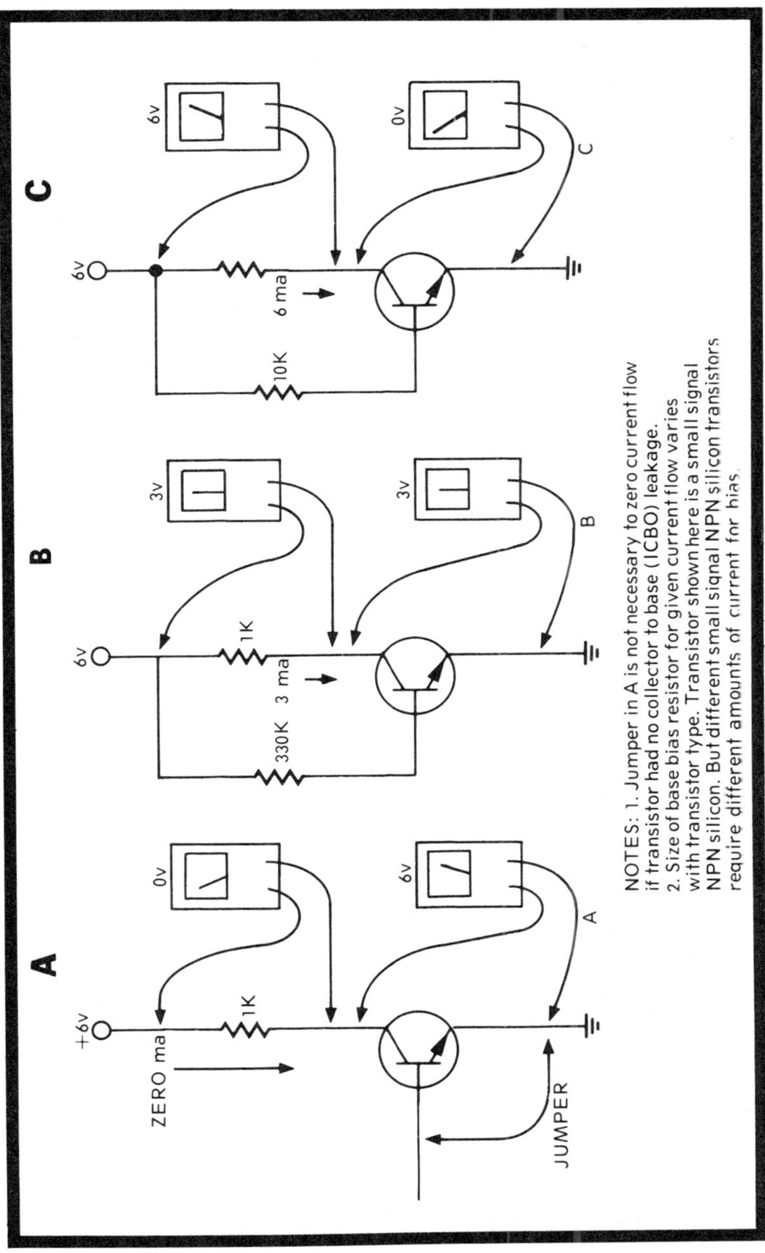

Fig. 1-3. Change in transistor resistance and voltage drop as bias changes.

But even if the amplifier is not stereo, some circuits, such as the one shown in Fig. 1-4 may be checked for certain defects by comparison. For example, distortion in this circuit, or lowered volume, might be caused by a defective transistor, especially one with excessive ICBO leakage. If, for instance, the base-to-emitter voltage reads 2 volts on Q2 and the correct 0.7 volt on the base of Q3, the trouble could be a leaky Q2 or it could be a leaky C2 but obviously in either case there is trouble because the circuit readings should be practically identical. In a push-pull circuit of this sort that is giving trouble, check the temperature by feeling each transistor—if one seems to be overheating, it is likely the one that is giving trouble or else there is trouble in its external circuit.

When emitter voltages can be measured, such as in Fig. 1-4, these measurements too can show quickly whether one transistor is drawing more current than the other.

VOLTMETERS

Bipolar transistors, in most circuits, have fairly low impedance and are not so affected by circuit measurements, especially in low frequency circuits, as might be expected from either vacuum tubes or field-effect transistors.

A 20,000 ohm-per-volt meter (VOM) is a good all-purpose test instrument so long as you don't use too low a voltage range. Unfortunately, the voltages on transistors are generally small, and switching to, say, a 3-volt range on a 20,000 ohm-per-volt meter is like putting a 60,000 ohm shunt across the circuit you are measuring. If you happen to be measuring across a 1K emitter resistor, the 60K shunt means little. But in the base circuit of a silicon transistor which has a 1-megohm resistor to supply bias, a 60K shunt could completely upset the performance of the transistor.

If there is doubt, then, when using a 20K opv meter, use the highest voltage range that provides a usable reading.

A better test instrument than the VOM is a battery-operated field effect transistor (FET) meter which normally has about 10 megohms of loading for any voltage range. With such a meter, you can switch to a 1-volt range to read bias voltages and know that the meter will have virtually no effect on the DC bias reading. Usually these meters also have a resistor isolation right at the tip of the probe lead, which tends to reduce the loading even in RF circuit such as oscillators, video amplifiers, etc.

The use of a VTVM is also possible, though in many cases not so practical as the FET meter simply because the VTVM

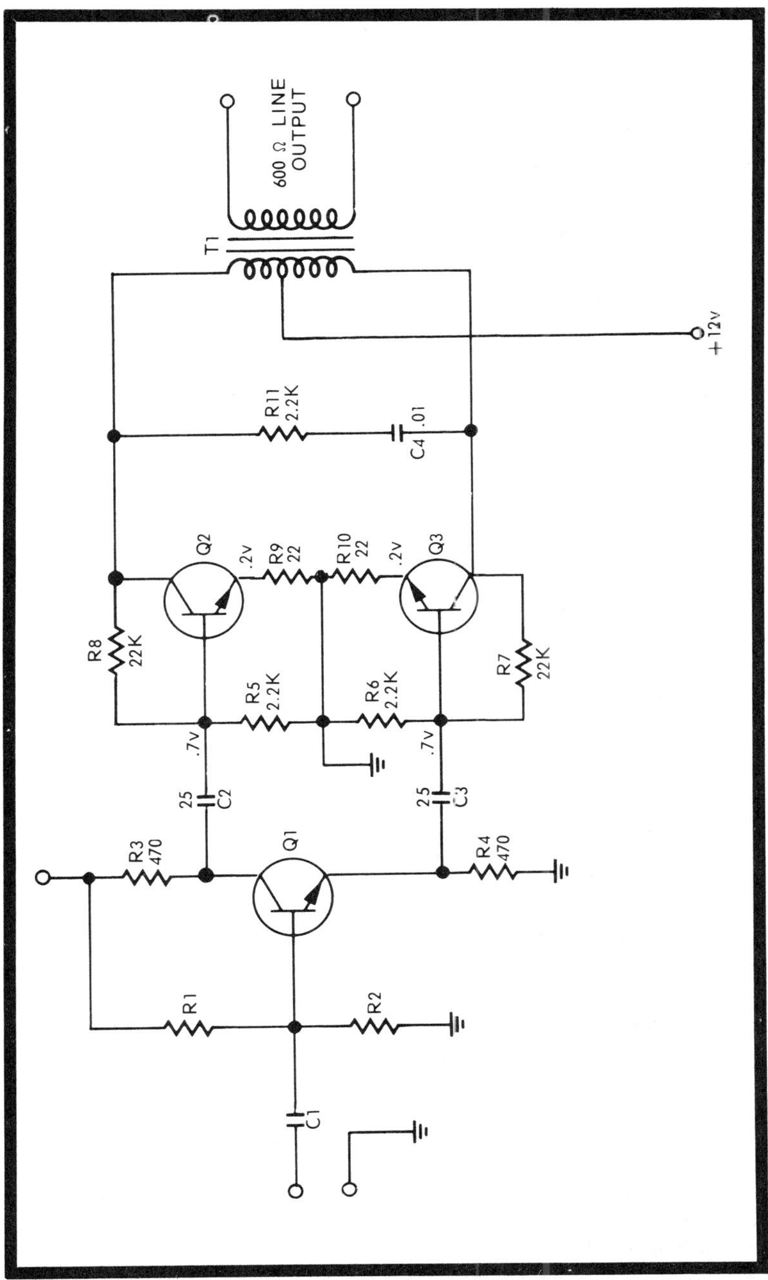

Fig. 1-4. Line amplifier output circuit using transistor phase splitter.

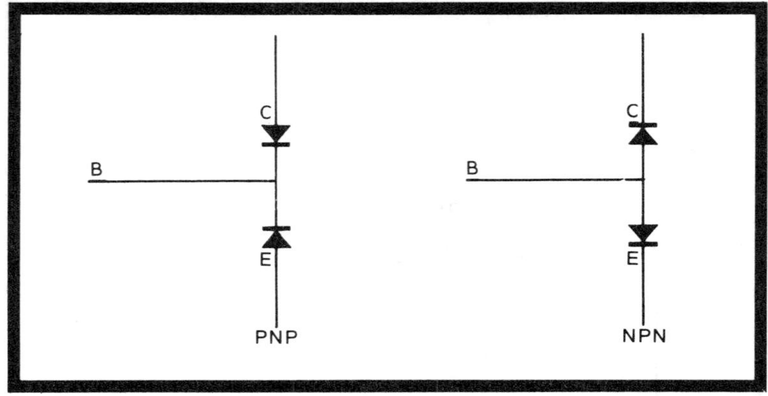

Fig. 1-5. What an ohmmeter "thinks" is inside a transistor.

usually must be connected to the power line to derive its power. Otherwise, the VTVM, with its high input impedance is extremely useful for testing transistor circuits.

OHMMETERS

An ohmmeter is a useful instrument even for in-circuit checking (at least a rough check) of transistors. To an ohmmeter, a transistor seems to be two diodes back-to-back or face-to-face (Fig. 1-5). When you connect the ohmmeter leads across base to emitter, for example, in one direction the resistance reading will be low because the ohmmeter battery has forward-biased the "diode." When the ohmmeter leads are reversed across this "diode," it is reverse-biased and the reading should be a high resistance. If there is no difference in the readings when the ohmmeter leads are reversed then the transistor must be at fault.

Most VOMs, are built so that, although the red lead goes to + when used in the voltmeter function, the red lead usually goes to the negative side of the ohmmeter battery or power source when switched to ohms. If this is true of your VOM when you measure a PNP transistor, place the red lead on the base and the black lead on the emitter. Since this places a negative voltage on the base with respect to the emitter, the base-emitter diode conducts and the ohmmeter should read less than 500 ohms. Reversing the leads, with the black lead on the base and the red on the emitter, you'll now have a positive voltage on the base with respect to the emitter and the diode is reverse-biased, and there should be a high resistance of at least 100K in germaniums and 1 megohm or more in silicons.

The base-collector diode can be checked in the same manner. The collector to emitter should read a quite high resistance in both directions of the ohmmeter leads, though not necessarily the same amount of resistance.

The foregoing of course suggests that with just an ohmmeter you can determine whether an unknown transistor (out of circuit) is an NPN or PNP type.

When checking a transistor in the circuit the method is just the same except that you must recognize that shunt resistances in the circuit make the test somewhat less definitive.

Fig. 1-6 shows that there is 3.3K resistance normally in the circuit (not counting other possible shunt resistance through the power supply) and so when taking an ohmmeter reading, the high reading indicates the external shunt resistance in the circuit, the low reading represents the forward-biased resistance of the base-emitter junction inside the transistor.

Shunt resistances usually are not a big problem in in-circuit testing except where the external resistance is low as compared to the diode resistance, then the ohmmeter readings

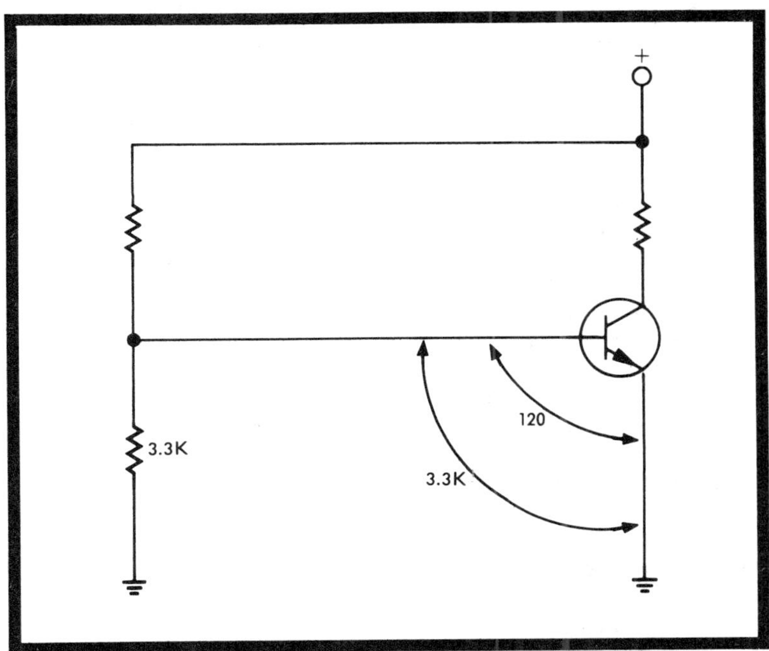

Fig. 1-6. Why reversing ohmmeter leads when checking a transistor in-circuit produces differing readings.

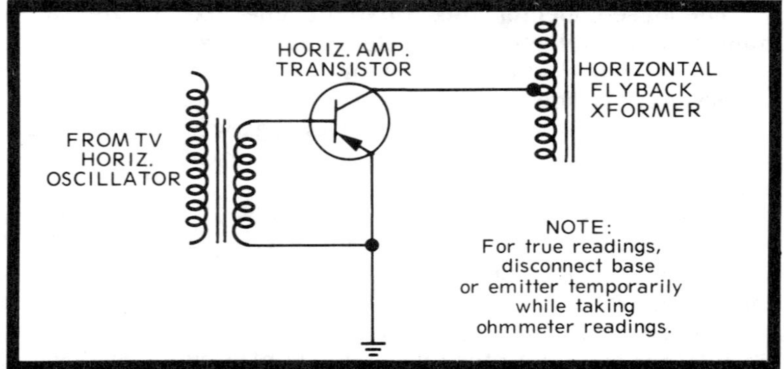

Fig. 1-7. Inconclusive testing by ohmmeter because of shunt resistances.

may not be interpretable or at least can be misleading. Fig. 1-7 shows a type of circuit that has low external resistance between base and emitter. But there are only a few circuits like this.

NOTE: When testing in-circuit between collector and emitter you may get a rather marked high-low reading because in one direction the collector may supply enough bias to the base through the bias networks to "turn on" the transistor.

SPECIAL OHMMETERS

There are now several ohmmeters available that use very low voltage in the ohmmeter circuit, so low in fact that the voltage applied will not supply enough bias to cause a transistor to conduct. This means that any reading of a resistor, coil, etc., is not affected by a diode or transistor in the circuit and so it is not necessary to reverse the leads for reading the resistance of components. Usually this kind of ohmmeter also has a switch to a higher ohmmeter voltage so that the ohmmeter test for transistors and diodes also can be made.

BEST WAYS TO CHECK TRANSISTORS

The ohmmeter method just described is useful, although not an absolute test (as few tests are). Probably the best way to test a transistor is to see how it performs in its own circuit. DC voltage readings, as indicated throughout this book, will tell you probably 90 percent of the time whether or not the transistor is bad. The single most important first test is to determine the presence or absence of transistor current flow.

The best way to make this test is to measure the voltage across the emitter resistor, and if there is no emitter resistor then across a collector resistor—there will nearly always be one or the other. You can determine current by Ohm's law, I equals E divided by R. If there is a 1-volt drop across a 1K resistor then the current flow through the resistor is 1 ma, meaning logically that if there is a 2-volt drop across a 1K resistor the current through it is 2 ma and if there is a 3 volt drop across a 500 ohm resistor, the current through the resistor is 6 ma.

Transistor testers may do a good job in many instances but out-of-circuit testers require that you remove the transistor from the circuit (a process that may ruin the transistor if you are not careful). Also, the in-circuit testers are difficult to connect and suffer from misleading indications due to shunt circuits, especially in direct-coupled circuits, or in circuits which use diodes besides transistors.

FIELD-EFFECT TRANSISTORS

Field-effect transistors (FETs) have many of the advantages of bipolar transistors and also of vacuum tubes; they work with low voltages like other transistors, but have high input impedances like tubes.

The simplest of the field effect transistor types is the junction (JFET) type. (Fig. 1-8.) A semiconductor bar with connections at either end is the "channel" for the FET. The resistance of this bar is generally from around 250 to 800 ohms. The bar alone cannot act as an amplifier since its resistance is fixed, but the amount of resistance in the channel can be varied and controlled by making a junction into the channel using the opposite type semiconductor material (P or N as the case may be). To explain this further, let's look at Fig. 1-9.

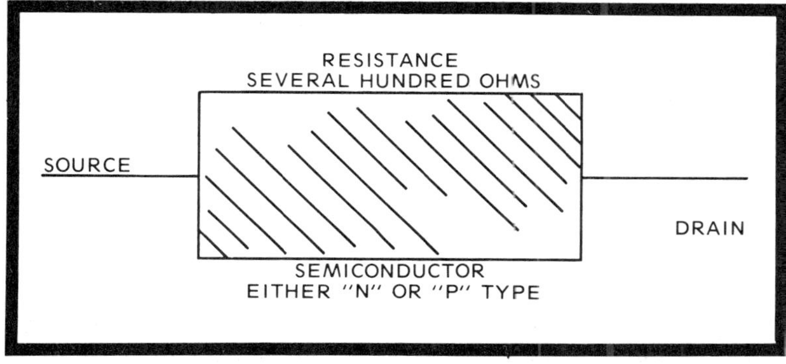

Fig. 1-8. Semiconductor bar with connections at either end.

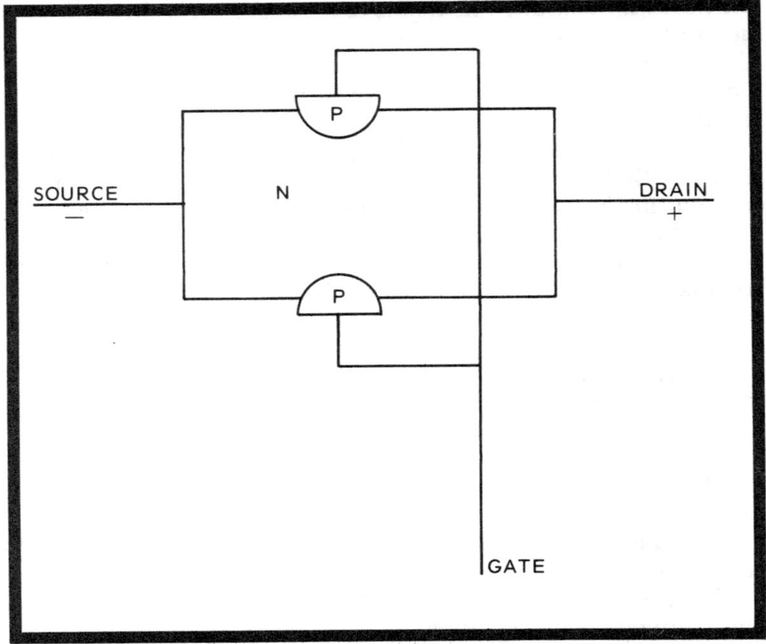

Fig. 1-9. P-gate junctioned into N channel.

This is an N-channel FET. Placing a voltage between the "source" and "drain" will produce a current flow through the channel resistance. But if we apply a negative voltage to the P "gate," this reverse-biases the PN diode between gate and channel so no current flows between them. However, the negative voltage also creates a negative "field" which repels the flow from source to drain, essentially reducing the path where electrons can travel and "squeezing" off the current flow. If the negative voltage is large enough, the current will be cut off (in FETs, this is called "pinch-off"). If the negative voltage is such that the current flow is about half of normal, then a signal voltage can be added to this negative bias. The signal excursions will add and subtract from the bias and thereby change the source-drain current in much the same way as grid modulation in a triode vacuum tube.

Note that this action is with a REVERSE-biased gate-channel, so the entire control is by voltage only and no current is required. This means that the input impedance of the circuit is very high, making it possible to amplify a voltage without reducing it in the input circuit.

Although we have discussed here the N-channel FET because presently it is most popular, the P-channel is identical except that the channel is P material and the gate is N material. Also, the gate voltage must be positive with respect to the source in the P-channel in order to reduce the current flow and keep the gate-channel diode reverse-biased.

Fig. 1-10 shows the schematic symbols for N-channel and P-channel FETs. The difference is the direction of the arrow on the gate terminal. In any semiconductor symbol the arrow always points toward the N material so when the arrow is pointing toward the channel it is an N-channel transistor, pointing away, it is a P-channel. Circuits for either N- or P-channel FETs are identical except the voltage polarities are reversed. **The drain is positive with respect to the source in an N-channel FET and negative in a P-channel FET.**

If a JFET is forward-biased accidentally, the current should not increase; but because current will flow in the gate-channel junction, the gain of the stage will decrease due to loading on the input signal. Excessive forward bias will destroy the transistor. Excessive reverse bias could also destroy the transistor because of "zenering," but current in the gate circuit would have to be high to do so, such as a direct connection to a power supply with no series resistor.

The JFET can be tested with an ohmmeter with normally excellent results. If you measure between source and drain, the reading should be from about 250 to 800 ohms unless the

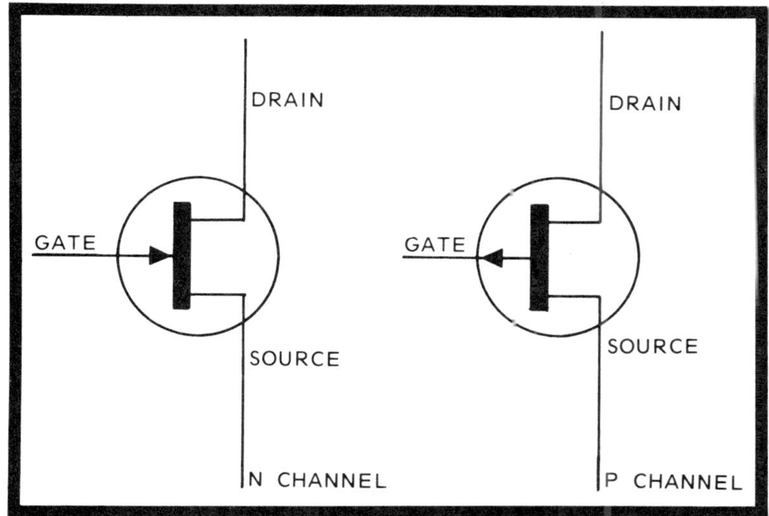

Fig. 1-10. Symbols for JFET.

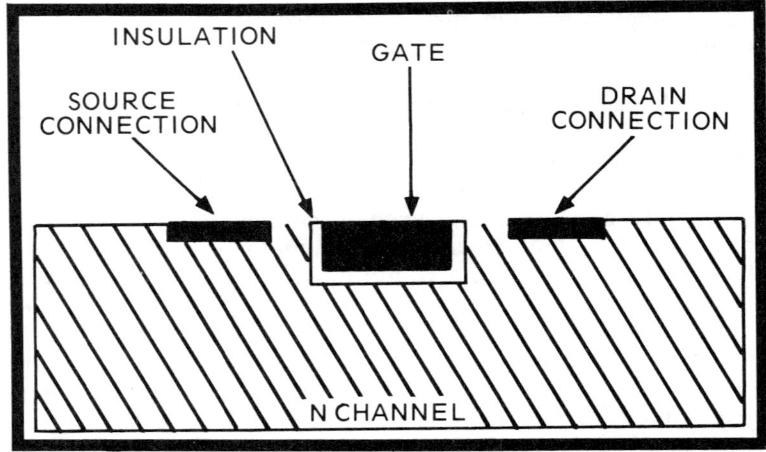

Fig. 1-11. Representation of a depletion type MOSFET.

gate circuit is floating and then the resistance may rise to 10K or more.

Measuring between the gate and channel should give a low resistance reading for one direction of hookup of the ohmmeter leads and a high resistance reading in the other hookup direction.

METAL OXIDE SEMICONDUCTOR FIELD EFFECT TRANSISTORS

The Metal Oxide Semiconductor Field Effect Transistor (MOSFET) differs from the junction FET type because the gate is actually insulated from the channel by a thin oxide insulation. (MOSFETs are also called IGFETs, for "insulated gate.") What this means is that the gate cannot draw current even though forward-biased. It also means that the ohmmeter no longer is useful for checking gate connections inside the transistor.

There are three types of MOSFET:
Type A—depletion
Type B—depletion-enhancement
Type C—enhancement

and these are described further below, first type A, then type C, and finally type B which is a hybrid. Keep in mind that a JFET is a type A depletion transistor.

Depletion Type MOSFET

The type A is called a depletion type transistor. This simply means that bias on the gate depletes the number of electrons (or holes) that can flow and so there is less current, or in other words, with zero bias the conduction between the source and drain is maximum.

Fig. 1-11 is a representation of a depletion type MOSFET. The N-channel has metallic connections at either end and maximum current flows with zero bias on the gate. As the gate is made more negative, the channel current is pinched off more and more until finally, when the gate is negative enough, there will be no current flow at all between drain and source. But even if the gate should go positive, the input impedance still remains high because no current can flow between the gate and channel due to the oxide insulation.

Fig. 1-12 shows the schematic symbols for N- and P-channel depletion type MOSFETs.

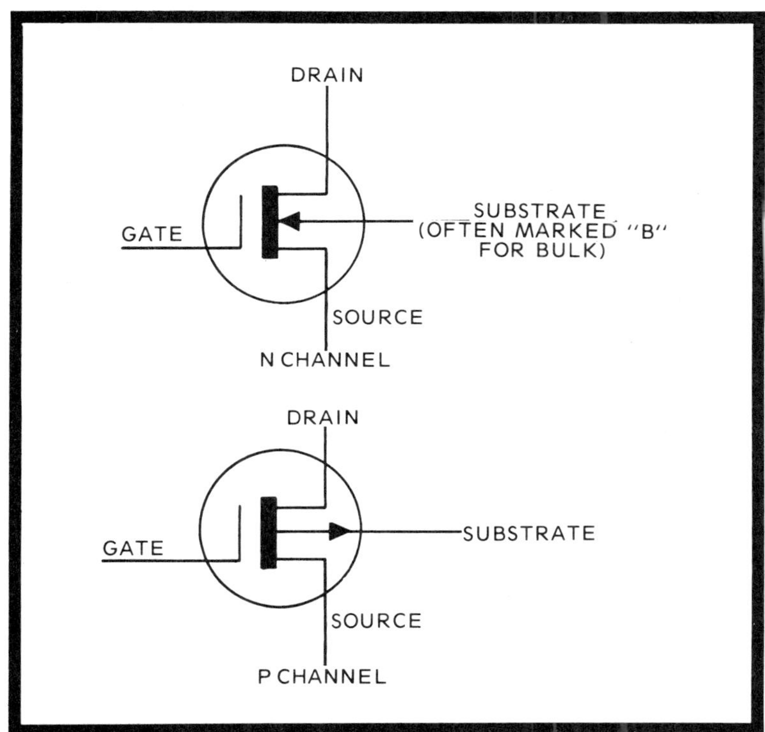

Fig. 1-12. Schematic symbols for depletion type MOSFETs.

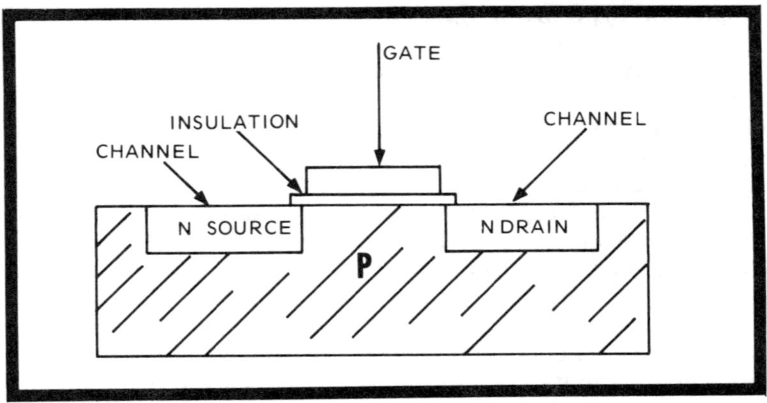

Fig. 1-13. Representation of an enhancement type MOSFET.

Enhancement Type MOSFET

A representation of a type C MOSFET is in Fig. 1-13. This is known as an enhancement type, that is, current flow between source and drain is zero if the bias is zero on the gate. To cause current to flow, the gate must be made positive. (Incidentally this is an N-channel transistor and the P section is called the "bulk" or substrate.) Keeping in mind that P material is basically holes (positive charges), we can see that with the P substrate between the two N channels, there can be no current flow; so the transistor is cut off until a plus voltage is applied to the gate. When this is done, the few electrons in the P material are pulled up into the region between the N channels and current can flow. The more voltage placed on the gate the more current flows until saturation is reached. Generally it takes around +1 volt to start conduction and around +4v to +5v to produce saturation.

Fig. 1-14 shows the schematic symbols for the enhancement type MOSFETs. Note that the symbol is broken up as shown in the representative drawing, in other words, **the source and drain are not connected until forced to be so by bias which pulls the current carriers into the spaces between them.**

Depletion-Enhancement Type MOSFET

The type B MOSFET has characteristics of both the enhancement and depletion transistors. It has some current flow at zero bias, is cut off with a negative bias on the gate (for N-channel types), and current flow increases with a positive voltage on the base.

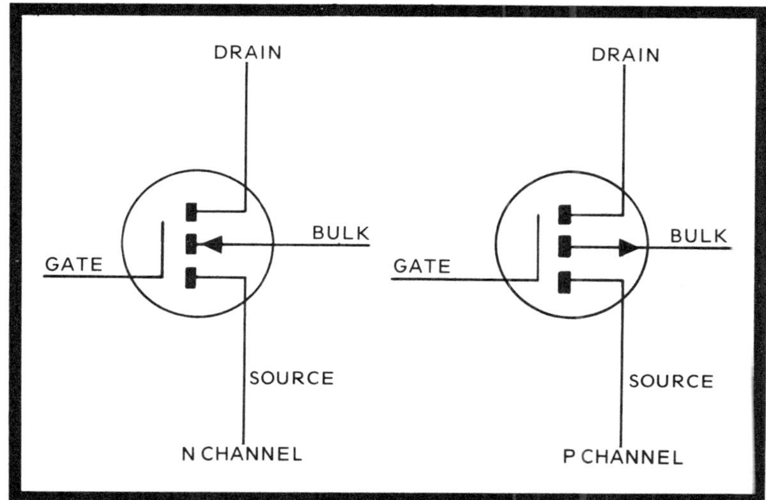

Fig. 1-16. Schematic symbol for P channel depletion-enhancement (IG) MOSFET.

Fig. 1-15 is a representation of this type. The source and drain bars are heavily-doped N type material. Between the two is another piece of N material that is not so heavily doped. Current can flow from source to drain through the lightly doped N material, even without gate bias. If negative gate bias is applied, the electrons in the N material are depleted and current stops; conversely, if the gate is made positive, the electrons from the substrate are pulled into the channel and the current flow from source to drain increases.

As a general rule, about 1 to 2 volts negative bias will pinch off the drain-source current and about the same amount positive will produce saturation. The "median" point on the

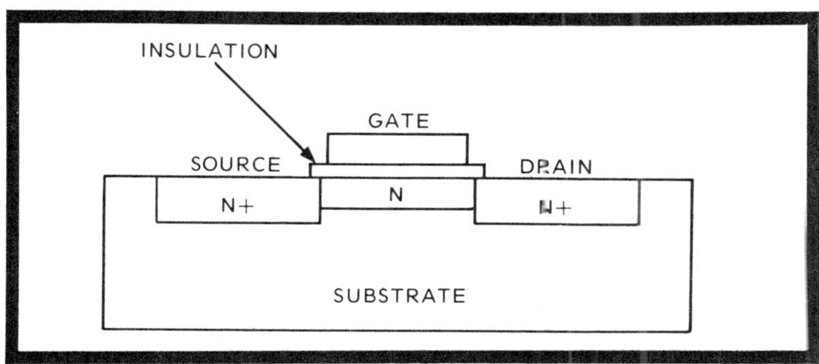

Fig. 1-15. Representation of a depletion-enhancement type MOSFET.

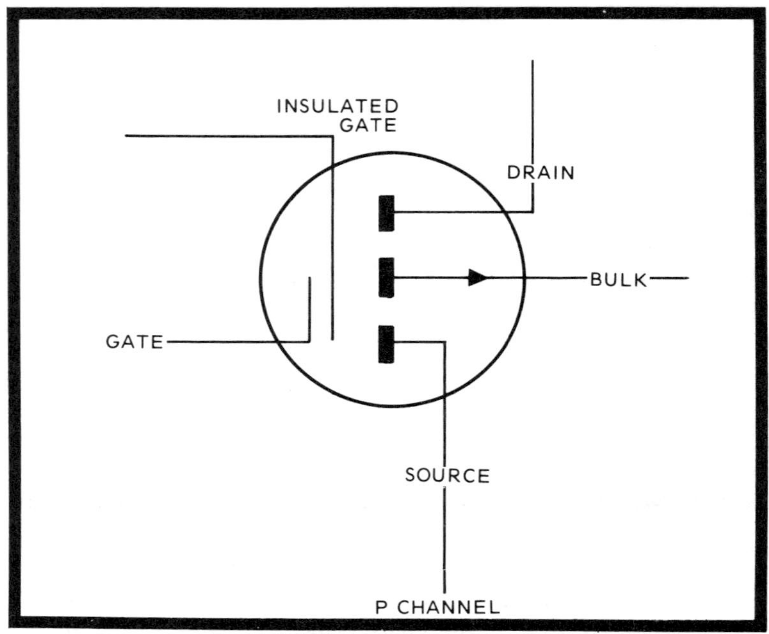

Fig. 1-4. Line amplifier output circuit using transistor phase splitter.

characteristic curve is usually with the gate a bit positive for N-channel transistors.

Dual-Gate MOSFET

The dual-gate MOSFET is now quite popular especially as an RF and IF amplifier. It is a type B depletion-enhancement type and is especially useful when the circuit is to be AGC-controlled since it has a wider and more linear response.

The dual-gate MOSFET is basically two type B MOSFETs in series, as shown in Figs. 1-17 and 1-18. Gate 1 is usually the signal gate since it is nearer the source potential. Gate 2 is usually the AGC gate. Both gates must be biased on before the transistor can saturate. If either gate receives enough negative bias, the transistor current will pinch off. In normal operation, the dual-gate MOSFET is generally operated with gate 2 a few volts positive and gate 1 nearer zero volts but often still a bit positive. Maximum gain may call for gate 2 to have as much as +5 or +6 volts while minimum gain may call for gate 2 voltage to be almost that far negative.

Note: The discussion above concerns for the most part N-channel MOSFETs because of their popularity. As with the

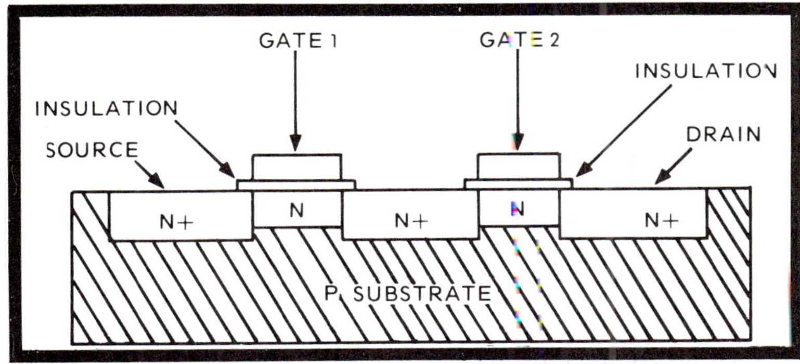

Fig. 1-17. Representation of dual-gate MOSFET.

JFETs, the only difference between the two types in circuit operation is that the supply polarity is reversed for the P channel type with the drain made negative with respect to the source, and the pinch off gate 2 voltage is positive rather than negative.

Testing the MOSFET

You can test a MOSFET best in the circuit where it is used. Measure the source resistor voltage to see whether

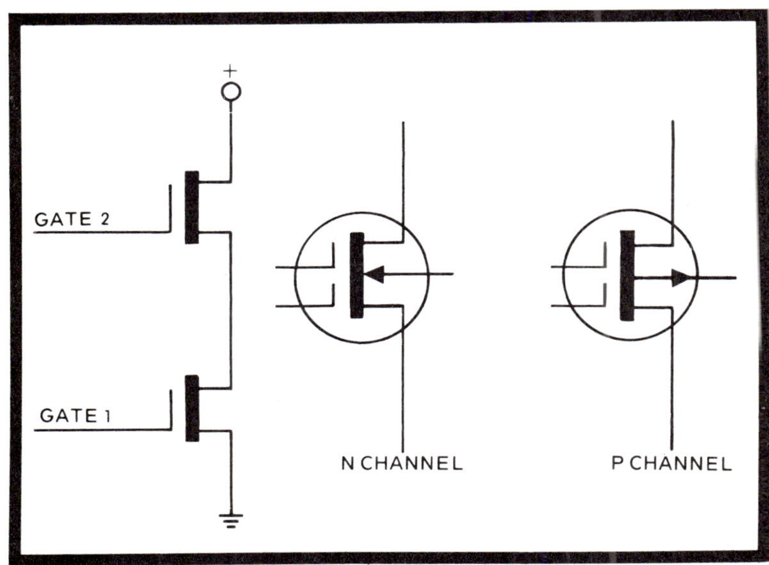

Fig. 1-18. Schematic symbols for dual-gate MOSFET.

current is flowing, or check the drop across a resistor in the drain circuit if no source resistance is used.

In depletion and depletion-enhancement types, an ohmmeter test of the transistor should produce a reading between the source and drain. There should never be any continuity reading between the gate(s) and any other transistor terminal in a MOSFET.

One of the problems with many MOSFETs is the possibility of damaging a transistor by breaking down the thin oxide insulation while making tests. Whenever the gate is floating there is danger of static electricity buildup which can puncture the insulation. Some MOSFETs have built-in zener diodes that short circuit any voltage buildup that exceeds about 10 volts. This feature has made MOSFETs much less delicate to test, and much less apt to be damaged during installation.

RADIO-FREQUENCY AMPLIFIERS

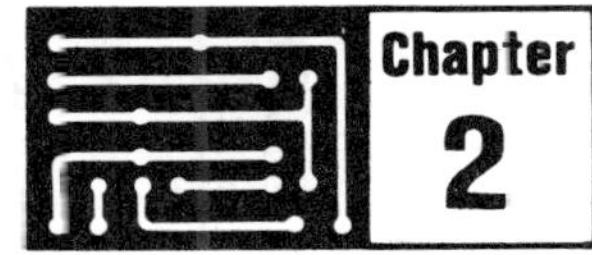

At high frequencies, the RF amplifier is needed generally to provide an impedance match between the low impedance of the antenna and the high impedance of the first tuned circuit. This transformation of impedance not only provides a match for good low-noise transfer of the signal, but also provides considerable voltage gain. The RF amplifier also provides isolation between the antenna and the local oscillator circuit, thus minimizing the reradiation of the local oscillator signal that can create interference in other nearby radios.

At low RF frequencies the most important function of the RF amplifier is to prevent spurious responses such as the image frequency response in superheterodyne radios. Since auto radios move into and out of strong RF signal areas, they are more apt to be troubled with spurious response, so nearly every auto radio has an RF amplifier stage.

There are a number of different RF amplifier circuits but the basic types are discussed here. Various other types may vary slightly in layout or performance, but the differences in test procedures will be minor.

AM RF AMPLIFIER (Common-Emitter)

Shown in Fig. 2-1 is a basic common-emitter circuit which uses a germanium PNP transistor; however, it would work almost identically with a silicon transistor, either NPN or PNP.

The signal is selected by L1 and the secondary coil on L1, a few turns of wire, matches the low impedance input of the RF amplifier transistor. Bias for the transistor is provided by R3 from the negative voltage source and also by the AGC circuit. The AGC circuit provides a more positive voltage as the signal input rises and this in turn reduces the current through the transistor. R2, the emitter resistor, is mainly a protective resistor to prevent transistor "runaway" as it warms up. The emitter bypass, C6, prevents signal degeneration caused by R2. If C6 opened, the gain of the RF stage would drop drastically.

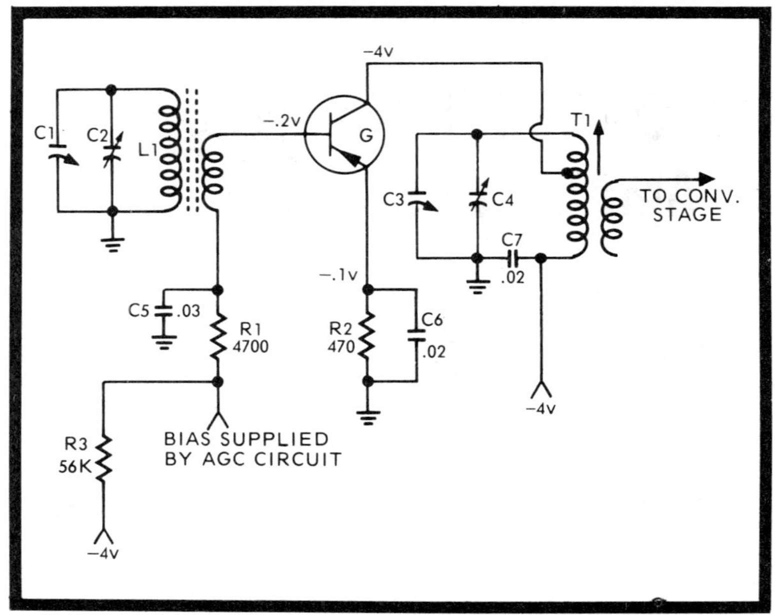

Fig. 2-1. AM RF amplifier (common-emitter) schematic.

A second tuned circuit is in the collector circuit. The collector is not connected to the "hottest" side of T1 but is tapped down. The reason for this is to reduce the gain of the stage, which at first might seem to be defeating the purpose, but gain here is traded for needed isolation and selectivity. Tapping down the collector improves the selectivity of the T1 circuit and also reduces the gain so neutralization of the circuit is not required. Therefore, the circuit is stable and relatively free of any tendency to develop spurious signals on its own. Good impedance matching is required in the input circuit to provide a low noise signal but in the output the matching does not have to be too close so far as signal-to-noise ratio is concerned.

Troubleshooting the Circuit

In an AM RF amplifier circuit it is generally quite easy to find out whether the circuit has gain. This is done by simply clipping a short wire, or touching a screwdriver to the collector. If doing this significantly increases the volume output of the radio it is a good indication that the RF amplifier is inoperative. Once this has been determined, check the bias voltages and the collector voltage. If the voltage drop is near zero across the emitter resistor, either the transistor or the bias circuit is defective. Always measure the bias between the base and emitter. For a PNP germanium transistor the voltage should be around—0.1 volt, while for an NPN silicon transistor the bias voltage will be around +0.5 volt.

If voltages are near normal, then check by shunting a known good capacitor across C5, C6, and C7 one at a time and see if the signal output increases.

Check to make sure that each of the tuned circuits will actually "tune." This is done by seeing whether or not the trimmer capacitors will bring the signal level to a peak when the radio is tuned to a station near the high frequency end of the dial. If the trimmers cannot be made to go through a peak then either something is wrong with the tuned circuits or the local oscillator circuit of the radio is considerably out of tune.

AM RF AMPLIFIER (Common-Base)

The AM RF amplifier in Fig. 2-2 uses a common-base circuit, which simply means that the input is to the emitter rather than to the base and the base is bypassed to ground. This circuit has a lower input impedance and a higher output impedance than the common-emitter circuit. It is often used

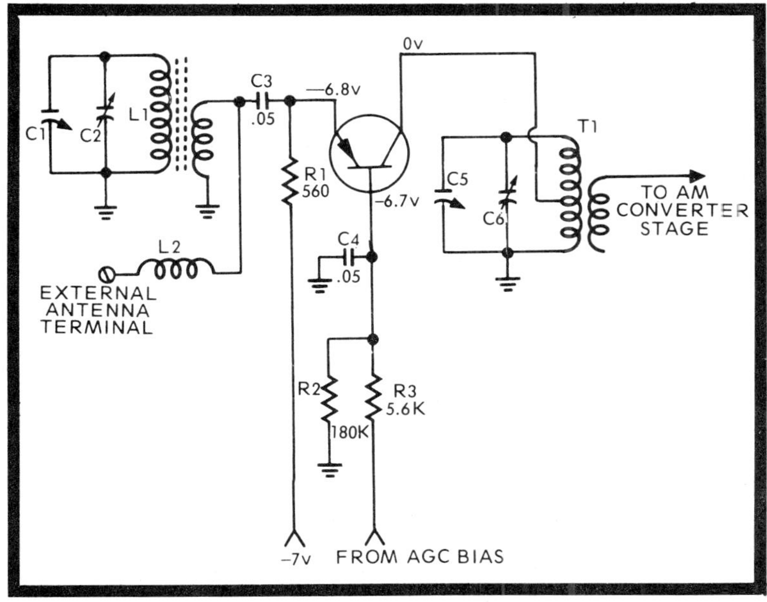

Fig. 2-2. AM RF amplifier (common-base) schematic.

for high frequency amplifiers and is discussed in more depth when these circuits are considered.

The input is matched, as in the previous circuit, by using a few turns of wire coupled to the tuned L1 circuit. The unusual part of this circuit is that the external antenna input is connected directly to the emitter coil (secondary of L1). (L2 is simply an isolation coil which prevents the external antenna from seriously upsetting the input match.)

Troubleshooting the Circuit

As with the previous circuit, gain of the stage can be checked by connecting a short external antenna to the collector of the transistor. If the radio volume increases and signal-to-noise ratio improves, the problem is in the RF stage. Make the voltage checks as described in the preceding discussion for Fig. 2-1. Check by shunt substitution C3, C4. Check for tuning as described for Fig. 2-1.

AM RF AMPLIFIER FOR AUTO RADIO

Nearly all automobile radios use "slug" tuning, that is, the tuning is changed by moving a ferrite slug in and out of the tuned circuit coil, and a fixed or adjustable capacitor establishes the band limits for the RF amplifier circuit only. Slug tuning is particularly adaptable to transistor circuits.

In the circuit shown in Fig. 2-3, the rod antenna of the auto radio is coupled directly to the top side of a tuned circuit. C1, is the trimmer, the "antenna compensator" which can be varied to compensate for the capacity of the antenna itself and the antenna lead-in cable. The secondary of L2 is made of a few turns of wire so as to provide a match to the input circuit of the transistor.

The collector circuit uses a "pi" network match, which is a match accomplished by capacities in the circuit. The collector is tied to the "hot" side of the circuit (L3) while the base circuit of the following stage is tapped off on the "cold" side of the coil, but this cold side still has signal at low impedance because capacitors C7 and C8 are part of the L3 resonant circuit.

L1 is not part of the tuned input circuit. This is a small coil usually about ¼ inch diameter and has about 20 turns of wire. Its purpose is to prevent or minimize strong high frequency signals, such as ignition pulses, from overloading the input stage and creating noise.

Troubleshooting the Circuit

As indicated for previous AM RF amplifier circuits, you can determine the operation of the RF amplifier circuit simply by touching the metal blade of a screwdriver to the collector terminal and noting whether stations can be tuned in at near-normal volume. If they can, and if they cannot with the screwdriver touching the antenna input terminal, then the problem is in the RF amplifier stage.

The most significant quick measurement for any transistor amplifier is probably across the emitter resistor (if used). If the voltage drop is correct here it is a good indication that the transistor and the bias circuits are working normally. If so, this result points to trouble in the signal circuits, either an open capacitor or coil, or that the circuit is drastically out of tune.

As with any tuned circuit, you should be able to tune the circuits to a peak output. If tuning either C1 or C5 does not change the amount of signal or changes it only slightly, then it is very likely that either a coil is defective or a tuning slug is broken or incorrectly positioned mechanically in the coil.

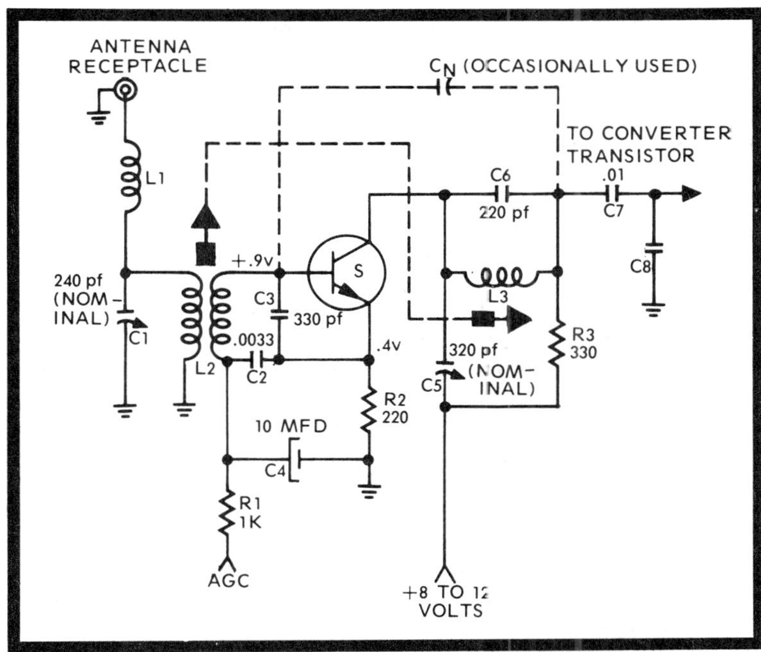

Fig. 2-3. AM RF amplifier for auto radio.

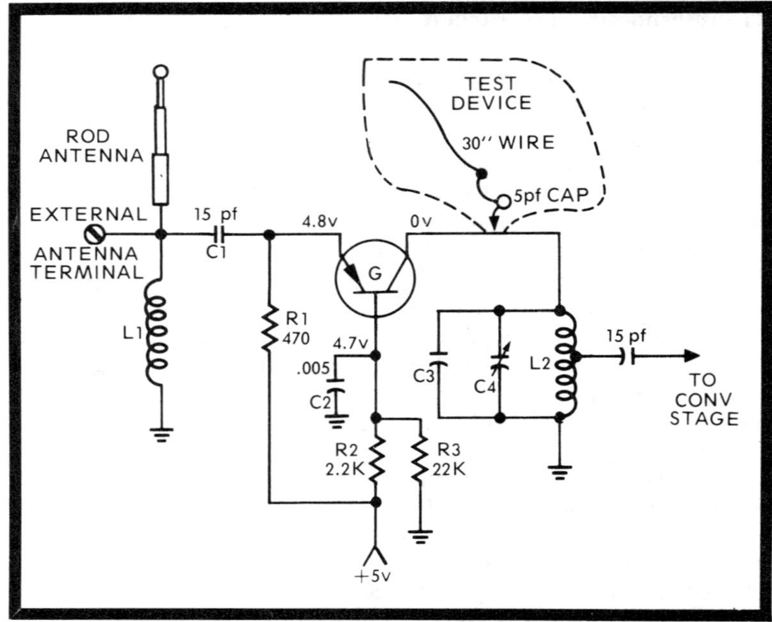

Fig. 2-4. FM RF amplifier using self-resonant broad-band input circuit (common-base).

Electrolytic bypass capacitors in any circuit should always be suspected. If C4 opens in this circuit the gain may be reduced, or (depending on the AGC circuit), there may be a "motorboating" effect in the output.

FM RF AMPLIFIER (Common-Base)

The most popular FM and high frequency RF amplifier is the common-base or grounded-base circuit. The grounded-base circuit is particularly suitable to high frequencies since it provides a low input impedance to match the rod antenna, a high output impedance to match the tuned circuit, and does not need neutralization to prevent feedback.

Coil L1 in Fig. 2-4 is a broadly resonant circuit for the FM band, in some cases, while in others it simply is a very high frequency (VHF) choke providing a low DC resistance to ground for the antenna circuit but acting as considerable reactance for the signal. The signal is coupled through C1 to the emitter. The base is grounded so far as signal is concerned by C2 but is not grounded so far as DC bias voltage is concerned.

Since this circuit uses a germanium PNP transistor, the base to emitter bias is approximately 0.1 volt negative. The designer here has chosen to place the "hot" side of the DC source voltage on the emitter and return the emitter tuned circuit to ground through R1, R2, R3.

In this circuit the collector is not tapped down though the output to the converter stage is tapped down on L2 so as to provide less loading on the tuned circuit thereby permitting it to tune more sharply).

The grounded-base circuit has high output impedance so the transistor collector loading of the tuned circuit is small.

Troubleshooting the Circuit

This circuit, too, can be checked by bypassing the stage but it can be a little more tricky than for lower-frequency RF stages. Probably the best way here, in most cases, is to touch a metal screwdriver blade, not to the collector of the RF amplifier, but to the base of the converter stage.

Another way is to use a 5 or 10 pf capacitor in series with about a 30 inch piece of wire and touch that to the RF stage collector to see whether the audio volume increases significantly. Try also touching the base of the converter stage with the same wire and capacitor before deciding for sure whether or not the RF amplifier is not passing sufficient signal.

If you can get an increase in signal by bypassing the stage, start by checking voltages in the circuit. Again the emitter resistor voltage drop is a good test. In this circuit the drop is 0.2 volt (+5 minus +4.8v).

The most common trouble in RF amplifiers of all kinds is the transistor itself. But as an almost universal rule, if the DC current through the transistor is near-normal, then the transistor is likely not at fault. However, there are enough exceptions to this rule that you should not overlook the possibility of a transistor with near-normal DC current failing to amplify a high frequency signal.

FM OR VHF RF AMPLIFIER (Grounded-Base)

This circuit (Fig. 2-5) is virtually identical to the previous circuit (Fig. 2-4). The only significant difference is that no input coil is used. Instead of the "hot" side of the DC source going to the emitter, it goes to the collector circuit instead. But this layout makes no difference in the operation of the circuit.

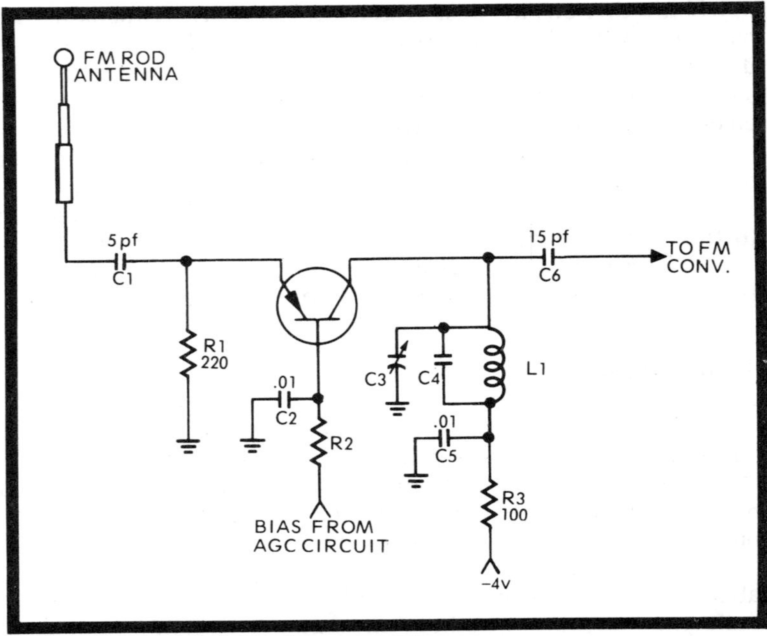

Fig. 2-5. FM RF grounded-base amplifier with untuned input.

Troubleshooting the Circuit

Troubleshooting techniques are the same as for common-base (Fig. 2-4) except that you must remember that bias is always measured between the base and emitter of a transistor. A significant test for transistor operation is to measure the voltage drop across the emitter resistor. For germanium transistors, the voltage across a 220 ohm resistor will be usually more than 0.1 but less than 0.25 volt. For silicon transistors, the voltage range will usually be between 0.2 volt and 0.5 volt across a 220 ohm resistor which represents a current flow in the transistor of from around 1 to 2.4 ma.

FM OR VHF RF AMPLIFIER (Grounded-Base)

This circuit (Fig. 2-6) is also similar to the previous two except that here there is a resonant input circuit. The circuit is rather broad and so is often fixed-tuned to cover a bandpass of several megahertz. Or it may be slug-tuned to provide some additional peaking and improved signal-to-noise ratio for a particular frequency.

Troubleshooting the Circuit

Generally the procedure is the same as for other grounded-base circuits already discussed. Measure the voltage drop across the 1K emitter resistor to determine transistor current flow. If emitter voltage is high, the transistor is probably shorted or very leaky. If emitter voltage is low or zero; (1) the transistor is probably open, (2) bias resistor R3 is open, or (3) capacitor C3 shorted or very leaky, (4) or the source voltage is low or zero (check the collector voltage to make sure).

VHF OR FM RF AMPLIFIER (Common-Emitter)

The common-emitter circuit has higher input impedance than the common-base circuit (typically around 1K as compared to about 150 ohms) and a somewhat lower output impedance (about 75K as compared to 500K for a typical circuit). The higher input impedance makes it easier to couple a tuned circuit into the input without having the circuit "swamped" by the input impedance. This means sharper tuning, and a better signal-to-noise ratio is possible.

The disadvantage of the circuit is that it either must be run at less than full gain or carefully neutralized. In the circuit here, no neutralization is used, but the collector circuit is tapped down on the tuned circuit. Tapping down lowers the

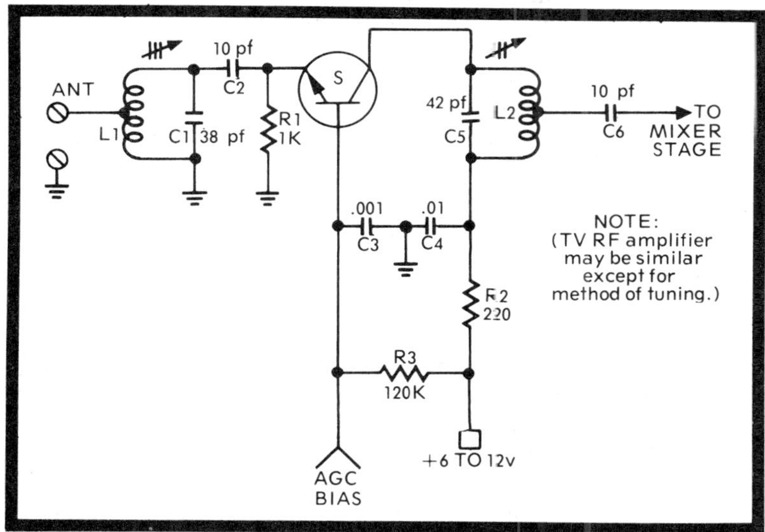

Fig. 2-6. FM RF grounded-base amplifier with tuned input.

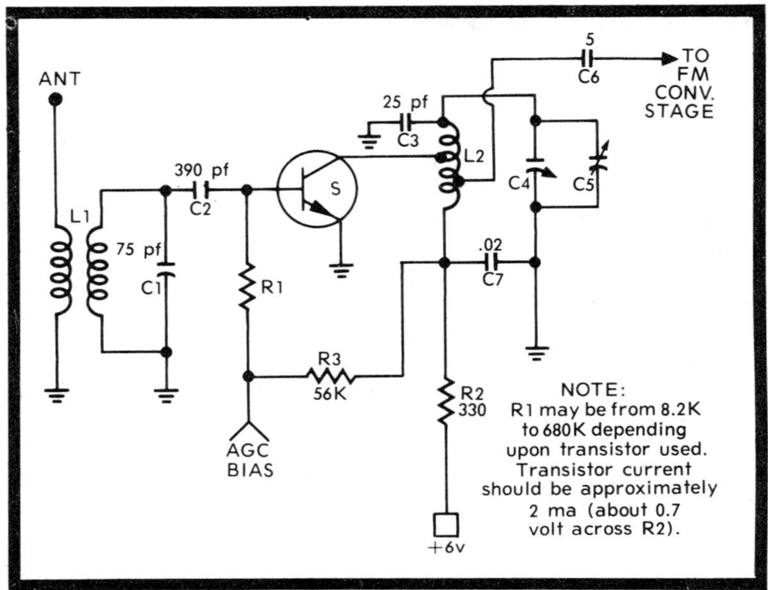

Fig. 2-7. VHF or FM RF amplifier (common-emitter).

output gain, but at the same time provides better selectivity in the resonant circuit due to less loading.

Since a silicon transistor is used in the circuit it is quite proper to use no emitter resistor. To find the transistor current, measure the voltage drop across the 330 ohm collector resistor, R2. Multiplying the DC voltage across R2 by 3 will indicate the approximate transistor current in ma. For example, if the voltage drop is 0.9 volt, the current will be approximately 2.7 ma.

Troubleshooting the Circuit

As already noted, there is no emitter resistor, so transistor current is checked by measuring the voltage drop across collector decoupling resistor R2.

To check bias, measure between base and emitter, which is the same in this case as between base and ground or common. A silicon transistor will have from about 0.4 to 0.6 volt bias normally or sometimes slightly more.

If collector voltage is low, it may be caused by a defective transistor, or by shorted or very leaky capacitors C3, C4, C5, or C7. Also, low collector voltage could be caused by excessive transistor bias.

VHF OR FM RF AMPLIFIER (Common-Emitter)

This particular circuit uses a common emitter circuit with the "hot" side of the DC source connected to the emitter (Fig. 2-8). Because the circuit is used with an AC-DC type power supply, isolation is used (R1, C1, R2, C2) between the antenna terminals and antenna coil L1. This prevents possible shock when attaching the antenna and also prevents possible antenna coil burn-out due to excessive ground current between the antenna and power line. Coil L1 is broadly resonant within the bandpass of the desired frequency range.

R3 is the bias resistor and its size is selected to provide about 1.5 to 2 ma of transistor current, and about 0.4 to 0.55 volt across the 270 ohm emitter resistor, R4.

This circuit does not use neutralization. Tapping down on the collector coil reduces the gain of the stage to insure stability.

Troubleshooting the Circuit

As with other RF circuits, you can determine if there is considerable loss in the stage simply by coupling the antenna into the collector circuit using a 5 pf capacitor or, better yet, by using a "gimmick." Simply connect one lead of the antenna

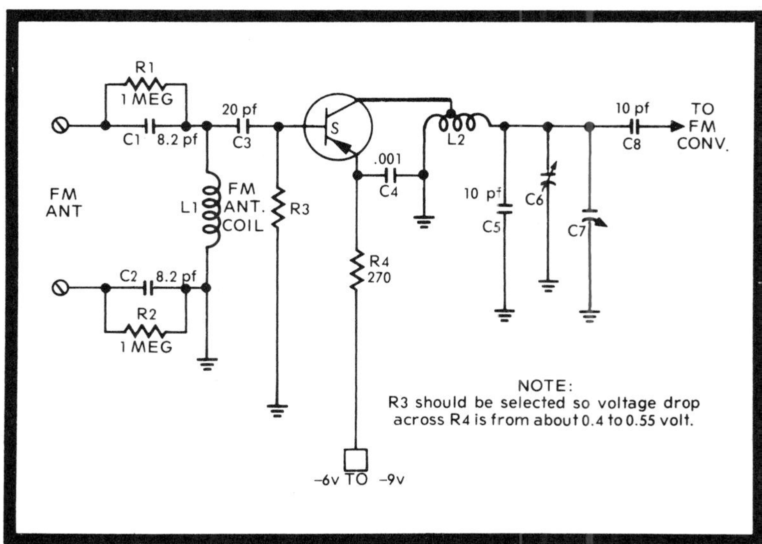

Fig. 2-8. VHF or FM RF amplifier (common-emitter) for use with AC-DC power supply.

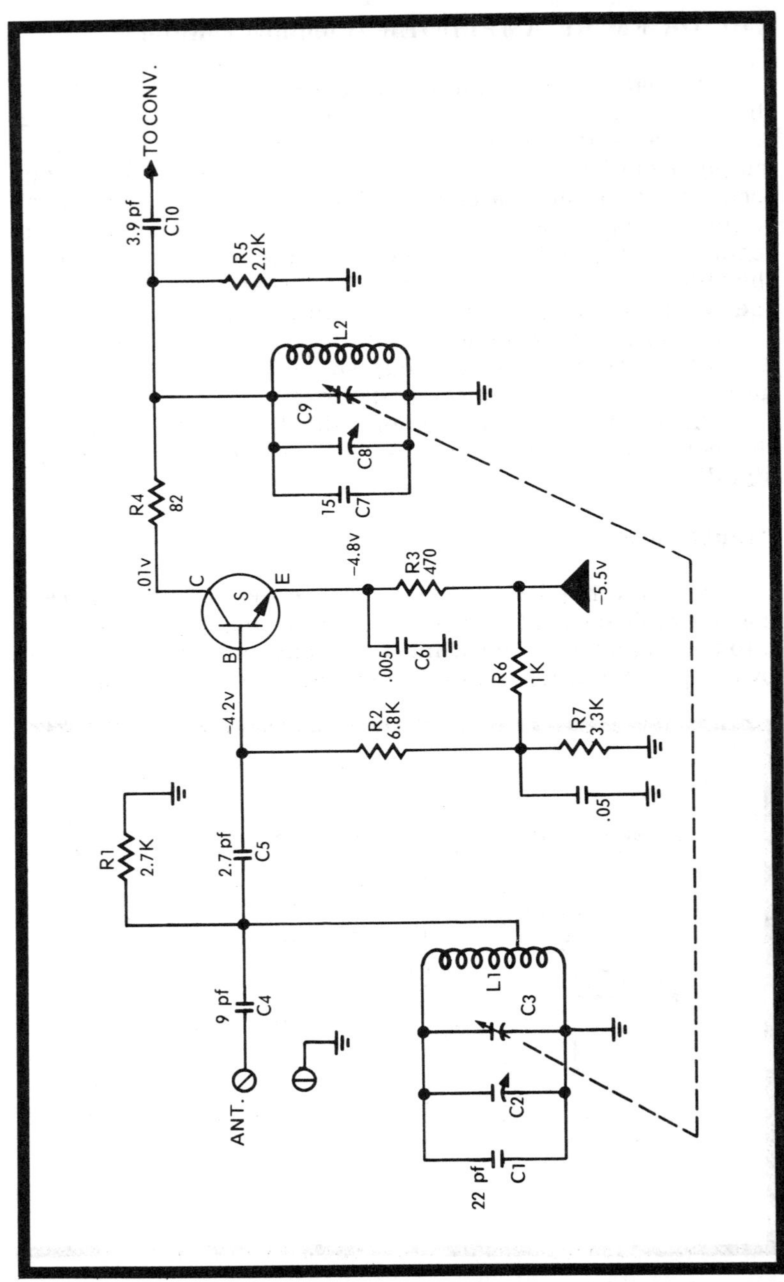

Fig. 2-9. FM and VHF RF amplifier (common-emitter).

to a piece of insulated wire and hook the wire around the collector lead, to couple enough signal into the circuit for a test and yet not load the tuned circuit so that serious mistuning would occur.

If coupling around the RF stage makes a significant improvement in the output volume and signal-to-noise ratio then you can assume that the RF stage is defective. Signal-to-noise ratio can be roughly determined by listening. Coupling in a signal to the collector may not noticeably increase the volume even if the RF stage is defective, but if the "hiss" level in the background drops, you know the RF stage is bad.

Excessive emitter resistor voltage drop may be caused by a defective transistor, incorrect transistor bias, or by C4 being shorted or very leaky. Low or zero voltage drop across the emitter resistor may be caused by low source voltage, by an open transistor, by an open R3 or leaky or shorted C3.

FM AND VHF RF AMPLIFIER

This is a common-emitter circuit using an NPN silicon transistor (Fig. 2-9). Coil L1 is tapped down to provide a better match between the tuned circuit and the input of the transistor. This tap-down results in less loading on the tuned circuit so the circuit tunes more sharply and signal-to-noise ratio should be better.

A 2.7K resistor (R1) tends to broaden the circuit slightly to accomplish the circuit stability required by the designer. The 470 ohm resistor, R3, also helps in stabilizing the amplifier, along with R4, 82 ohms.

Fixed padder capacitors C1 and C7 are nearly always desirable in a high frequency circuit since they help to prevent slight changes in the amplifier capacities due to warm-up or change in bias, from seriously affecting the resonant frequency.

The DC supply voltage is applied to the emitter circuit via R3 and the collector circuit is returned to ground through L2. This permits a rather easy way of tuning collector coil L2 without having any series capacitors between the coil and the tuning capacitor.

Troubleshooting the Circuit

To determine if the circuit is working, that is, providing some improvement in signal-to-noise ratio or gain, connect the antenna through a small capacitor (from around 3 to 10 pf) to the top of coil L2 or to the input of the converter. If the stations,

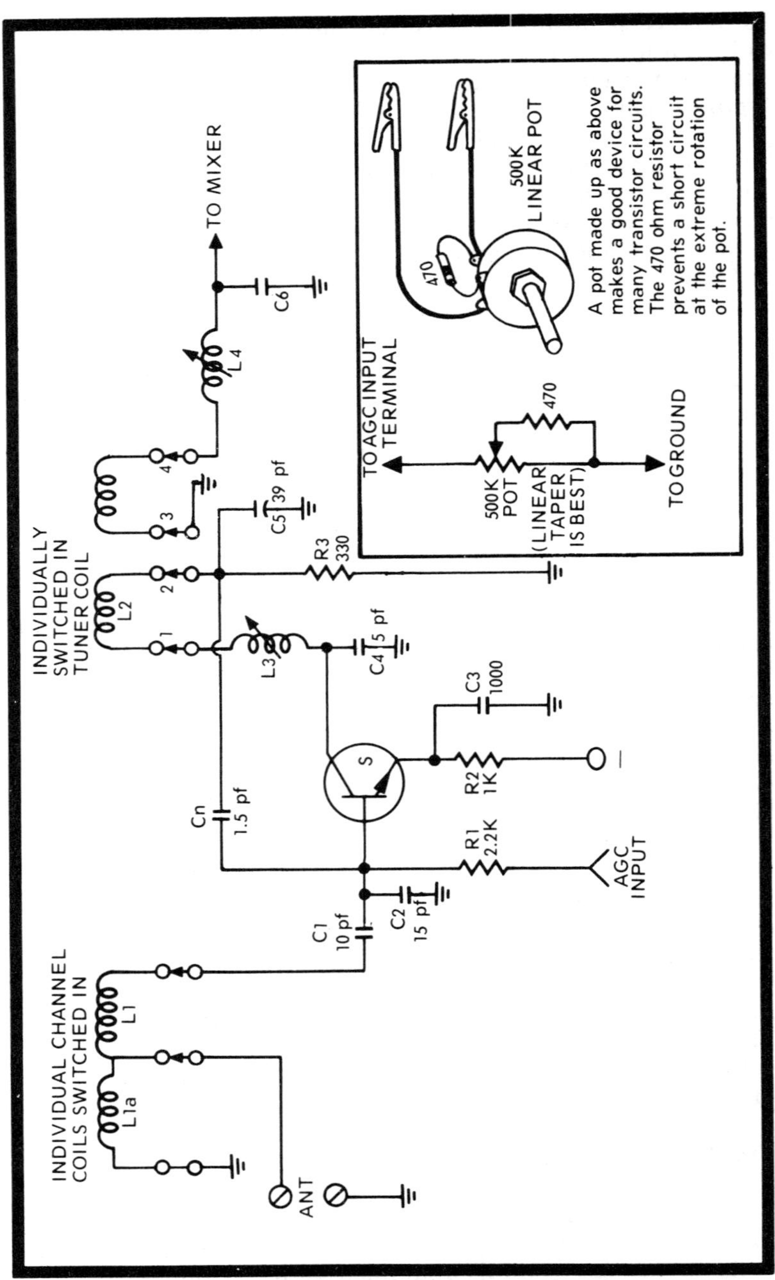

Fig. 2-10. Neutralized TV RF amplifier (common-emitter).

especially distant stations, are heard with more gain or with less hiss in the background, the RF amplifier is not working properly.

Check the bias voltage between the base and emitter; for an NPN silicon transistor, the bias should be positive on the base and should be at least 0.4 volt or usually somewhat more (0.6v shown). To check transistor current, measure the voltage drop across R3 in the emitter. For every volt across a 470 ohm resistor, the current through the resistor will be about twice that many milliamperes. For example, a 0.7 volt drop indicates about 1.4 ma.

If voltages appear normal, the transistor is probably not defective. Check to see if trimmers C2 or C8 will peak the signal. If they will not, the corresponding resonant circuit has some problem. It could be an open fixed padder capacitor, an open coil, or a shorted tuning capacitor or trimmer.

Low gain, with DC voltages normal, could also be caused by an open C6 in the emitter.

Capacitors C4, C5 and C10 are such small sizes that they seldom open unless physically damaged. A quick check though for C4 and C5 would be to simply connect the antenna through a 5 to 10 pf capacitor direct to the base of the RF amplifier. (Any open C10 will be found in the very first step.)

TV RF AMPLIFIER (Common-Emitter, Neutralized)

This circuit (Fig. 2-10) uses a "hot" negative DC supply going to the emitter of an NPN silicon transistor. This is a "turret" tuner in which the individual coils for each channel are rotated into place. The input coil L1 is called the antenna coil and the antenna is inductively coupled to L1, the base coil. (Most TV tuners have an FM trap between the antenna lead and the input coils; to simplify the circuit, this is not shown here.)

The base is coupled from L1 through a 10 pf capacitor, C1, and C2 goes to ground from the base C1 and C2 are shunted across the base coil of L1 and so make it resonant to the required frequency. By connecting the base at the junction of these two capacitors, there is a better impedance match between the base and the tuned circuit. This "tapping down" results in the same kind of match as if the coil were tapped appropriately.

The total bias for the RF stage is supplied by the AGC circuit which supplies a negative voltage but one that is more positive than the emitter voltage. Forward AGC is used, which means that the AGC voltage will go more positive with an increase in signal, thus driving the transistor toward saturation rather than toward cutoff. (Either saturation or cutoff means that a change in signal will not have any affect on the output so there is no gain.) Forward AGC results in a more nearly constant load on the tuned circuit than reverse AGC which can cut off the transistor and remove all load from the tuned circuit.

The 330 ohm resistor, R3, in the collector circuit limits the transistor from drawing excessive current when the bias is increased toward saturation, as does the 1K resistor in the emitter, R2.

Collector resistor R3 is also an impedance across which it is possible to develop a neutralization voltage. Note that terminal 2 on L2 has a 39 pf capacitor to ground, rather than some larger size such as 1000 pf. The reason for this is so the total RF in the output circuit is not bypassed to ground, therefore a small portion still remains across C5 and R3. A 1.5 pf neutralizing capacitor Cn is then connected from this point back to the base. Since the RF at terminal 2 of L2 is out-of-phase with that at the collector and terminal 1, it can be used to cancel the effect of any signal fed back through the capacity of the collector and base of the RF transistor. Sometimes either Cn or C5 is adjustable.

C4 is the tuned circuit capacitor for the output circuit and L3 is the "band set" adjustment which is effectively in series with all the rotating channel coils.

The signal from the output is inductively coupled through L2 to the mixer, and L4 and C6 make the output circuit resonant, forming a bandpass circuit between the RF amplifier and the mixer. (A bandpass circuit is two resonant circuits coupled together and tuned in such a way as to provide a somewhat wider than normal frequency passage than might be expected with only one tuned circuit, but with sharper cutoff, i.e., more selectivity for signals outside the bandpass. For example, this circuit could be around 6 MHz wide with sharp cutoff to frequencies above and below, while a single circuit might pass 12 MHz but work best for only a 2 MHz bandwidth.)

Troubleshooting the Circuit

Like all (or most all) RF amplifiers, a simple way to prove whether or not it is working is to shunt around it. This you can do by connecting a 5 pf capacitor (capacitor size is not too critical in most cases) between the antenna lead and the collector (or at terminal 1 on L2 if it is easier to get at) with the other antenna lead connected to ground nearby.

If the TV picture improves (snow is reduced), the problem is sure to be in the RF amplifier. This may be due to the transistor or other components or may be due to incorrect AGC voltage. The AGC voltage supplies the entire bias for the stage, and ground in this circuit is positive; therefore, grounding out the AGC may cause the transistor to saturate, since this places a high positive voltage on the base.

You can check, however, to see if the AGC is the problem by connecting a 500K potentiometer (Fig. 2-10) between the AGC terminal and ground, and then adjusting the bias until the circuit starts working or refuses to work. If it does start working normally, the trouble is in the AGC circuit; if not, then the AGC can probably be eliminated as a suspect. (Note that the potentiometer-to-ground method here works only when the circuit has the collector returning to ground, as in this case, through L2 and R3. In a circuit where the collector is returned to the "hot" side, the potentiometer would have to be from the AGC terminal to the "hot" side of the power supply rather than to ground.)

If bias (from the AGC) is not the problem, then use an ohmmeter to check the transistor to ensure there is a "one high-one low" reading between base and emitter and between base and collector, and that there is no short between collector and emitter.

Next, measure the terminal voltages on the transistor. Collector current can be determined either by measuring the voltage across R2 or R3, whichever is easier. The voltage across R2 is in direct relation to the current numerically, that is, a 1-volt drop across R2 (1K) indicates a 1 ma current flow through R2. The voltage across R3 should be multiplied by 3 to obtain the current through it; for example, a 0.33-volt drop across R3 indicates approximately 1 ma of current through it.

This circuit has fixed neutralization (no adjustment), and so stage oscillation would most likely be caused by either an open C2 or C5. Since small ceramic capacitors of this type seldom open except when physically damaged, the trouble is rare that cannot be "seen."

The transistor in this circuit should be replaced with an identical type whenever practical, because a different type number, even though designed for TV RF amplification, may require different values of adjacent parts in the circuit for good neutralization. A mismatched transistor and-or poor neutralization, of course, will give less than optimum performance.

If a substitute transistor must be used, check its performance on all active channels, making sure that sensitivity

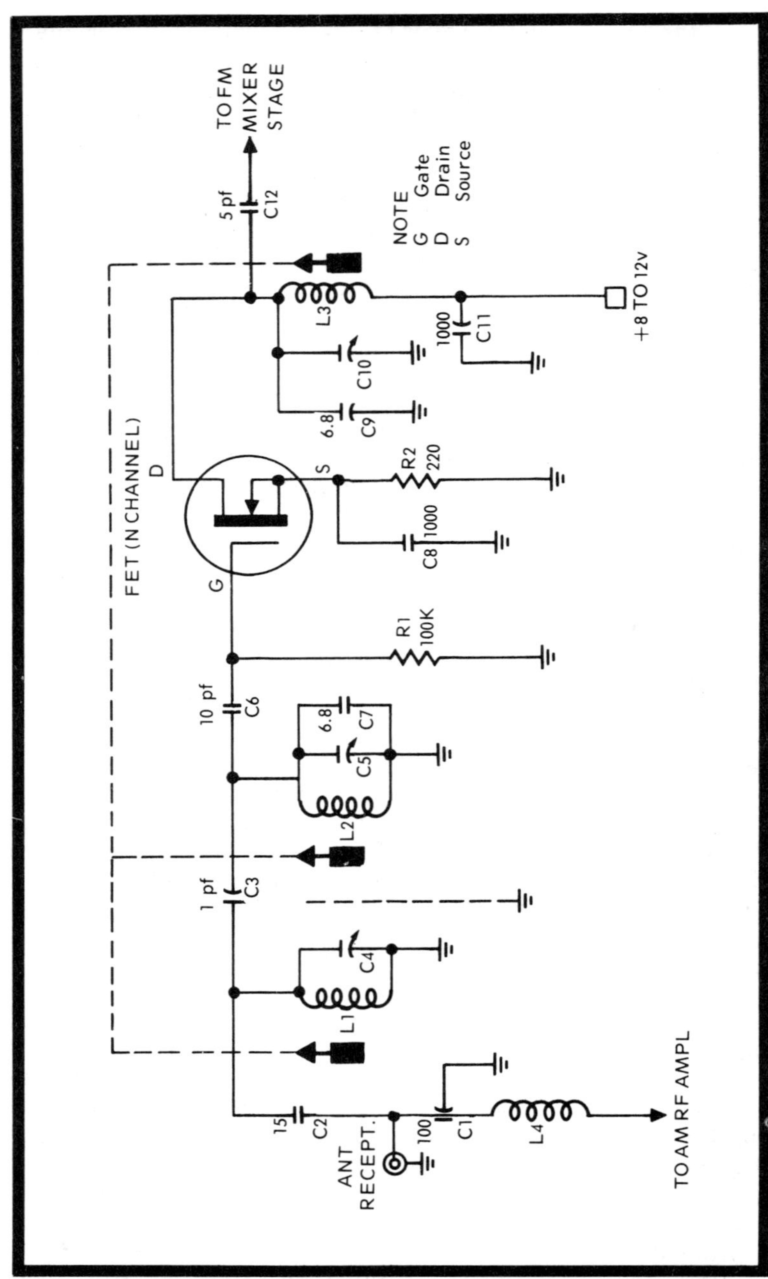

Fig. 2-11. FM RF amplifier using field effect transistor (auto radio).

is adequate and that there are no spurious diagonal lines in the picture (such lines would indicate oscillation of the RF stage).

Any tuner, such as this one, which uses individual coils that are rotated into position, may develop noise when channels are changed or may be subject to intermittent drop-out of signal, due to dirty contact surfaces. Use a good tuner spray, not haphazardly but directly on the contacts as the channel knob is rotated. Whenever noise is severe or persistent, remove the coil drum, if possible, and clean it with a soft cloth and cleaner, and adjust the spring contacts for equal tension.

RF AMPLIFIER USING FET

The circuit shown in Fig. 2-11 is similar to what might be used in an automobile radio for an FM RF amplifier. Slug tuning is used, and to provide additional selectivity, two separate tuned circuits are included in the input.

The field-effect transistor (FET) has a high impedance input and so circuits for it are similar in many ways to those for pentode vacuum tubes.

This particular circuit uses a single insulated-gate transistor and no AGC voltage is applied. The output (drain terminal) is connected directly to the "hot" side of the tuned circuit. Because of the low voltage used, there is no problem in returning the adjustable tuning capacitors (C9, C10) to ground. C11 provides continuity for the tuned circuit while offering DC isolation, and it also acts as a bypass for the source voltage line.

The 220 ohm resistor (R2) in the source circuit provides self-bias and prevents excessive current in the FET should the input signal level be extremely high. C8 bypasses the source resistor to prevent degeneration of the RF signal.

L4 in this circuit is a VHF RF choke which prevents the FM signals from being "bled off" by the AM circuits, but of course L4 still allows the AM signals to pass to the AM circuits without attenuation.

Troubleshooting the Circuit

The field-effect transistor can be tested in the circuit with reasonable success with either a voltmeter or an ohmmeter or both. In RF circuits, the current in a FET generally is a bit higher than for bipolar transistors. It is not uncommon to have 5 ma of current flow. If there is no current flow, then the voltage across source resistor R2 will be zero. This could be caused either by a defective transistor or by a high negative

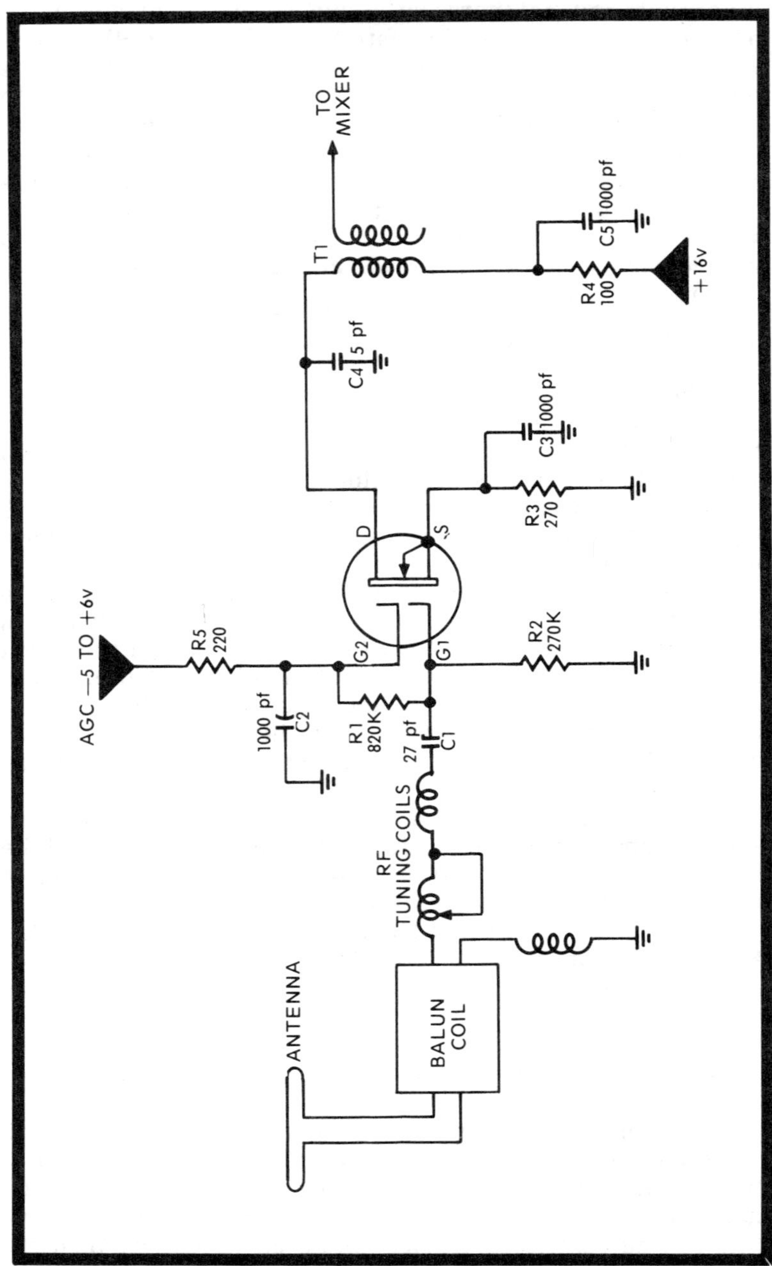

Fig. 2-12. Dual-gate MOSFET TV RF amplifier.

voltage on the gate, which is unlikely. It could also be caused by low or zero DC source voltage.

Measuring with an ohmmeter between the drain and source, you should read a fairly low resistance (be sure no DC power is applied to the circuit when taking resistance measurements) and R should be the same when the ohmmeter leads are reversed.

In the insulated-gate type FET, such as used here, there should be no reading (open) between the gate and drain and between gate and source terminals.

If the transistor DC circuits are performing normally, and gain is low, check to see that C4, C5, and C10 each will peak up on a received signal. You can check gain or lack of it by the same methods as discussed with other transistor RF amplifiers, that is, by coupling a signal into the drain to see if the signal-to-noise ratio improves. Also check C8 by shunt substitution with a known good capacitor. If C10 will not peak on a signal, check for an open C11.

MOSFET TV RF AMPLIFIER (Dual-Gate)

The dual-gate (DG) MOSFET in this circuit (Fig. 2-12) is a "depletion-enhancement" type meaning that to cut it off (pinch off) one of the gate voltages must be made negative but for the transistor to saturate both gates must go positive.

The gates are electrically insulated from the channel by a very thin coating of oxide and are delicate so far as spurious pulse voltages are concerned, meaning that the insulation can be ruptured if the gate is left floating and then touched suddenly. Some MOSFETs (metal-oxide semiconductor field effect transistors) have built in, back-to-back zener diodes across the gate and source terminals to prevent surge voltages from damaging the insulation. For those MOSFETs that do not have such protection, be careful when installing them so that gate leads are kept from picking up some surge voltage. One way is to wrap a tiny bare wire around all the leads close to where the leads enter the transistor case and then not removing the bare wire until all solder connections have been made into the circuit.

In a dual-gate circuit, generally the signal is applied to one gate and the AGC voltage to the other. In this circuit, full AGC is applied to gate 2 and the signal is applied to gate 1. Gate 1 also has some AGC applied through R1.

Note that the AGC voltage swings from -5 volts (on a strong input signal) to +6 volts (when the input signal is weak). Gate 1 voltage swings from about -1.6 to +2 volts.

The source resistor (R3) is essentially a limiting resistor to provide some self-bias for the transistor.

Because of the high output impedance of the FET, it can be connected directly to the top side of the output tuned circuit. Here a transformer (T1) is used to provide an impedance match between the output of the RF amplifier and the mixer input, which uses a bipolar transistor.

Troubleshooting the Circuit

Measure the terminal voltages. These will vary because of AGC action, but with no signal input, the voltage on the source terminal will be highest and the drain voltage the lowest. If the voltages seem normal, this is a good indication that the transistor is working, but for further proof you can use a bias box and vary the voltage at the AGC input terminal. Making the voltage more negative should reduce the source terminal voltage and finally drop it to zero when the bias voltage exceeds about 5.5 volts.

You can check to make sure the gate insulation is not punctured by removing the AGC line and then measuring the voltage on the gates. There should be practically zero voltage on the gates. If the voltage reads positive (0.1 volt or more) it is very probable that the transistor needs to be replaced due to leakage between the gate and the channel.

As with most RF circuits, you can determine whether they are causing a loss in signal simply by loosely coupling the antenna circuit into the output circuit of the amplifier. If the signal is significantly improved, then either the RF stage is defective or the AGC voltage is holding it pinched off.

In this particular circuit, simply grounding the AGC terminal should establish whether the AGC is at fault.

One word of caution when testing by coupling the antenna around the RF stage: remember that the problem could be in the antenna balun coils, so first bypass the balun coils and then the whole stage. The easiest way to do this probably is to connect one of the antenna leads to ground and then connect a 5 to 15 pf capacitor in series with the other lead. Touch the capacitor lead to the output terminal of the balun coil; if the signal is improved, the balun coil is defective. If the signal is not improved here, but is improved when the drain terminal of the FET is touched, the problem is in the RF stage itself.

JFET FM RF AMPLIFIER

The junction field effect transistor (JFET) has not been too popular as a VHF amplifier because of its general need of neutralization to keep it stable. In this respect a JFET is much like a triode tube.

The tuned circuits (Fig. 2-13) use variable capacitor tuning. Fixed padders C1 and C6 set the band and minimize capacity drift. C3 and C9 are trimmers used to make minor adjustments in tracking between the two circuits.

R1 is the gate return resistor and its size is not critical within the range of 47K to 1 meg generally; however, a larger resistor tends to prevent signal overload better because it will provide some self-bias in conjunction with C4.

The source resistor, R2, acts as the bias resistor to keep the gate reverse-biased in respect to the JFET channel. Current in this particular circuit, as indicated by the voltage drop across R2, is about 2.5 ma.

For neutralization, a tiny bit of signal is tapped off L1 by L2 and fed back out-of-phase to the gate. Capacitor Cn is adjusted to provide essentially the same amount of neutralization over the entire bandpass of the amplifier. Cn could be adjusted by tuning in a fairly strong station, then removing the +12 volts from resistor R3, and tuning Cn for minimum output signal. Essentially, a neutralizing circuit returns an out-of-phase signal in the same amount as the in-phase signal fed from the gate to the drain by the transistor capacity.

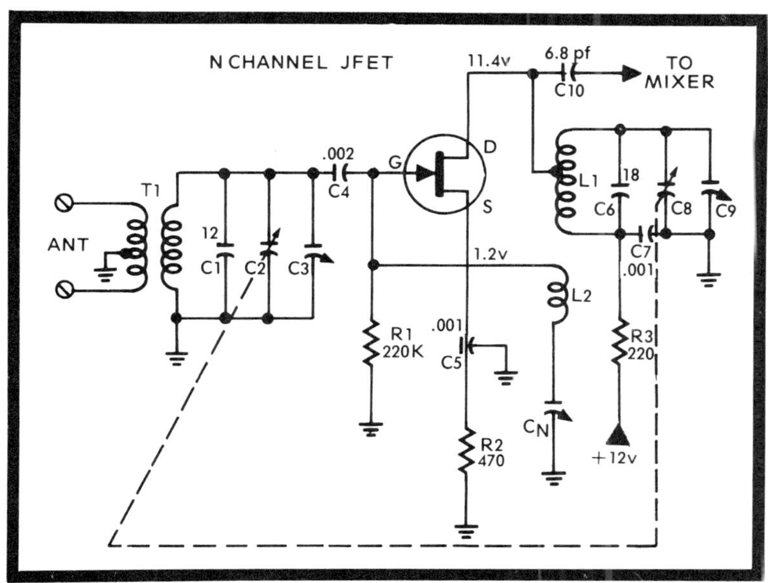

Fig. 2-13. JFET RF amplifier with neutralization.

Troubleshooting the Circuit

As with other RF amplifiers, you can determine a loss in the RF amplifier stage by simply connecting the antenna through a small capacitor to the output of the amplifier or the input of the mixer. If the signal improves by bypassing the amplifier, this is an accurate indication that the RF amplifier is causing a loss in signal.

Check the voltage across source resistor R2. It may vary somewhat from that shown on the schematic but should be within a range that indicates from 2 to 5 ma of current flow.

If the transistor is suspected, a JFET can be roughly checked with an ohmmeter. The gate is "junctioned" into the channel in this type transistor and so there is "diode action" when you check between either the gate and source or gate and drain. In other words, there should be a high resistance between gate and source with the ohmmeter leads connected one way, and when the ohmmeter leads are reversed the resistance should be fairly low. This is the same as when checking bipolar transistors between base and emitter or base and collector. Between drain and source the resistance should be fairly low and it should be the same regardless of which way the ohmmeter leads are connected (unless there is a possible shunt diode or transistor in the circuit that is directly coupled to the drain or source).

As with all amplifiers using tuned circuits, make sure the tuned circuits are tuning correctly by checking the action of the trimmer capacitor to see whether a peak can be reached.

If capacitor C5 in the source leg should open, the gain of the circuit will be lower than normal.

If Cn or L2 should open, the circuit may oscillate (cause whistles in the output especially as you tune from one station to another). If you suspect the RF stage is oscillating, **DON'T** start out by "twiddling" the neutralizing capacitor, Cn. Instead, tack about a 1K resistor across tuning capacitor C2. This will generally lower the gain enough to stop the oscillation and determines for sure whether the oscillation is in the RF stage or some later stage.

Neutralization adjustments for covering the whole band-pass of the amplifier can be tricky, and if the neutralization capacitor is a factory adjustment it may be difficult to reset without special instructions from the factory manual. However, as indicated earlier, the purpose of neutralization is to cancel the effects of capacity feedthrough of the signal from the drain back to the gate by coupling an exact out-of-phase signal back. Since this capacity is the same in either direction, you can normally check neutralization by removing the DC supply voltage and then feeding a signal into the input of the amplifier. When the neutralization capacitor is properly adjusted, the signal fed from the gate to the drain will be exactly cancelled by the signal fed in the opposite phase through the neutralizing circuit to L1, so while feeding in a signal, or even using a signal from the antenna, adjust the neutralizing capacitor for minimum output. Restore the DC supply voltage and check the circuit to see whether it works normally without oscillation. Another way to reduce the RF gain to make neutralization adjustments is to place a negative voltage on the gate (assuming an N-channel JFET) that is sufficient to pinch off the transistor current.

OSCILLATORS

The circuit probably used most often for VHF transistor oscillators is the grounded-base type. It has good stability; and because the collector and emitter voltages are in phase, it is a simple matter to provide feedback using a single, small capacitor between collector and emitter and an emitter resistor across which the signal voltage fed back from the collector can be developed.

The circuit (Fig. 3-1) is similar in many ways to the Colpitts oscillator for vacuum tubes. Its frequency is determined by the resonance point of L1, C4, C5 and the stray capacities and inductances. The oscillator frequency will also be changed slightly by increasing or decreasing the transistor bias and this is sometimes used in automatic frequency control (AFC) circuits.

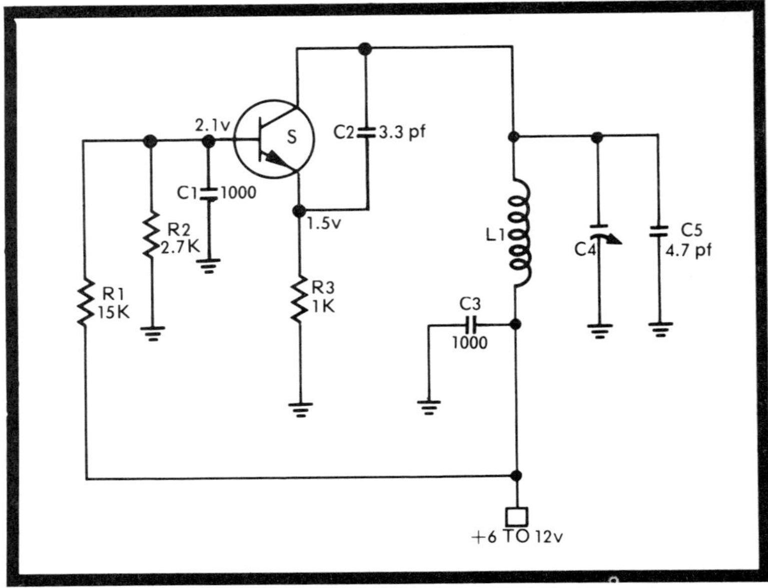

Fig. 3-1. FM oscillator (grounded-base).

Other AFC circuits may use a separate transistor or a diode that changes capacity with different amounts of reverse DC bias. The diodes especially produced for this use are called varicaps or varactors.

AFC is often needed in VHF oscillators, especially if the IF bandwidth is narrow, because relatively slight changes in stray capacity or in transistor current flow can make a considerable change in the oscillator frequency output.

FM OR VHF OSCILLATOR (Grounded-Base)

The circuit shown in Fig. 3-1 is a grounded-base amplifier with feedback from the collector to emitter through C2, from the tuning circuit, L1, C4. The base is grounded to signal by the 1000 pf capacitor, C1. Bias is supplied from the DC supply through R1 and stabilized by R2. R3, the 1K emitter resistor, is used not for protective bias but to provide an impedance across which the feedback signal can be applied to the emitter.

The circuit is simple to build and adjust. The frequency drift of the circuit depends largely on the stability of the collector and bias voltages, unless there is an increase in ambient heat around the tuned circuit components, in which case the oscillator frequency can change significantly. For good stability, the tuned circuit components should be mechanically sturdy.

At very high frequencies, capacitors C1 and C3 should be feedthroughs, and the leads from the transistor to the tuned circuit should be kept extremely short.

Troubleshooting the Circuit

Although you cannot tell by reading the bias of a transistor whether or not the circuit is oscillating, you can tell by reading the bias and then either tuning or in some other manner disturbing the oscillator circuit; the bias should change. In this circuit, the best way is to check the base voltage to ground (unlike other amplifiers where you check from base to emitter because the feedback to the emitter may be affected by the meter leads if you measured between base and emitter). Check the base voltage, then touch your finger to the collector of the transistor (which is the hot side of the oscillator tuned circuit); the base voltage should rise. If there is a resistor in the collector circuit, you can measure the voltage drop across it when you touch the collector—the voltage drop should increase if the circuit is oscillating.

If the circuit is not oscillating, check across R3. If the voltage is significantly high, it is likely that the transistor is

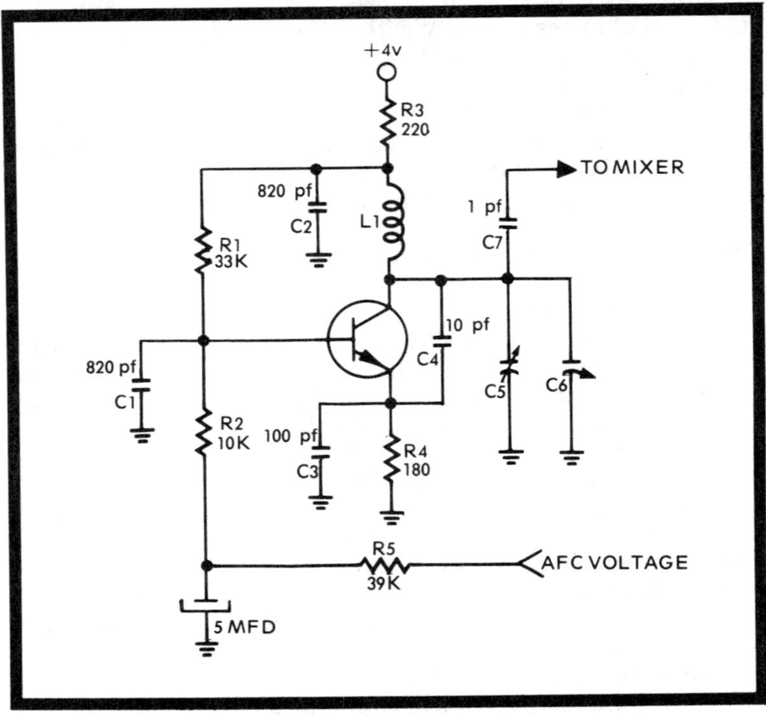

Fig. 3-2. FM oscillator with AFC.

shorted, or (rarely) C2 is shorted. If the voltage across R3 is low or zero, the transistor may be defective, the DC supply voltage may be low or zero, the 15K resistor, R1, may be open, or (rarely) C1 could be shorted.

If DC voltages are near normal and the circuit is not oscillating, check for either an open C1 or (rarely) an open C2.

FM OR VHF OSCILLATOR WITH AFC

This circuit (Fig. 3-2) has many similarities to Fig. 3-1. A smaller value resistor is used in the emitter circuit. The feedback circuit is a capacity divider made up of C3 and C4. L1 is the oscillator coil and C2 is the collector circuit bypass which also completes the tuned circuit between C5, C6, and L1.

C1 grounds the base so far as signal is concerned. The 33K resistor, R1, provides "turn on" bias for the transistor. The 10K resistor, R2, from the base and the 39K resistor, R5, to the AFC voltage circuit, are used in controlling the oscillator frequency. The 5 mfd capacitor slows down the frequency change to prevent "hunting" that could cause an audible output in an FM receiver.

The AFC voltage is taken from the FM detector and it normally is zero; however, if the oscillator frequency drops, this change is detected by the FM detector and its voltage goes positive. Applying this positive voltage to the base of the oscillator "speeds up" the oscillator and makes it operate at a higher frequency. The opposite effect occurs if the oscillator frequency goes too high, because the AFC voltage goes negative and "slows down" the oscillator.

Troubleshooting the Circuit

The troubleshooting here is identical to that for the circuit in Fig. 3-1 except for the AFC portion. If you suspect trouble in the AFC circuit, you can simply short across the 5 mfd capacitor. This "zeros" any voltage on the AFC line and if the trouble clears then you can be sure the trouble is in the AFC circuit. Most radios will have an AFC switch which usually does exactly the same thing, grounds out the AFC line. The AFC switch should be "off" when tuning in a station, it is then turned "on" to hold the station locked in.

VHF OSCILLATOR FOR TV (Grounded-Emitter)

This is a grounded-emitter oscillator which uses "switched coil" tuning for each of 12 channels. The circuit is similar to the "ultraudion" tube circuit. Feedback is from collector to base across the tuned circuit. A 3.3K collector load resistor (R2) is the impedance used to prevent "grounding out" the oscillator signal on the collector. Bias to the base is R1, an 82K resistor. C2 is part of the resonant circuit, as well as C1, C3, C4, and C5 and L1. This is a "preset" fine tuning tuner and so no separate fine tuner is used. If it were, it would likely be a small capacitor, or an inductor in series with a capacitor connected between the collector and ground. In this circuit, an individual fine tuning slug is used in each of the 12 VHF coils.

Troubleshooting the Circuit

Any VHF oscillator is affected when test leads are placed on it to find out whether it is working. Not only will its frequency change but sometimes it will stop working altogether when the test leads are placed on "hot" points in the circuit. Here both the collector and base are "hot" and with no resistor in the emitter there is no easy way to check for transistor current.

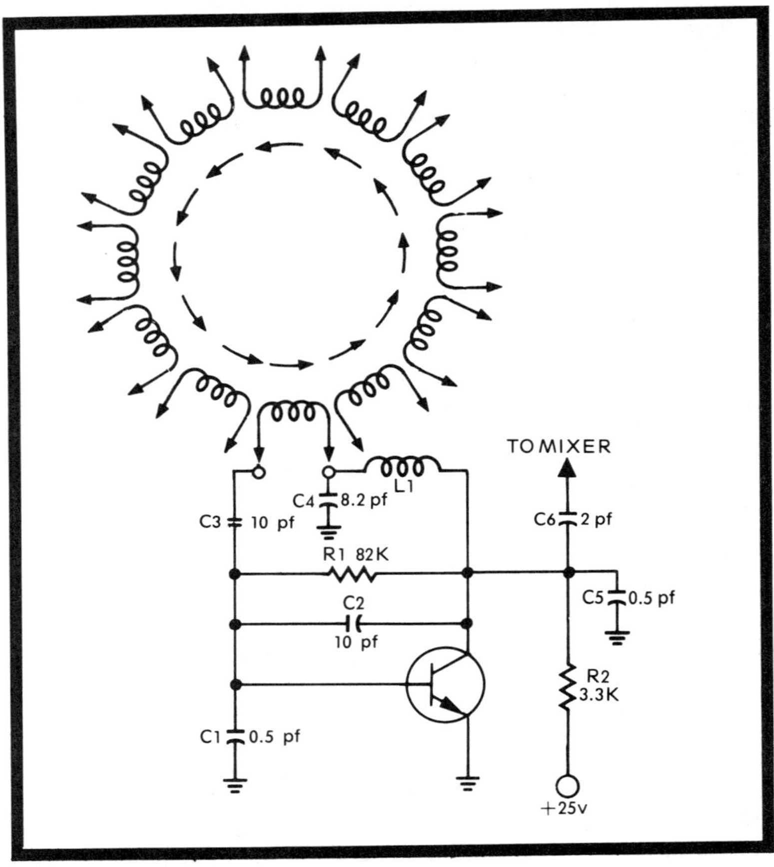

Fig. 3-3. VHF TV oscillator.

You can check for bias between base and emitter because it makes no difference whether or not you upset the oscillator performance, base bias should be about 0.6 volts for a silicon transistor plus or minus perhaps one or two tenths of a volt.

In TV tuners, mechanical failures are probably the most common source of trouble, e.g., perhaps the coils are not making proper contact, or perhaps broken. Check first to see if the trouble is on all channels rather than on just one or two.

If you suspect the oscillator in a TV set is bad, one way to prove it is to tune the set to a known operating channel, then couple a signal generator into the input of the mixer circuit through a tiny capacitor or gimmick (an insulated wire wrapped once around the mixer input lead). Tune the signal generator to around 40 MHz higher than the selected channel and if you can get a picture or sound or both you know that the TV oscillator must be defective.

Negative temperature coefficient (NTC) capacitors are often used in TV oscillator circuits to compensate for variations in temperature inside the set. If you are sure there is no mechanical trouble, and if you find that you cannot adjust an oscillator to the correct channel but perhaps it will adjust so that, say, channel 8 can be tuned in on channel 7, check the NTC capacitors first since they are more apt to become unstable or open than most regular capacitors.

LHF AND MF OSCILLATORS

Separate low frequency oscillators are sometimes used in radios for the broadcast and shortwave bands. The oscillator uses a separate transistor and the output is fed, usually through a capacitor, to the mixer circuit. This kind of oscillator circuit is also used in signal generators used for testing radio receivers.

Because of the lower frequencies, the inherent capacities in the transistor and in the wiring are not sufficient for feedback and so some sort of inductive feedback is generally used. The feedback may go either to the base or to the emitter. The grounded-base circuit is somewhat more popular. With the grounded-base circuit, DC bias is applied to the base and the base is "grounded" (so far as the signal is concerned) by a bypass capacitor. The oscillator feedback signal is generally capacity-coupled to the emitter which usually has a 1K or larger resistor in series to provide an impedance across which the feedback signal is impressed. The emitter resistor also provides a protective bias for the transistor to limit current flow in the event of circuit or transistor troubles. Limiting current flow in the transistor is also helpful in maintaining the oscillator stability since any heat in a transistor tends to increase the transistor current and this will usually increase the oscillator frequency. Germaniums are more sensitive to heat than silicons but both are affected to some extent. At low frequencies, the oscillator frequency drift is usually not a serious problem. But it becomes much more a problem as the frequency increases, and this is the reason many higher-frequency radios use automatic frequency control (AFC).

AM OSCILLATOR NO. 1 (Grounded-Base)

The AM oscillator shown in Fig. 3-4 uses a grounded-base circuit with feedback provided through transformer coupling

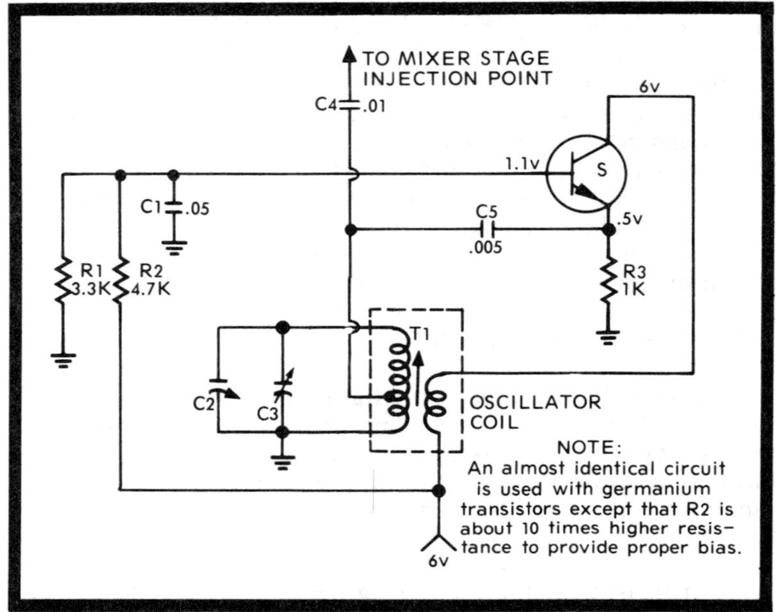

Fig. 3-4. AM oscillator (grounded-base).

and a capacitor to the emitter. Base bias is provided by the bleeder, R1 and R2, and the base is signal-grounded by C1.

The circuit shown here uses a silicon NPN transistor. Bias voltages shown are approximate since the bias changes with the frequency.

The oscillator tap-off to the mixer stage is at fairly low impedance and this is why a relatively large capacitor (C4) is used for coupling.

The 1K resistor in the emitter circuit (R3) reduces the oscillator current flow. R3 also provides an impedance in the emitter circuit across which a feedback signal is developed.

The voltage source for this circuit may vary within rather wide limits without serious modification of the circuit.

Troubleshooting the Circuit

A radio that will amplify a noise input, such as a fluorescent lamp noise, but will not tune in stations, generally has a defective local oscillator.

You can check to see if the oscillator is operating by measuring the bias between base and emitter and tuning the radio from one end of the dial to the other. While this is done, the base-emitter bias should vary a few tenths of a volt at least. If it does not, the oscillator is not working.

Of course an oscillator may be working and still be off frequency. Tune the radio near the low end of the dial; then hold the set close to a noise source, such as a fluorescent lamp, and adjust the slug in T1 until the noise peaks. If the noise will not peak then the oscillator is not on the correct frequency even though operative. Obviously, to make the preceding test, the rest of the radio must be in good working condition.

If the emitter voltage is low or zero, check the supply voltage and collector voltage. If collector voltage is normal, either the transistor is defective or the base bias is low, so check R2.

If emitter voltage is high, check for excessive bias, such as might be caused by an open R1. If bias is near normal, the transistor is likely shorted.

If DC voltages seem near normal and yet the stage is not oscillating, check for continuity of T1 windings. Also shunt test C5—it may be open.

AM OSCILLATOR NO. 2 (Grounded-Base)

This circuit is similar to that of Fig. 3-4 except that the DC source voltage "hot" side is to the emitter rather than to the

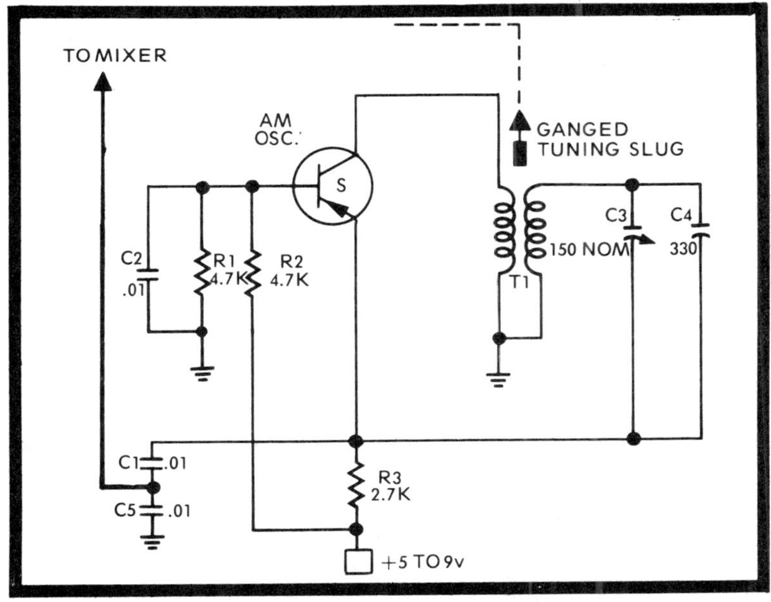

Fig. 3-5. AM oscillator (grounded-base).

collector circuit. The emitter resistor in this case is 2.7K as compared to 1K in the previous circuit. This emitter resistor is selected by the designer to provide the necessary waveform and output signal desired.

Here the tuned circuit capacitors, C3 and C4, are returned to the emitter, and the bypasses for these capacitors to complete the tuned circuit are C1 and C5.

This circuit is used in an automobile radio which uses slug tuning.

Troubleshooting the Circuit

The same techniques as described for AM oscillator No. 1 are applicable. Measure the DC bias on the transistor while tuning across the band. If the circuit is oscillating, the DC bias will change by several hundredths of a volt.

To take measurements in any circuit which has the "hot" DC source voltage to the emitter circuit, use the emitter as common and make all transistor readings to the emitter.

To measure transistor current, measure the voltage drop across R3, between the "hot" DC source and the emitter. Since a 2.7K resistor is used here, a voltage of 2.7 volts will be developed for 1 ma of current flow. Typically this circuit should have about 0.5 ma current flow so the voltage reading across R3 should be around 1.35 volts.

If the current flow through the emitter resistor is high, check for a shorted transistor, or for an open R1. If current flow is low, check for a bad transistor or an open R2.

If the collector voltage in this circuit is about the same as the DC source voltage (measured to ground), check for an open T1. If T1 is open and you measure between collector and emitter as suggested, the voltage will be zero.

If oscillator frequency is incorrect, check for mistuning of C3, or, possibly, an open C4. Sometimes C4 is made up of two capacitors in parallel, with one considerably smaller in value than the other. The small one may have a negative temperature coefficient for holding the oscillator stable. If drift occurs regularly, replace this NTC capacitor.

AM OR LOW FREQUENCY OSCILLATOR (Base Feedback)

This circuit (Fig. 3-6) is similar to the previous two circuits, with the main difference being that the base is used as the feedback terminal rather than the emitter. T1 is similar to the oscillator transformers used in the two previous circuits and the transformers could be interchanged by simply reversing the leads of the tickler winding. (In the two previous circuits, the small "tickler" winding was in the collector circuit with the "tap down" connection on the oscillator coil being capacitivly coupled to the emitter.)

Fig. 3-7 shows another variation of this same circuit, but with the tickler coil in the collector circuit rather than in the base circuit.

Troubleshooting the Circuit

Either circuit (Fig. 3-6 or Fig. 3-7) can be checked just like Fig. 3-4 or Fig. 3-5. If the DC bias varies as the frequency of the oscillator is changed then the circuit is oscillating, though not necessarily at the right frequency.

You can also check for oscillation by measuring the DC bias and then touching your finger to a "hot" point in the circuit such as the top side of the tuning capacitor. This touching loads the oscillator circuit and the DC bias will change only if the oscillator is working.

Another way to check the oscillator is with another radio tuned to a station and placed nearby. As you rotate the dial on the defective radio, if the oscillator is working, you will hear a whistle in the good radio when the oscillator beats against the station frequency or against the oscillator in the other set.

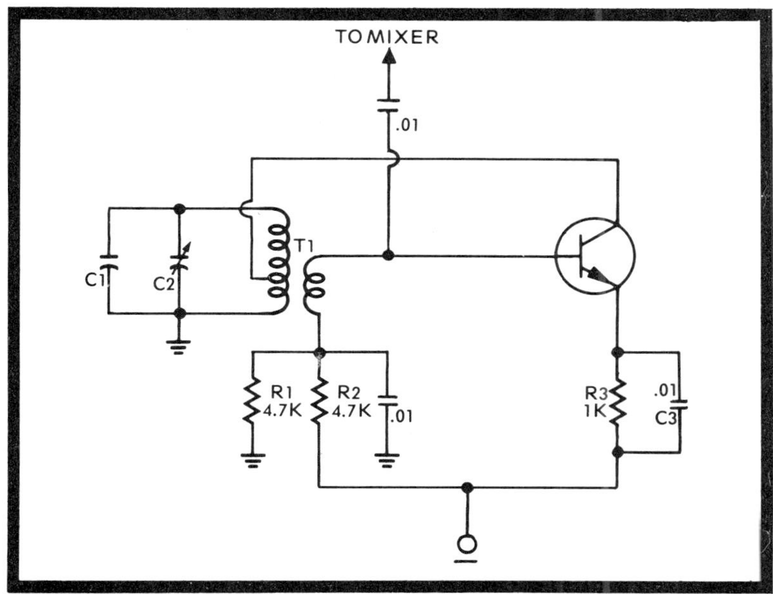

Fig. 3-6. AM oscillator (base feedback).

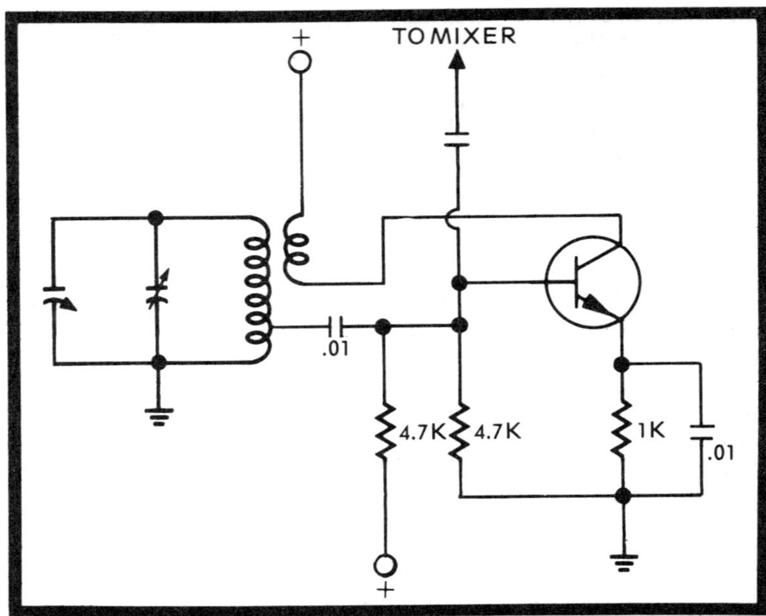

Fig. 3-7. AM oscillator (collector feedback).

Remember that it is less confusing to check a transistor circuit, regardless of whether the DC supply is to the collector or to the emitter, if you use the emitter as common and measure the base and collector voltages with respect to the emitter. To measure transistor current, measure across the emitter resistor. For every 1K of resistance and every 1 ma of current, there will be a 1 volt drop. For example, 0.6 ma through a 1K resistor means a voltage drop across the resistor of 0.6 volt.

CONVERTERS

A converter is both a mixer and a local oscillator, and the stage uses just one transistor for both functions. The converter not only accepts and amplifies the desired RF input signal, but it also oscillates at the required frequency above the RF signal to produce an IF (intermediate frequency). Fig. 4-1 shows a converter for low to medium frequencies. The antenna signal is fed to the base of the transistor, and the feedback from the collector circuit is tuned by the oscillator coil and capacitor and fed through the oscillator coupling capacitor to the emitter to sustain oscillation. In this instance, the collector circuit IF coil is tuned to 455 kHz and the oscillator feedback is developed across the primary winding of the oscillator coil.

As examples of the frequencies in a converter circuit (in kHz):

Point A	Point B	Point C
550	1005	455
800	1255	455
1200	1655	455
1440	1895	455

The real purpose, then, of a converter, is to change the desired incoming frequency to another lower frequency which remains at a fixed frequency regardless of which radio frequency is tuned in. This permits a fixed-frequency IF amplifier to be used on all incoming signals. A fixed-frequency amplifier can be designed to have more gain and also more selectivity with fewer parts, especially fewer complicated mechanical parts, than if the radio used only dial-tunable amplifiers.

It is the converter stage, or a mixer-oscillator stage, that makes the superheterodyne radio possible. Before the advent of the frequency conversion receiver, all receivers had every RF circuit tunable and all circuits were changed in tuning when another station was tuned in. For example, if a 560 kHz

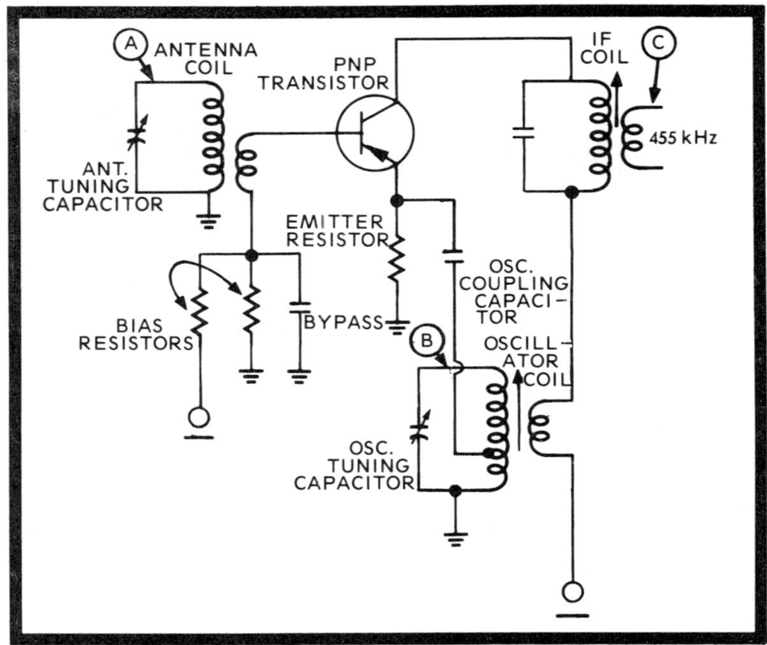

Fig. 4-1. Simplified converter stage for lower frequencies.

signal was tuned in, every tuned radio circuit was resonant at 560 kHz. Then if a station at 750 kHz were tuned in, all the circuits were changed, as the dial turned, to 750 kHz. This was called a tuned radio frequency (TRF) receiver. The many advantages of the superheterodyne have made the TRF totally obsolete except for a very few applications where the local oscillator signal might create interference in some other nearby electronic device or another receiver.

AM CONVERTER CIRCUITS

There are two general types of AM converter circuits, and they are similar in operation. One type has the oscillator feedback circuit to the base (Fig. 4-2) and the other has the feedback circuit to the emitter of the transistor (Fig. 4-3). Either germanium or silicon transistors are suitable for these circuits, and circuit values for both will be similar except for some slight differences in the base bias circuit or the emitter resistor. Testing is also similar.

The basic idea of the circuit in Fig. 4-2 is, with one transistor, to amplify an incoming AM signal, mix it with a locally generated "oscillator" signal, and produce an output at an IF, usually 455 kHz in home type radios but at 262 kHz in some automobile radios.

The oscillator circuit is tuned higher in frequency by the amount of the intermediate frequency. For example, if the signal to be received is 1000 kHz and the IF is 455 kHz then the oscillator is tuned to 1455 kHz.

In Fig. 4-2 the "tickler" coil in the collector circuit feeds back some of the output signal through T1 to the oscillator tuned circuit. A tap on the oscillator coil couples the signal through C3 to the base so as to sustain oscillations.

In Fig. 4-3 the signal is fed back via T1 to the emitter instead, through C6. The oscillator transformers (T1) can be interchanged for use in either converter circuit. The only difference is that the connections to the tickler coil must be reversed, depending upon which circuit is used.

The emitter resistor is an essential part of both these circuits since it provides a sort of self-regulating bias for the transistor. In any converter circuit, the amplifying device, whatever it is, must operate nonlinearly. The emitter resistor and bypass tend to hold the transistor near cut-off, except on the negative excursion of oscillator voltage (positive ex-

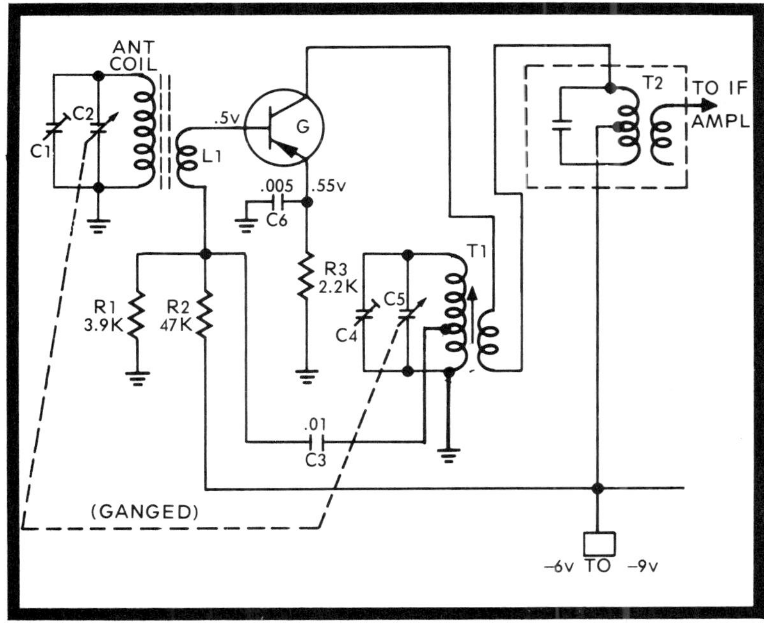

Fig. 4-2. AM converter, base feedback.

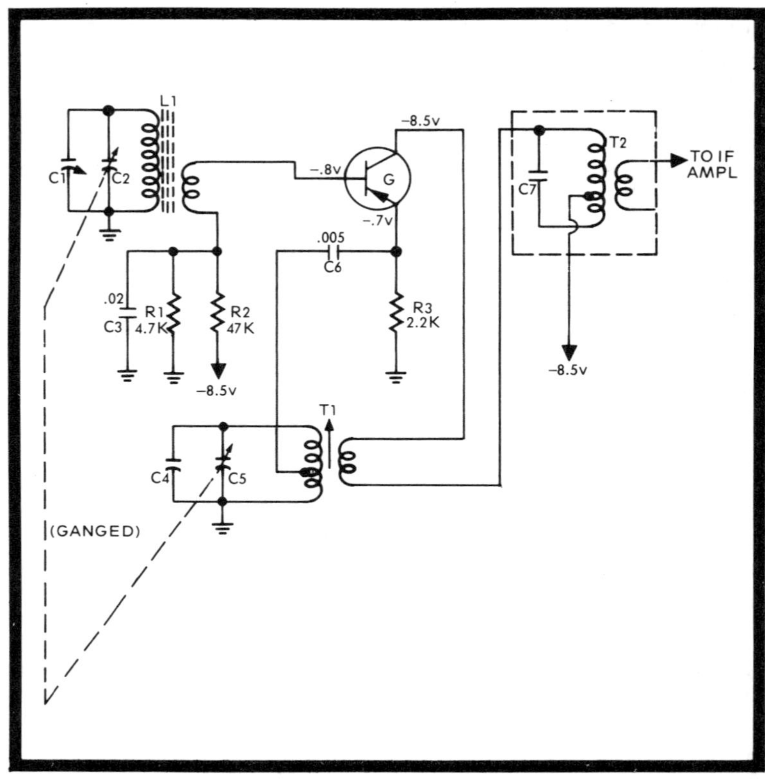

Fig. 4-3. AM converter, emitter feedback.

cursion if the transistor is an NPN). For this reason, the DC bias on a converter transistor is affected, depending upon the strength of the oscillations.

L1 of this circuit is the antenna coil. The tuned part of the circuit consists of several turns of wire wound on a ferrite core (ferrite is powdered iron). The base coil generally has no more than 6 or 8 turns. This provides the necessary change in impedance between the tuned circuit (high Z) and the transistor input circuit (low Z). Without this impedance match, the gain of the circuit would be low, and the tuning would be extremely broad.

T2 is the first IF transformer. It can be connected in the collector circuit in series with the oscillator tickler coil, since the tickler coil has very few turns and thus has little effect on the overall impedance in the collector circuit.

The voltage input to this circuit is generally not too critical.

Troubleshooting the Circuit

First measure supply voltage readings. If they are within 25 percent or so, the circuit likely will operate normally. To find out whether the circuit is oscillating, there are a number of methods you can use.

One method is to use another similar AM radio and tune it to a station near the middle of the band. Hold the radio with the suspected oscillator near the radio that is playing. Rotate the dial of the suspected radio and see whether or not you can produce a whistle in the output of the playing radio at some dial setting. If you can, this means that the oscillator in the suspect radio must be working. If you hear no whistle, then either the oscillator is not working or it is considerably off frequency.

Another method is to measure the transistor bias. This bias is the result of two things; the DC supplied by the bias resistors, and the additional bias supplied due to base-emitter rectification of the oscillator signal. To check, use a VTVM or a FET voltmeter or even a 20,000 ohm per volt VOM, and while measuring the base-emitter bias, tune the radio from one end of the dial to the other. Because the oscillation strength changes with frequency, if the oscillator is working there should be a change of DC bias on the transistor when the dial is moved.

Another method is to measure the transistor bias and then touch a "hot" point in the oscillator circuit with your finger. If the oscillator is working, the detuning caused by touching will cause the transistor bias to change.

If the oscillator is not working, and if DC bias seems to be near normal, check for open capacitors by shunting each suspected one with a known good one. Check to make sure there is continuity in all coils and transformers, and to all taps on the coils.

Sometimes either the tuning capacitor or the trimmer capacitor may be shorted. Disconnect the coil from the "hot" terminal of the capacitors and check across the capacitors with an ohmmeter—there should be no reading on the ohmmeter even on the R X 1000 scale.

Whistles or squeals in the radio output that appear to originate in the converter circuit may be caused by an open electrolytic capacitor either on the B+ line or in the AGC circuit, if it should be connected to the converter circuit. Another cause is an open capacitor in T2. Sometimes this capacitor will be connected from collector to ground rather than across the T2 coil, or there may be two capacitors, one in the coil and one connected from the collector to ground.

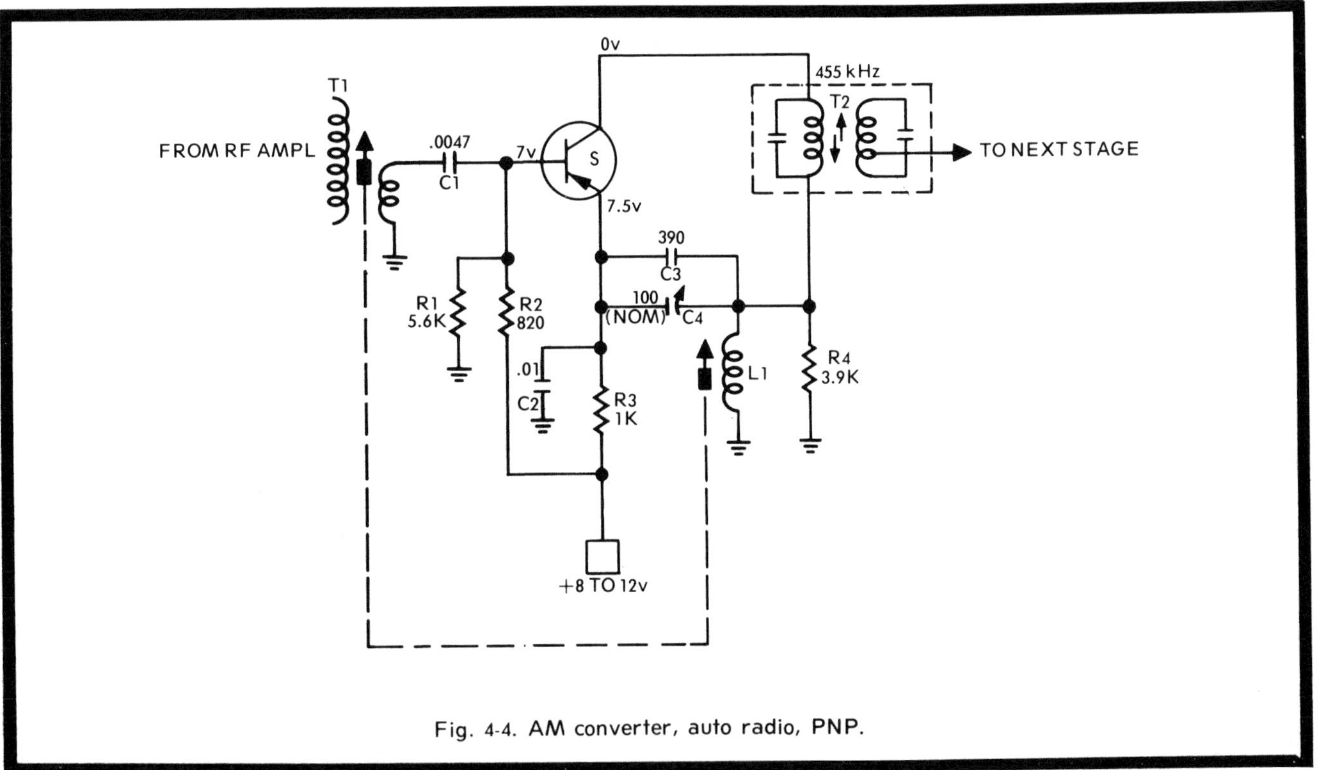

Fig. 4-4. AM converter, auto radio, PNP.

A defective transistor can cause whistles or squeals and often a replacement transistor may cause this problem. Sometimes it can be corrected, if the right transistor is not available, by connecting a 10K or so resistor across T2 or a 100K or so resistor across the tuned circuit of T1. Sometimes changing the emitter resistor to one of higher or lower value is essential to good performance when a replacement transistor must be used that is not an exact replacement.

When the oscillator is not working, the radio will often still pick up noise, such as from a fluorescent light. If you can hear this noise but hear no stations, then check the oscillator circuit carefully.

If an AM broadcast-band radio picks up only short wave signals, check for an open in the tuned circuit part of the antenna coil, L1.

AUTO RADIO AM CONVERTER

Nearly all modern automobile radios use "slug" tuning, that is, a ferrite core is moved in and out of the tuned coils to change the resonant frequency. Consequently the converter circuit is often simpler when compared with a home radio circuit.

In this circuit (Fig. 4-4) the feedback for the oscillator is to the emitter of the transistor. Instead of a "tap down" on a coil, the tap down is at the junction of C3, C4, and C2. Resistor R4 tends to reduce the impedance of the oscillator coil, not so much that it affects the tuning significantly, but enough to prevent the circuit from "taking off" into spurious oscillations or parasitics.

C4 is a screwdriver adjustment to adjust the oscillator circuit so it will track with the RF and antenna coil circuits.

A silicon transistor is used although this circuit works equally well with germanium types.

Auto radios often use the "dual-tuned" IF coils (T2) as shown here, since better selectivity is desirable in the car radio to help eliminate noise and interfering signals.

Troubleshooting the Circuit

Troubleshooting in this circuit is almost identical with that already discussed.

In addition, with this or any other AM oscillator circuit, you may find that an oscilloscope is useful to determine whether the oscillator is working. An oscilloscope with a good low-capacity probe will indicate a clean oscillator signal at

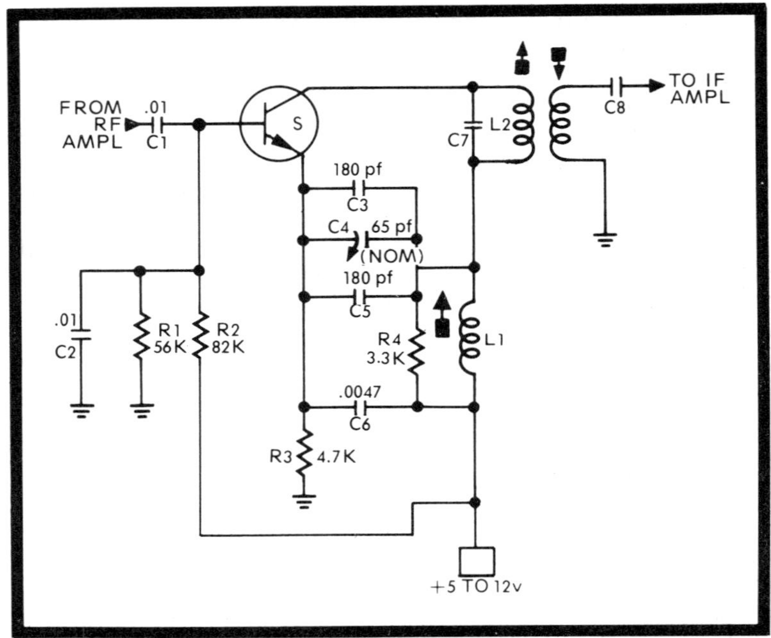

Fig. 4-5. AM converter, auto radio, NPN.

several points. A point that will have little effect on the oscillator frequency, even with a direct probe, is at the emitter of the transistor since the impedance here is low. If you measure across the oscillator coil (L1), be sure to use a low-capacity probe for best results.

At the collector of the converter transistor, you can also see the oscillator output, as well as a composite output, if a station is tuned in and everything is working normally up to that point. Again, be sure to use a low-capacity probe, or if you have only a direct probe, connect a 10 pf capacitor in series with the probe tip.

Fig. 4-5 is very similar to Fig. 4-4 except that an NPN rather than a PNP transistor is used. Testing for both circuits is identical.

MIXERS

A mixer circuit is just what the name implies, a circuit in which two different signals are mixed and a third produced. For example, in an FM receiver, if the radio is tuned to a station at 90.3 MHz, the local oscillator will generate a signal at 101 MHz. Inside the mixer the two signals will beat together and produce a 10.7 MHz signal. (The mixer would also produce a 192.3 MHz signal—the sum of 90.3 and 101 MHz—if the mixer output were tuned to around 192 MHz, but if the mixer output is tuned to 10.7 MHz then the mixer output will be the difference between the two signals.)

Such a stage, in order to be a good mixer, must be nonlinear, that is, it must actually distort the signals so they will mix readily. (By comparison, an audio amplifier has many different frequencies mixed within it and so long as the amplifier is linear the mixing and producing of other frequencies is virtually nonexistent and distortion of the output is low.)

A mixer stage should not be confused with a converter stage. A converter stage does double duty, not only as a mixer but as the local oscillator as well. A mixer stage doesn't have a local oscillator; that's a separate circuit. Fig. 5-1 shows the

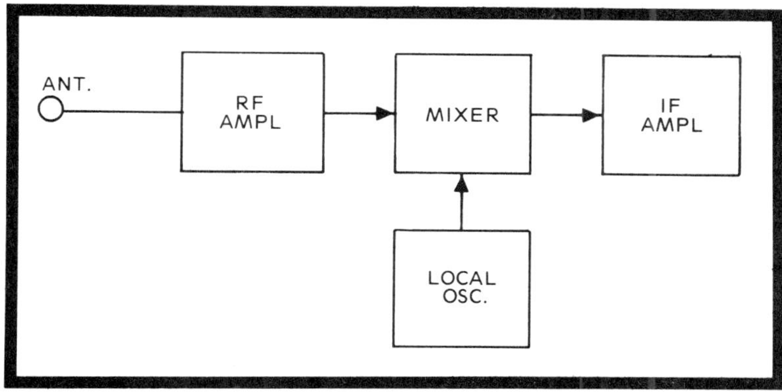

Fig. 5-1. Mixer position in typical radio, block diagram.

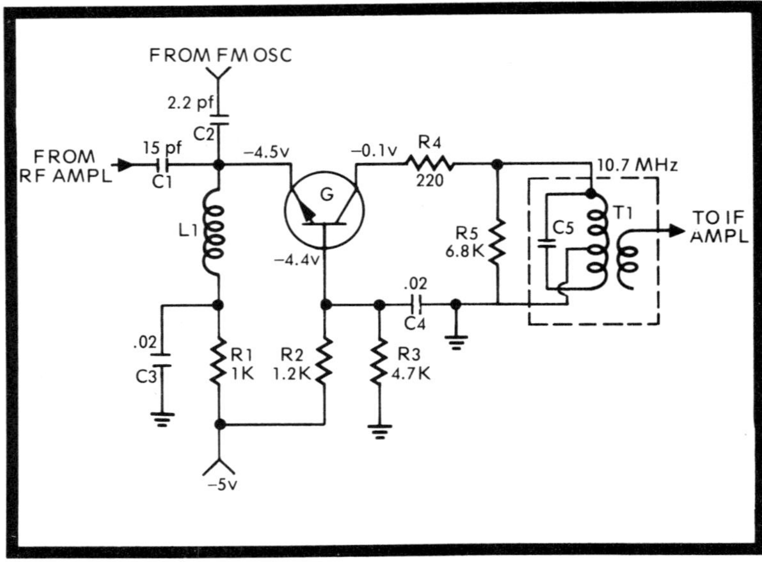

Fig. 5-2. FM mixer (used with separate FM oscillator).

arrangement in block form of the front end of a receiver and 1st IF amplifier.

FM OR VHF MIXER (Grounded-Base)

Fig. 5-2 shows a grounded-base circuit with the RF signal input and the oscillator input both to the emitter. The base is grounded for signal voltages by bypass C4. Base bias is applied through R2 and R3. Protective resistor R1 (1K) is bypassed by C3 to prevent degeneration of the signal.

To give additional stability to the circuit and prevent spurious oscillation, a 220 ohm resistor, R4, is connected between the collector and IF transformer T1. Also, the coil is tapped up and resistor R5 is connected across the coil to reduce gain and thus reduce any tendency for the circuit to oscillate on its own.

Troubleshooting the Circuit

This particular circuit uses an NPN germanium transistor; however, the circuit would be very similar for a silicon transistor. To check the DC circuit, measure the voltage drop across R1. Each volt across a 1K resistor is equal to 1 ma of current through it. A mixer circuit usually has less than 1 ma of current flow. About 0.5 ma is indicated here since the drop across R1 should be 0.5 volt.

If the emitter voltage is low, measured to ground, check for a shorted or leaky transistor, or possibly an open base bias resistor R2. If the emitter voltage is equal to the source voltage, it means there is no drop across R1 and so either the transistor is open, or the base bias resistor R3 is open.

If C4 should short, the transistor will draw excessive current, and the emitter voltage will be near zero measured to ground.

Note: Measuring voltages to ground can be misleading, especially when the DC source voltage is applied to the emitter rather than to the collector circuit. For this reason it is often less confusing if the technician measures all voltages in the transistor circuit with respect to the emitter. In this circuit, for example, the base bias, measured between base and emitter, reads —0.1 volt which is about right for a germanium transistor. Measuring between the —5 volt source and the emitter indicates the voltage drop across R1 and in turn the transistor current, etc.

FM OR VHF MIXER (Common-Emitter)

This circuit (Fig. 5-3) uses an NPN silicon transistor in a common-emitter circuit. The signal input as well as the oscillator input is to the base across a VHF choke, which is usually only a few turns of wire wound on a small form.

Base bias is supplied by one resistor R1 (390K). This use of just one resistor is practical in silicon transistor circuits because they are much less susceptible than germaniums to increased leakage due to heat. The 1K resistor (R2) is not for protective purposes but rather to provide a nonlinearity in the circuit for better mixer characteristics. Current in the circuit is 0.45 ma as indicated by the voltage drop across R2, the 1K resistor (Ohm's law).

A losser resistor, R3, and tuned-circuit loading resistors, R4 and R5, reduce the gain of the circuit to insure stability and thus keep the mixer circuit from oscillating at some spurious frequency on its own.

The two 10.7 MHz coils, L2 and L3, are "high C" coupled through C5. There is no mutual inductance coupling between L2 and L3 since each is inside a separate shield can.

Although 4 volts is shown here as the DC source, the circuit will work with either slightly higher or lower voltages.

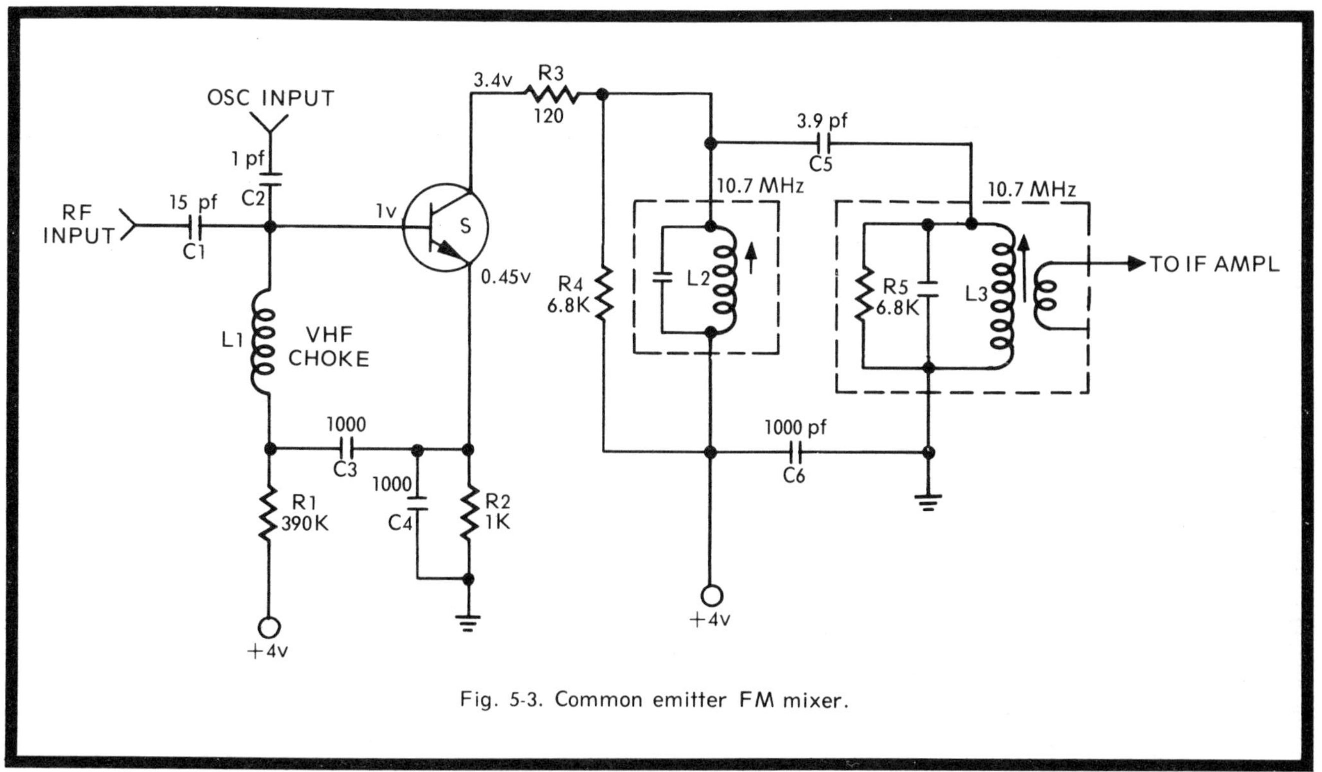

Fig. 5-3. Common emitter FM mixer.

Troubleshooting the Circuit

Measure the voltage drop across emitter resistor R2. If the voltage drop is high, check for a defective transistor or possibly, though rarely, the 390K resistor (R1) could have changed to a considerably lower value.

If the emitter voltage is very low or zero, check the DC source voltage. If okay, check for an open 390K base bias resistor (R1) or for a shorted C3, or possibly, though rarely, a shorted C4. Also check L1.

If either C3 or C4 should open, the circuit will have low gain and there will likely be a strong hiss in the radio output.

If either L2 or L3 fail to "peak up" the signal, the coils should be replaced. Because of the resistive load across these coils, the peak will not be as sharp as in other portions of the IF circuit, but there should be a definite rise in signal strength at some point in the slug adjustment.

TV CASCODE MIXER

On first glance at Fig. 5-4 it might seem foolish to use two transistors when many circuits use only one to do the same

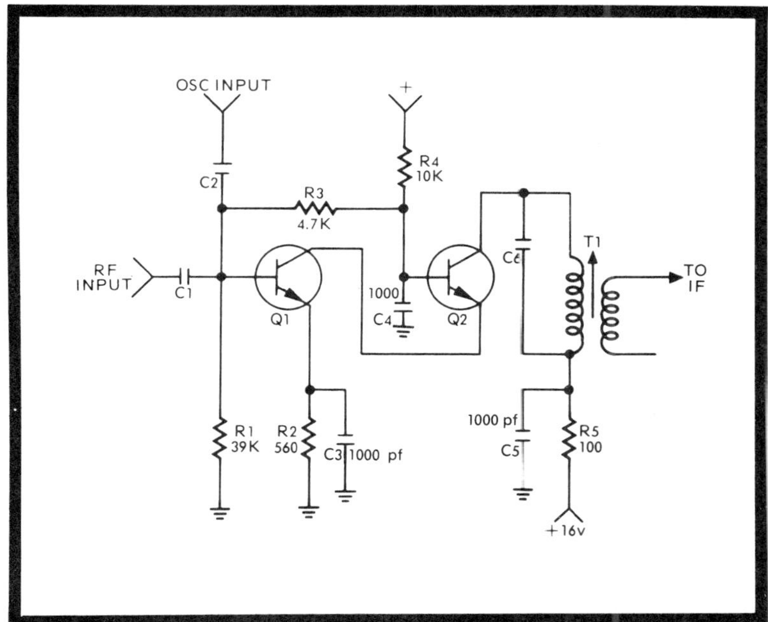

Fig. 5-4. TV cascode transistor mixer.

mixer job. The advantage of two transistors is the inherent stability of the circuit. The first transistor (Q1) is connected in a common-emitter circuit with the output connected into the emitter of a grounded-base amplifier (Q2). The stability occurs because the input and output have a high degree of isolation.

Base bias for the transistors is provided by the network R4, R3, and R1, with the bias adjusted to provide the most efficient mixer action.

Troubleshooting the Circuit

Since the transistors in this circuit are in series, both must be biased correctly for either to work. If the voltage drop across R2 is correct, then the chances are great that the bias on both transistors is correct.

If DC voltages are normal, yet the mixer is not working properly, check for an open C4 or C5. C1 and C2 are very small capacitors and seldom become defective unless actually physically broken or leads not properly connected.

FET MIXER

The field-effect transistor (FET) is not so popular as a mixer as it is an RF or IF amplifier. This is because the bipolar transistor makes an efficient low noise mixer. Such problems as higher cross modulation, or poor AGC control ability, that can plague the bipolar transistor used as an RF or IF amplifier, are not a consideration in the mixer circuit, since, by nature, the mixer needs no AGC control and must operate nonlinearly to be a mixer in the first place.

The FET mixer (Fig. 5-5), here using a dual-gate MOSFET, somewhat resembles the older multigrid tube mixers. The radio signal is applied to one gate, the local oscillator signal to the other gate. A positive "enhancement" bias is applied to both gates, through R3 and R2. R1 reduces the enhancement bias to the required level. R1 is necessary since the gates are insulated from the channel and thus draw no current. Without R1, the gates would have 12 volts on them which is the same voltage as the drain terminal has, so there would be no control possible by the gates.

R4 is the source resistor which provides some self bias for the circuit, limiting the current to a safe value (along with the drain decoupling resistor R5).

Because of the high output impedance of the FET, the drain is connected directly to the "hot" signal side of T1, similar to the old tube circuits.

Troubleshooting the Circuit

The best method here, once you suspect the mixer stage is defective, is to use a voltmeter. The voltage across R4 should be as shown on the factory schematic. In this particular circuit, the voltage is 1 volt indicating a FET current of about 3 ma. Obviously there should also be about a 1 volt drop across R5, meaning that the drain voltage to ground, assuming a 12 volt supply, would be 11 volts.

This particular FET has built-in, back-to-back zener diodes between the gates and the source so that it is not easily damaged as earlier insulated-gate transistors were, so it is quite practical to remove the gate leads from the circuit for testing. To test the gates for leakage, measure the voltage on the floating gate lead. It should be less than 0.1 volt as measured with a VTVM or a high impedance FET voltmeter.

The insulated-gate FET should NOT have diode action between the gates and the source.

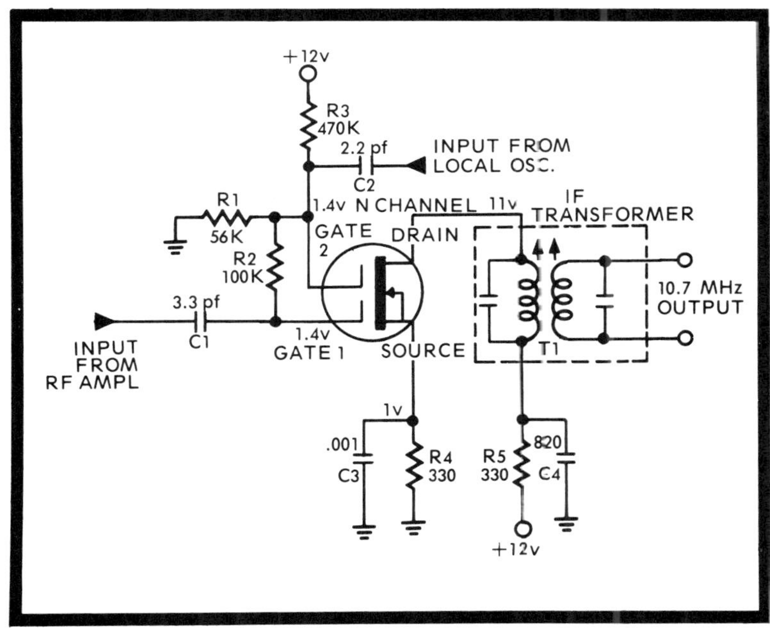

Fig. 5-5. FET FM mixer.

For signal tracing, to make sure that the mixer is the trouble, set the signal generator to 10.7 MHz and feed a signal to each gate through a 100 pf capacitor. If the transistor is working you should be able to get out a stronger signal than if you apply the same amount of signal to the input of the 1st IF amplifier. You should be able to tune T1 to a peak while feeding in the 10.7 MHz signal to either of the FET gates.

The input from the signal generator should be no stronger than needed.

AUTOMATIC FINE TUNING

Automatic fine tuning (AFT) is the same thing for TV as automatic frequency control (AFC) is for FM radio. The basic idea is that when the oscillator is at the correct frequency, a phase detector will put out no error voltage and so have no effect on the oscillator frequency. But if the oscillator frequency does change, a DC voltage is developed by the phase detector, and the "error voltage" is fed to a control element to increase or decrease the frequency until the oscillator frequency returns to normal.

Fig. 6-1 shows two kinds of control elements. The varactor is the most common. Any diode when reverse-biased will act as a variable capacitor by changing the amount of reverse

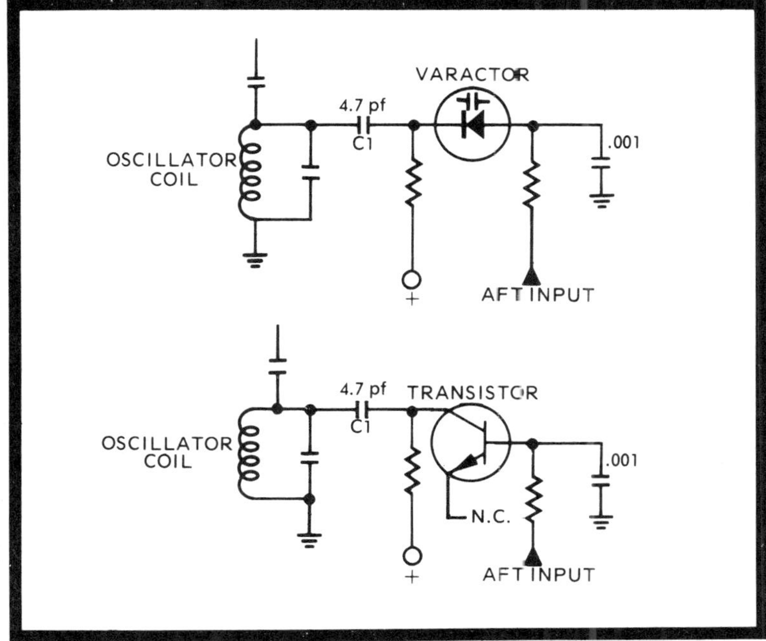

Fig. 6-1. Automatic fine tuning control devices.

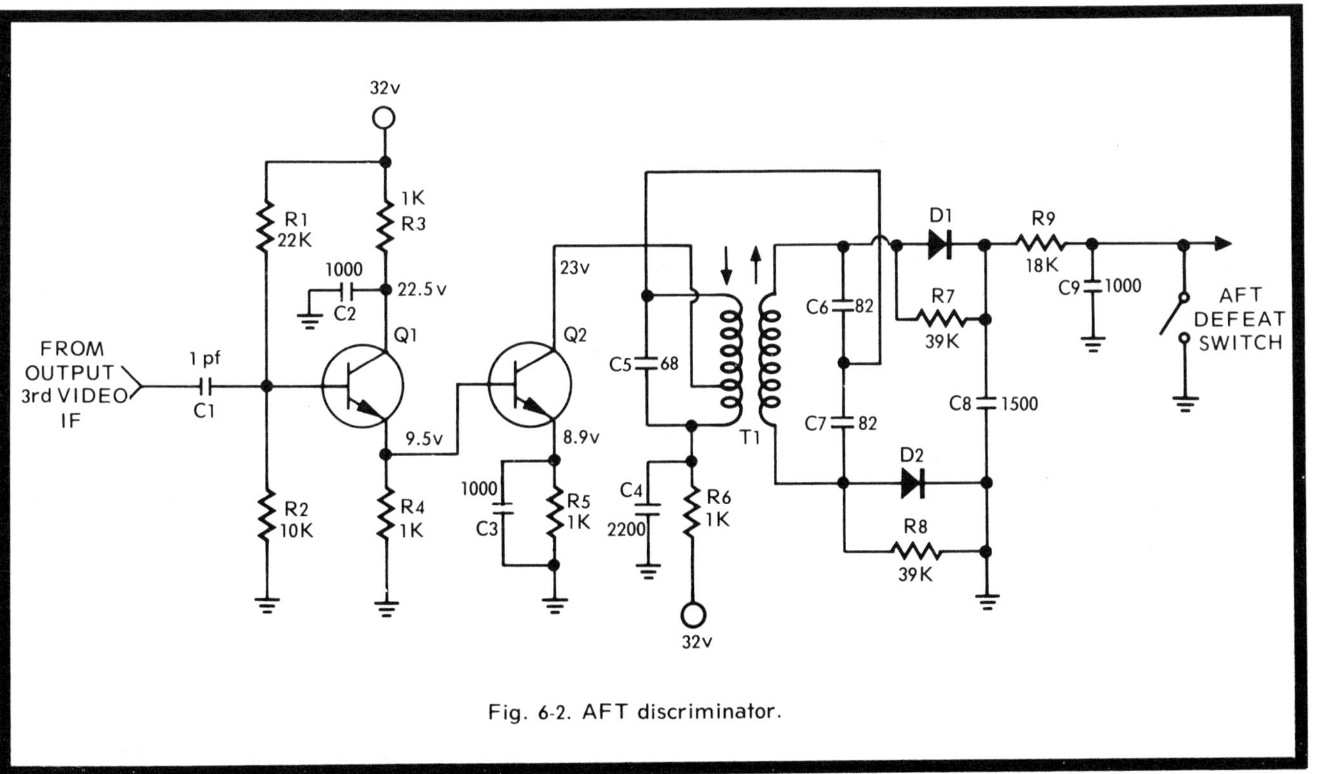

Fig. 6-2. AFT discriminator.

bias (the more reverse bias the less the capacity). Diodes specially processed to exhibit this effect best are called varactors. The varactor is reverse-biased with a fixed plus voltage on one side, and the amount of bias on the other side is varied by the AFT error voltage. The AFT error voltage changes the varactor capacity and the varactor changes the oscillator tuning, slowing down the oscillator when the reverse bias is lowered and speeding up the frequency when the reverse bias is raised. Obviously the AFT input does not have to be both positive and negative, it can simply be more or less positive.

Another element sometimes used for control is a transistor using only two terminals, generally the collector and base junction, that is, a diode. The operation is the same as for the varactor, reverse-biasing a diode junction and then varying the amount of reverse bias to change the capacity across the junction and thus change the oscillator tuning.

AFT DISCRIMINATOR

In Fig. 6-2, the IF signal from the last video IF stage is fed through the 1 pf capacitor, C1, to transistor amplifiers Q1 and Q2. Transformer T1 feeds the diodes D1 and D2, which are in an unbalanced discriminator circuit which develops zero voltage output when the IF signal is the same as that to which T1 is tuned. If the frequency of the signal is either higher or lower than desired, the discriminator develops either a positive or negative DC "error" voltage that is fed, in turn, to a varactor in the tuner oscillator circuit to correct for the change.

The AFT defeat switch grounds out the AFT line and so sets a zero voltage reference. With the AFT defeated, the fine tuning on the set can be adjusted for the best picture, and then when the AFT is switched on again it will hold the picture at this point regardless of reasonable amounts of tuner oscillator drift.

This circuit works identically to an FM discriminator detector, with either diode D1 or D2 receiving more signal depending upon whether the frequency is high or low. When D1 has the most signal, the output voltage will be positive. When D2 receives more signal, the DC output voltage will be more negative. Resistor R7 permits the rectified voltage from D2 to be applied directly to the cathode of D1, while R8 permits a DC return for D1.

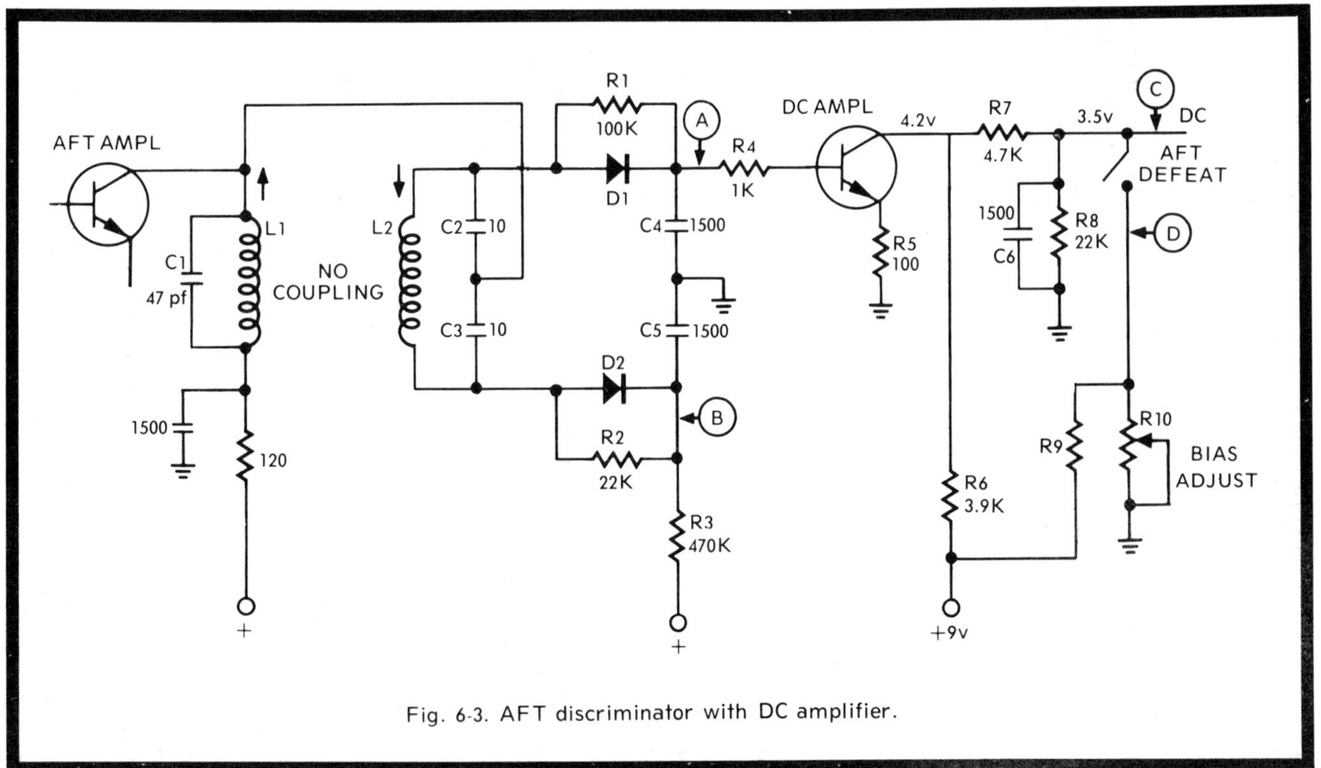

Fig. 6-3. AFT discriminator with DC amplifier.

Troubleshooting the Circuit

Adjustment of the circuit is usually not complicated. For touch up adjustments, close the AFT defeat switch (AFT OFF) and tune in a good color picture (or black and white on a monochrome set) by adjusting until the picture gets "wormy" (moirė effect) and then until the "worms" nearly disappear. Now switch on the AFT. If the picture pulls in normally, no adjustment of the AFT circuit is needed. If, however, the picture is pulled back into the "worms" or in the other direction into a smear, carefully adjust the slug in the secondary of T1 until the picture is good. Now close the AFT switch (OFF). There should be no more than a tiny change in the picture, corresponding to the picture you originally tuned in with the AFT defeated (OFF). Try all active channels including UHF to make sure that the picture will pull out of the "worms" (moire effect) when the AFT switch is on.

To check the AFT circuit to see whether trouble is in it or in the control circuits in the oscillator, check the AFT voltage with a voltmeter. The AFT voltage should go through zero when a station is tuned in and the fine tuning is rotated throughout its range. If the AFT voltage is normal but the oscillator will not pull in when the AFT is switched on, the trouble is probably in the varactor or its associated circuitry in the tuner. Some tuners use a transistor as the control device rather than a varactor, and sometimes only the collector-base junction of the transistor is used as a diode (emitter not connected).

If the AFT voltage does not change or changes very little, it is most likely caused by a defective transistor, or by serious mistuning of transformer T1. Check the transistors by measuring the emitter voltage, comparing it with the schematic. Here the voltage drop across the emitter resistors indicates that Q1 has a current flow of 9.5 ma and Q2 has 8.9 ma (the voltage drop across a 1K resistor and the number of milliamperes through the resistor are the same).

If either diode D1 or D2 should become defective, replace both diodes with a matched pair.

AFT DISCRIMINATOR WITH DC AMPLIFIER

It is sometimes desirable to increase the amount of DC change provided by the automatic fine tuning (AFT) circuit. In Fig. 6-3, a DC amplifier is used to provide an output voltage which does not reference around zero voltage but around some fixed voltage, in this case, about 3.5 volts. This 3.5 volt reference represents an "in tune" condition, and less than 3.5 volts represents an error correction voltage to speed up the oscillator while more than 3.5v represents an error voltage to slow down the oscillator frequency.

The DC amplifier can easily produce a voltage swing that is 10 times larger than the discriminator output can swing. With this circuit, the transistor must be biased to conduct, and bias voltage is provided by R3. This bias establishes the collector voltage at around half the B+ voltage. If the voltage to the base goes more positive because of discriminator action, the transistor conducts more and the collector voltage will go less positive; on the other hand, however, if the base voltage goes less positive, the collector voltage will go more positive.

Obviously, the AFT defeat switch cannot short the AFT line to ground since this would change the DC voltage on the varactor in the tuner by an average of 3.5 volts. To prevent this from happening a bias circuit is provided which can be adjusted to 3.5 volts so that when the AFT defeat switch is closed there is no change on the AFT line.

Troubleshooting the Circuit

This particular circuit uses unshielded coils for L1 and L2 and little or no coupling between the coils. Adjustment of the circuit is essentially the same as for Fig. 6-2 so far as the discriminator circuit is concerned. The critical adjustment is L2.

One way to adjust the bias is to short across between points A and B to assure that the discriminator output is zero. Using a high impedance voltmeter on a low range, adjust the bias until there is zero voltage between points C and D with the AFT defeat switch open.

Close the AFT defeat switch and tune in a picture that is just barely into the moire (squiggly effect around the outlines of the pictures). Open the AFT defeat switch and the picture should pull in cleanly. If not, adjust L2 until the picture is correct. (Don't forget to remove the short between C and D.)

This is a fairly rugged and straightforward circuit, and it is not too likely to give trouble if it is properly adjusted, since the diode and the transistor currents are low. However, if the AFT voltage is high, first short across points A and B so the discriminator circuit can have no effect; if the voltage returns to normal, the trouble is in the discriminator components or the tuning. If the voltage is not affected by shorting points A and B, then check for an open transistor, and also for an open 470K resistor, R3.

The same checks should be made for low collector voltage, by shorting points A and B to see whether the trouble is in the discriminator or in the DC amplifier. Low collector voltage, if the discriminator is not at fault, could be caused by a leaky transistor, or an increase in value of R6.

Chapter 7 INTERMEDIATE-FREQUENCY AMPLIFIERS

Nearly all modern receivers contain a superheterodyne circuit which uses a local oscillator that beats against the incoming signal to produce the same fixed-frequency output for all input signals. The resultant signal is then amplified by the intermediate-frequency (IF) amplifier(s). This method of receiving, using an IF amplifier instead of, say, TRF, provides better gain, better selectivity, better stability, and greatly simplifies the mechanical arrangement necessary to tune in stations.

Intermediate-frequency amplifiers are generally tuned to certain specific frequencies such as 455 kHz for AM broadcast radios (262 kHz is also used, especially in some automobile radios), 4.5 MHz for television sound, 10.7 MHz for FM broadcast radios, and around 40 MHz for television video, etc. Low-frequency IF and high-frequency amplifiers have much in common. The higher-frequency types are more often neutralized for better stability. High-frequency IFs may also have resistive loading across one or more windings to broaden the frequency response or to lower the gain slightly for better stability.

The IF amplifier usually has one or more stages that are controlled by automatic gain control (AGC). In transistorized radio circuits, this AGC is usually polarized so that as the signal increases the AGC voltage tends to cut off the transistors. In TV, forward AGC is more often used, tending to saturate the transistors whenever the signal increases. Either cutting off the transistor current or increasing the current to saturation will reduce the gain of the stage. Forward AGC has the advantage that there is less impedance change in the input circuit with change in AGC voltage and so less tendency toward detuning of the resonant circuits.

Transistor IF amplifiers using bipolar transistors (not FETs) require a step-down impedance between the output of one stage and the input of the next. Fig. 7-1 shows four ways of coupling between IF stages. "A" might be called the conventional method, using a single tuned winding with a low-

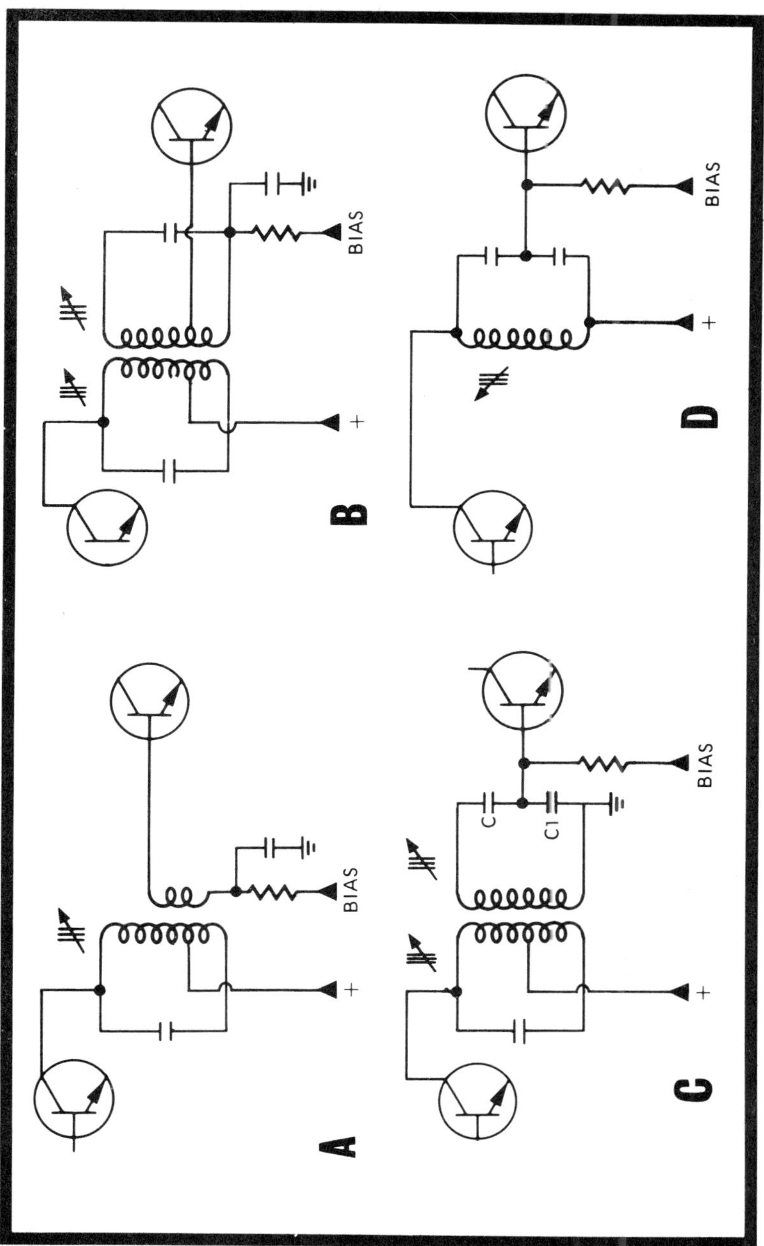

Fig. 7-1. Different coupling methods for IF amplifier stages.

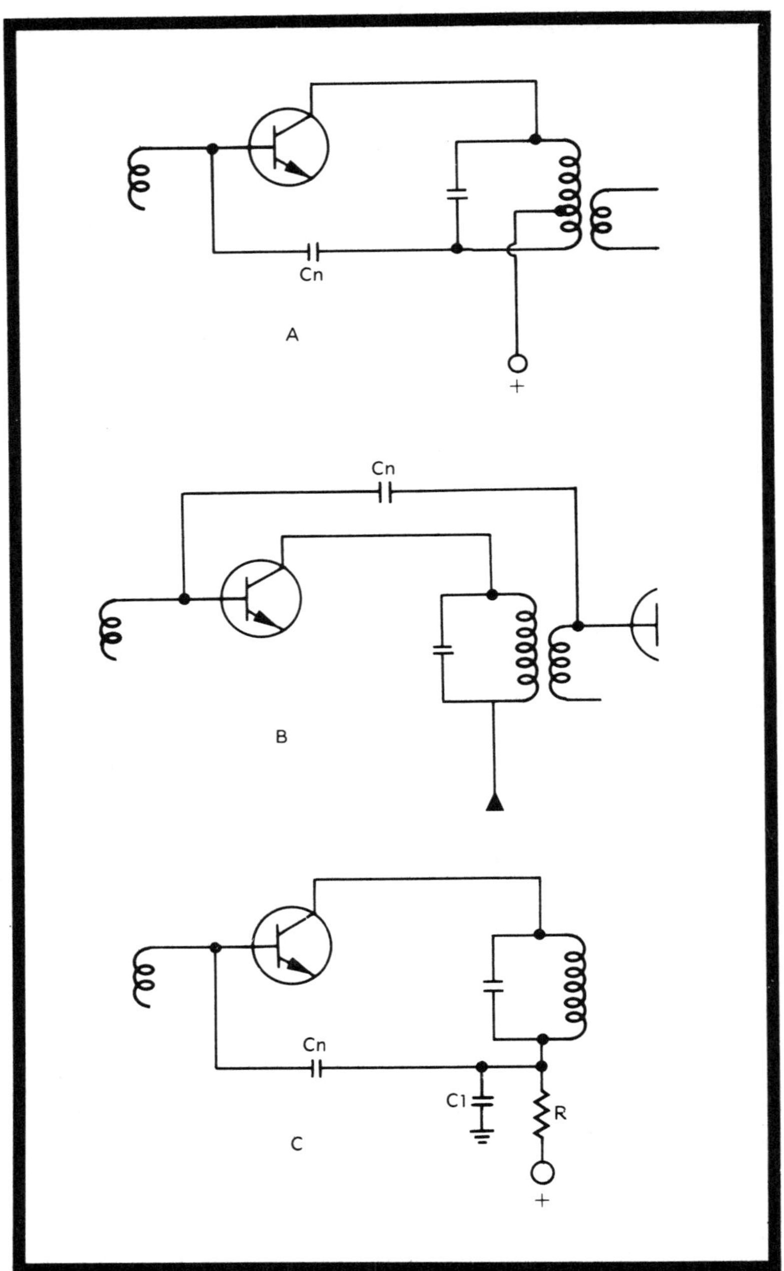

Fig. 7-2. IF amplifier neutralization methods.

impedance winding coupled to the tuned circuit to feed the base of the transistor in the next stage. "B" is a dual-tuned IF transformer with a step-down tap for the base. (Note that the collector is also tapped down, that is, the transistor output is not connected across the total tuned circuit; this provides a better match and less loading on the tuned circuit so that it tunes more sharply.) "C" is about the same circuit as "B" except that the impedance match to the base is by capacitors. Capacitor C is often about 2 to 4 times smaller than C1. This gives an almost identical effect to tapping down on the coil. "D" is a modification of the circuit in "C" so that only one tuned circuit is used. Usually, "C" has more selectivity and somewhat more coupling efficiency than "D."

NEUTRALIZATION

A neutralized circuit generally has better stability and a somewhat better noise factor than an unneutralized circuit. However, neutralization is not so necessary if circuit gain is reduced below the point where any tendency to oscillation exists. The idea of neutralization is to cancel out, in the external circuit, the internal capacity in the transistor. Obviously the capacitor between the collector and base is direct and in-phase so any cancellation must be reversed in phase. Fig. 7-2A shows one of the most common methods of neutralization. The tap in the IF coil where B+ is applied places an AC ground there and so the lower end of the coil provides a 180 degree phase shift to ground which can be coupled through Cn to the base for neutralization. The size of Cn is selected to exactly cancel the internal capacity of the transistor.

Fig. 7-2B shows a method sometimes used when the primary is not tapped. The secondary is connected so that the following base is 180 degrees out of phase with the collector, and the signal can be fed back through Cn to the preceding base to neutralize the stage.

The circuit in Fig. 7-2C has become quite popular in recent years. It is used more often in RF circuits where tuning is changed than in IF circuits. The idea is to select C1 so that it is not as large a bypass as normal, and this means that there is some signal always across the capacitor. This signal, 180 degrees out of phase with the collector signal, can be fed back to the base for neutralization. Resistor R is also selected to help in providing the right amount of signal impedance in the collector circuit. Both R and C1 size are not overly critical if Cn is adjustable. Sometimes the neutralization is adjusted by selecting the size of C1 rather than Cn.

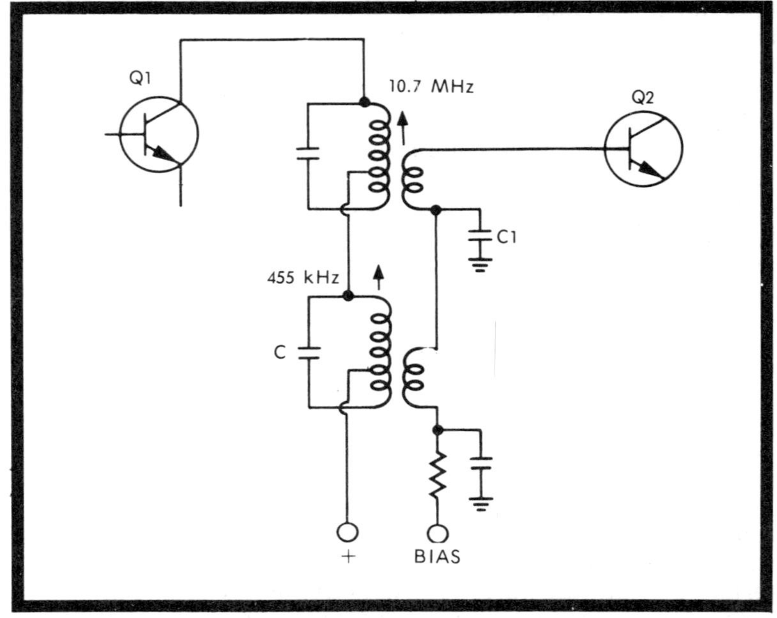

Fig. 7-3. Combination IF stage for AM-FM.

Setting neutralization is probably easiest by simply removing the B+ voltage from the collector, feeding a signal into the previous stage and adjusting neutralization for minimum IF signal in the following stage. The idea, of course, is that the signal fed through the capacity of the transistor is exactly cancelled by a 180 degree signal through the external neutralization circuit.

COMBINATION IF AMPLIFIERS

In AM-FM broadcast radios it is fairly common practice to use the same transistor to amplify both the 455-kHz and the 10.7-MHz IF signals. This is not too difficult to do so long as the transistor selected works well at 10.7 MHz. The difference in frequency of the two signals makes series coupling of the IF transformers practical.

Fig. 7-3 shows the most common method of coupling used. The high-frequency coils are placed nearest the transistor since they are the most sensitive to length of leads. Capacitor C is the tuned circuit capacitor for the 455 kHz primary, but it also acts as an excellent bypass for the B+ tap on the 10.7 MHz primary. C1 may or may not be used, depending upon several factors including the capacity of the secondary winding on the 455 kHz transformer. The reason for C1 is to provide a low end bypass for the 10.7 MHz secondary, but it must also be small enough not to appreciably affect the 455 kHz signal going to the base of Q2.

The windings on the 10.7 MHz transformer have very low inductance and so they do not have any noticeable effect on the 455 kHz signal.

Some designs will have a switch to short out the 455 kHz winding when the radio is switched to FM. This switching out may be to provide slightly better gain than otherwise but is often a simple way to eliminate any possible IF "feedthrough" at 455 kHz.

Sometimes the designer will combine an IF amplifier with an AM converter circuit. A circuit of this type is shown in the converter section of this book.

AM IF AMPLIFIER FOR 455 kHz

This circuit, Fig. 7-4, uses a PNP germanium transistor with the emitter circuit tied to B+ and the collector circuit grounded. (When a circuit has the DC connected in this manner, the bias readings to ground are difficult to interpret so a bias reading is much more meaningful, as it most often is, by measuring between the base and emitter.)

The signal to the base is fed from the preceding stage by a low impedance windings. (Low impedance simply means that

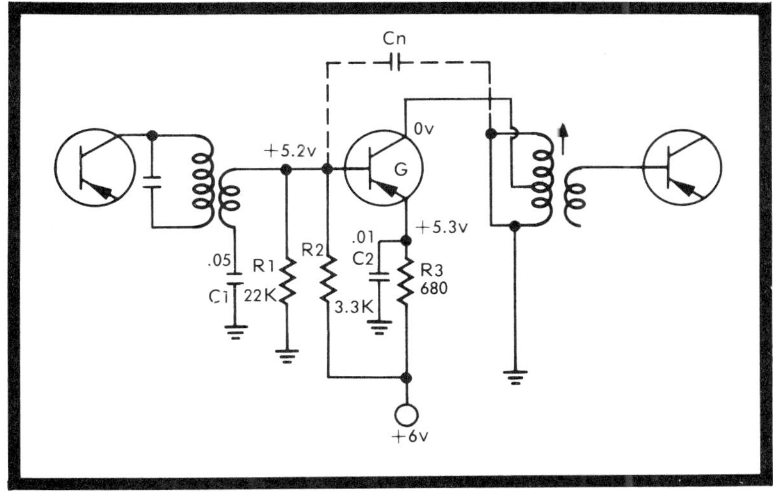

Fig. 7-4. A 455 kHz IF amplifier.

the winding has a few turns as compared to the primary winding, in other words, a voltage step-down and a current step-up.) Bias for the stage is provided by R1 (R1 goes to ground, the negative side of the power supply, and a PNP transistor base and collector require negative bias with respect to the emitter). R2 is the bleeder for the bias circuit and helps prevent any collector-to-base leakage in the transistor from seriously affecting the overall transistor bias. C1 connects the low end of the base input coil to ground so far as the signal is concerned and also blocks the DC bias voltage so that the bias won't be shorted to ground.

R3, the emitter bias resistor, protects the transistor from excessive current. Remember, this is a germanium transistor; as the transistor current tends to increase with warmup, the bias on the emitter goes more negative and this subtracts from the base bias.

C2 is necessary to bypass the signal voltage around the emitter resistor, otherwise the gain of the stage would be very low. (This lowering of the gain if C2 should open is caused by degeneration; in other words, with C2 open, when the signal on the base goes negative, transistor current would try to increase but this would increase current flow through R3 which would make the emitter go more negative and cancel out a considerable amount of the increase. C2 allows the 680 ohm resistor (R3) to provide degeneration for DC current but to have no effect on the signal voltage.)

The collector is tapped down on the primary of the IF coil. This method provides a better match between the medium output impedance of the transistor and the higher impedance of the tuned circuit. Matching the impedance provides less load on the tuned circuit and so the tuning is sharper and the gain is higher.

The neutralizing capacitor is connected to the "floating" terminal on the IF transformer, but is not used in all circuits of this general type. However, most radios using germanium transistors do use some form of neutralization in the IF circuit.

Troubleshooting the Circuit

As with all transistor circuits, the best place to start is by determining if the transistor is drawing the approximate normal amount of current. For germanium transistors this will usually be from about 0.75 to 2 ma in an IF amplifier, with around 1 ma being considered pretty much the norm.

Note that this circuit has a "hot" emitter so far as DC voltage is concerned. The B+ voltage shown here is +6 and the emitter voltage is 5.3v read to ground, meaning that the drop across R3 is 0.7 volt. Calculation will show that a 0.7 volt drop across a 680 ohm resistor is just slightly over 1 ma. The voltage shown here on the base is +5.2v, meaning that the base is 0.1 volt more negative (less positive) than the emitter, and this is about normal for a germanium transistor.

The easiest way to check current flow, of course, is not to subtract the emitter voltage from the B+ voltage but rather, if possible, to measure the voltage drop directly across R3, which in this case would be 0.7 volt. And the most direct and most accurate way to measure bias is not to subtract the base voltage from the emitter voltage (when both are measured to ground) but rather to simply measure between the base and emitter terminals. Why? Consider this: What might happen if C2 shorted? This would reduce the emitter voltage to zero and since the collector voltage is zero, there would be no drop across the transistor and therefore no current could flow. Of course, there would be +6 volts across R3 and this could make it appear that the transistor was drawing heavy current when in reality it was drawing none. The base voltage would still be near normal because the transistor is reverse-biased and so no base-emitter current is flowing.

What might be wrong if the collector reads about +6 volts to ground? This would likely indicate that the primary of the IF transformer is open. The voltage read would be the result of transistor current flow, or said another way, there is a resistance connection between the collector and emitter which causes the voltmeter to read the emitter voltage.

What happens if C2 opens? The gain would be very low, caused by excessive degeneration. With C2 open, and signal on the base goes negative, transistor current would try to increase. But this would increase current through R3, causing the emitter to go more negative, thereby cancelling a large portion of the increase.

AUTO RADIO IF AMPLIFIER

The circuit in Fig. 7-5 is similar in many ways to the previous circuit, but uses an NPN transistor with an emitter ground circuit. Bias is applied directly to the base, as in the previous circuit, but the blocking capacitor is in the "hot" side of the input IF coil rather than the "cold" side. But the blocking capacitor does more; it is part of the tuning of the L1 IF output winding so that in reality the base is connected in a

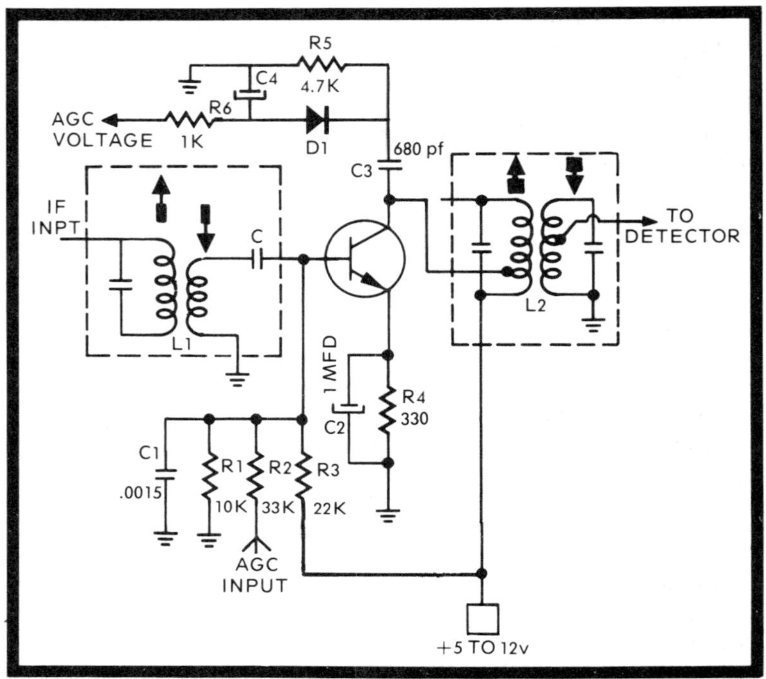

Fig. 7-5. Auto radio IF amplifier with AGC diode.

capacity divider circuit, C and C1, providing a low impedance match to the base.

The output IF transformer L2 also is dual-tuned but, in this circuit, taps on the coil are used for matching.

The AGC voltage input through R3 to the base is negative-increasing as the signal strength increases. The AGC is developed by a separate diode, D1, which rectifies the signal voltage from the collector, thereby developing a negative voltage that is proportionate to signal strength.

Auto radios often use only one IF stage, that is, one transistor and two IF transformers and this layout is usual if the IF used is 262 kHz. But at the same time, auto radios almost invariably use an RF amplifier stage. Dual-tuning of the IF transformers makes for a more complex transformer but raises the selectivity and gain.

Troubleshooting the Circuit

The most likely trouble spot here is the transistor itself. Measure the emitter voltage. It should be in the neighborhood of 0.7 to 1.2 volts, indicating the transistor is drawing around 2 to 3.5 ma. Collector voltage should be the same as the supply voltage unless there is a resistor in the collector circuit. Base bias, measured to the emitter, should be above 0.4 volt.

If the stage has low gain, check emitter bypass capacitor C2. Also check the tuning of the IF transformers; if either winding fails to "peak" the signal output, it is likely that transformer needs replacing.

Excessive gain, noted by overload and distortion when trying to listen to strong local stations, can be an indication of loss of AGC, caused by an open or shorted diode D1. Check to see that the AGC voltage changes when a station is tuned in and out. Often, AGC voltage will have a fixed + or - voltage due to the bias circuits it is feeding, so the thing to look for is change of voltage with a change in signal. Even this effect can sometimes be misleading because the overloaded transistor will start rectifying on its own and produce some bias voltage changes.

10.7 MHz IF AMPLIFIER FOR FM RADIO

The circuit in Fig. 7-6 is similar to amplifiers already described. It uses an NPN transistor which is neutralized by feeding back an out-of-phase signal through Cn. The collector circuit is returned to DC ground and the emitter goes to the B- source.

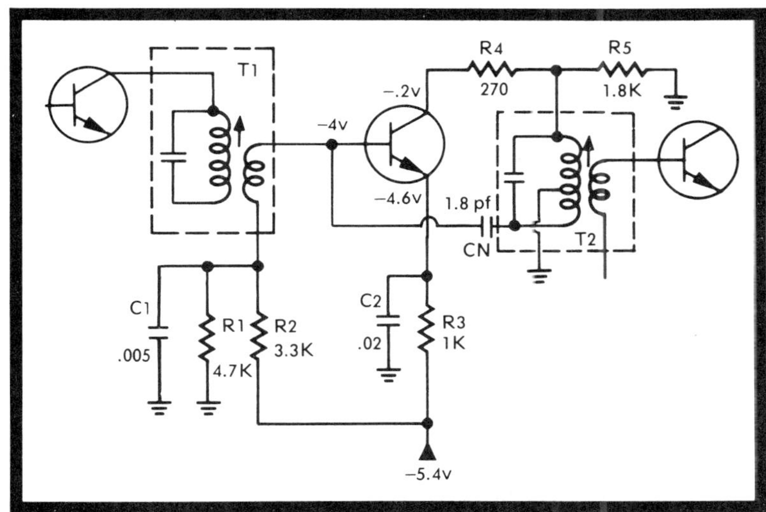

Fig. 7-6. Typical 10.7 MHz IF for FM broadcast radio.

A 270-ohm resistor, R4, is a "losser" resistor which tends to stabilize the circuit by lowering the gain a bit and also by decoupling slightly the internal capacity of the transistor from the tuned circuit. R5, the 1.8K resistor across part of the primary winding of T2, serves to "broaden" the response so as to better pass the FM signal. At the same time, R5 also lowers the stage gain somewhat.

Troubleshooting the Circuit

When the collector circuit is grounded it is even more important to check DC voltages between the transistor elements, when practical, to determine bias voltage. Here the normal bias is about 0.6 volt. The NPN transistor requires a positive polarity on the base with respect to the emitter. Here the base is 0.6 volt less negative (more positive) than the emitter.

Measuring across R3 indicates the transistor current, and the calculation is always easy across a 1K resistor since the voltage drop and the milliamperes are identical. Here the voltage drop is 0.8 volt (the difference between -5.4 and -4.6) and this means the current is 0.8 ma as well.

There should be a small amount of voltage (say 0.2v) on the collector since the 270 ohm resistor is in series with the collector current which is virtually identical to the emitter current of 0.8 ma. (0.8 ma times 270 is about 0.21 volt.) If there should be voltage at the junction of R4 and R5, it is a strong indication that the primary of T2 is open since for DC, the 1.8K resistor is shorted by the primary winding of T2 and that junction is nearly at ground.

If transistor current is low or zero, check for a changed value or an open R1 by measuring bias. If bias is present, that is, the base voltage is lower (less negative) than the supply, check the transistor.

If the emitter voltage is zero, about the only cause would be a shorted C2, assuming that source voltage is normal.

TV IF (40 MHz)

This circuit (Fig. 7-7) is similar to others already discussed except that it operates in the 40 MHz range. The neutralization is of the type discussed in the early part of this chapter, with Cn feeding back an out-of-phase signal derived from the junction of R4 and C3, and with the capacity of C3 selected to bypass part of the IF signal.

The resonant capacitor for T2 is C4. It is not connected directly across the coil but is connected to ground instead.

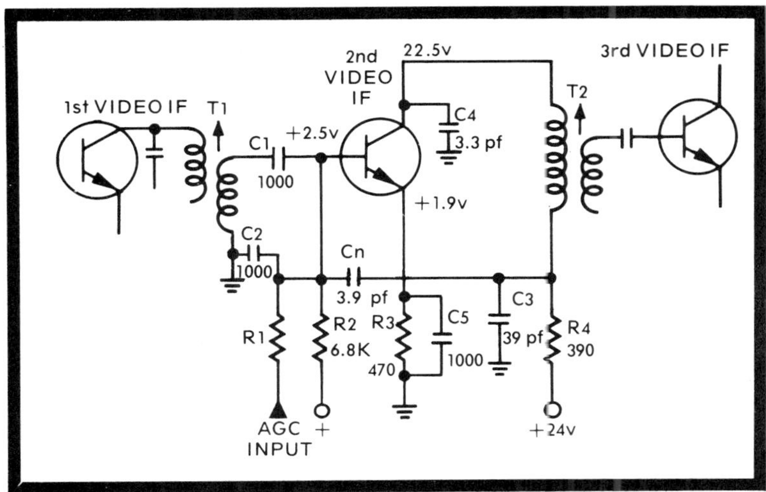

Fig. 7-7. Video IF, 40 MHz range.

This is a rather common practice and physically the capacitor is connected directly from the collector terminal of the transistor to ground. This is because at high frequencies even a short length of wire can look like an RF choke. Fig. 7-8 shows why this happens; in "A" the wire connecting the coil to the transistor becomes part of the resonant circuit and so there is

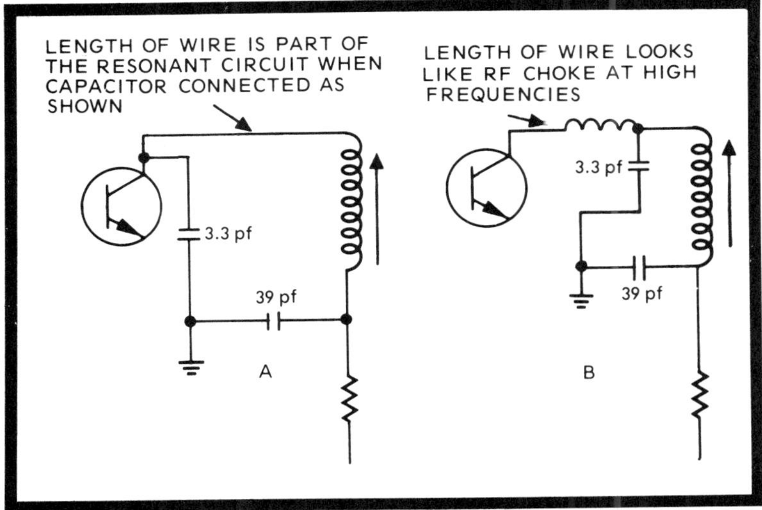

Fig. 7-8. How connecting a capacitor across transistor improves performance of HF IF.

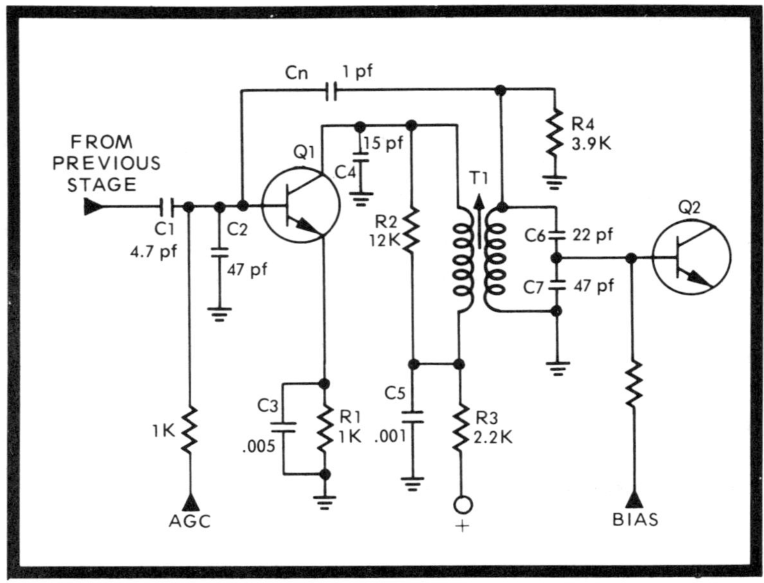

Fig. 7-9. TV IF amplifier, capacity-tapped Z match.

no loss across it, while in "B" the wire is not part of the circuit and at higher frequencies acts as a small RF choke, reducing the gain of the stage and possibly resulting in spurious instabilities.

The AGC in this circuit is the "forward" type, meaning that as signal input increases the AGC goes more positive, thus increasing the current flow of the NPN transistor toward saturation. Because of R4, saturation occurs more quickly, since, as the transistor current increases, the voltage drop across R4 increases, and this, in turn, reduces the supply voltage to the collector.

Troubleshooting the Circuit

The normal current flow in video IF amplifiers is generally greater than in small transistor radios mostly because the collector voltage is higher. This particular circuit has a normal current of around 4 ma but this will vary greatly with bias. With a strong signal, current flow may be 15 ma or more.

What if the emitter voltage is zero? This could be caused by a defective transistor or by a lack of transistor bias. Zero bias might be caused either by an open R2 or it could be caused by an excessive negative voltage coming from the AGC circuit. One way to find out if the transistor will respond to bias is to place a small resistor of about 5K from collector to base while measuring the emitter voltage. This should increase the emitter voltage because the transistor will be biased in a more positive direction.

If, on the other hand, the emitter voltage is already high, try connecting a jumper between the base and emitter and see if the voltage on the emitter drops to zero; if it doesn't, the transistor is almost surely defective.

Excessive emitter voltage can also be caused by the AGC system being out of adjustment, or it could be caused (rarely) by a leaky capacitor Cn. A leaky transistor can also cause excessive transistor current flow, but if leakage is the problem, shorting the base to emitter will reduce the transistor current flow. One way you can check leakage is to disconnect the base lead from other components in the circuit and then connect it through a 47K resistor to the emitter; if the emitter voltage indicates transistor current flow, the transistor is leaky.

VIDEO IF WITH CAPACITY IMPEDANCE MATCH

This circuit (Fig. 7-9) uses the capacity-type impedance match rather than tapped coils. The input comes from a resonant circuit with a 10 to 1 (4.7 pf to 47 pf) step-down in impedance. Transformer T1 is a bifilar-wound coil using C4 to resonate the primary winding and C6 and C7 the secondary. (A bifilar winding is a pair of wires wound around a coil form the same number of turns, with one coil becoming the primary and the other the secondary, giving a one to one ratio with unity coupling. Only one tuning slug is needed if capacities are carefully selected.) The base of Q2 is tapped off between C6 and C7. The 12K resistor, R2, broadens the primary winding circuit so it will pass the necessary bandwidth for video, as does the 3.9K resistor, R4, in the secondary winding.

Neutralization is taken from the secondary of T1 through the 1 pf capacitor, Cn.

Troubleshooting the Circuit

Troubleshooting is similar to that described for Fig. 7-7. The NPN transistor must have a positive bias between base and emitter before it will conduct. Here the bias is supplied totally by the AGC circuit, so any trouble in the AGC circuit can either cut off this transistor or cause it to saturate, and either case will reduce the gain of the transistor to zero.

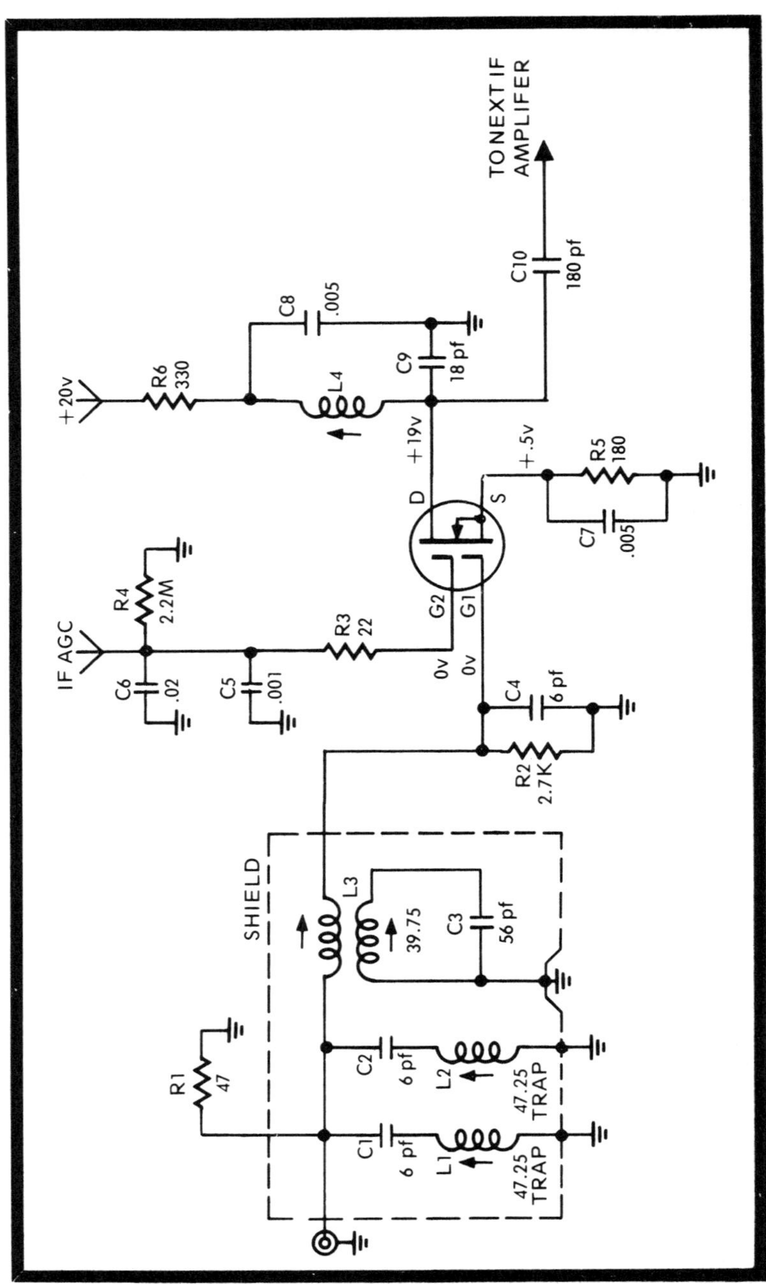

Fig. 7-10. FET TV IF amplifier.

Any tendency for this circuit to oscillate could be caused by an open neutralizing capacitor, though, many times, this circuit will show virtually no ill effects without the capacitor except for when it is receiving very weak signals, where gain is high in the stage.

A rather difficult trouble to diagnose is the refusal of the IF section in the TV to properly align. This can happen where bifilar transformers are used if one of the windings is no longer tuning properly due to an open capacitor, such as C4 or C7. It's rare, but an open R2 or R4 can also cause instability or poor tuning characteristics.

Loss in signal gain may be caused by an open C3, although this is a fairly rare trouble unless physical damage occurs in the capacitor.

FET TV IF AMPLIFIER

A low impedance input is used here (Fig. 7-10), but other circuits may be high input impedance. Output impedance is high, as is gain. Noise figure and AGC response is good. This circuit configuration is used over a wide range of frequencies with suitable tuned circuits.

The circuit in Fig. 7-10 is a dual-gate MOSFET circuit. The dual-gate compares to two cascoded amplifiers. The signal input is to gate 1. AGC is applied to gate 2. This arrangement allows the AGC voltage to be AC-grounded. The normal AGC voltage is about +4 volts, which should drop to about -0.5v when the signal is very strong. The signal input gate in this circuit is kept at 0 volts. In similar circuits, AGC is sometimes applied to gate 1 in small amounts which track with but are not as great as those applied to gate 2.

Troubleshooting the Circuit

Because this circuit is generally used at high frequencies, the FET will nearly always be soldered into the circuit. Because of the high frequencies, and without special equipment, it is best to troubleshoot this circuit by indirect methods such as making DC measurements. The nominal current in the circuit is from about 1 to 4 milliamperes. The actual current flow can be determined easily by checking the voltage drop across the source resistor (R5).

If an AGC voltage is applied to gate 2, you can ground it while measuring the source voltage. If a positive AGC voltage is grounded, the source voltage should drop.

You can check for possible leakage to the gate circuits by unsoldering the gate lead and reading the voltage on the transistor lead. Any DC voltage reading of more than 0.1 volt indicates excessive leakage and the transistor should be replaced.

Trouble Symptoms

No Drain Voltage: Check for correct supply voltage. Check for open resistor (R6) or open coil (L4). Shorted C10 (some circuits only).
Source Voltage High: Incorrect bias voltages. R5 open or changed to high value. Defective transistor.
G2 Bias Excessive: AGC circuit defective. Defective transistor.
Source Voltage Low: Incorrect bias. Defective transistor. C7 shorted (not too likely). No drain voltage, or drain voltage low.
Low Gain: Defective transistor. Incorrect bias or supply voltages. Source capacitor (C7) open. Incorrect tuning. Capacitors C4, C8 or C9 open.

Special Note 1: When DC voltages appear normal and gain appears low, check for variation in gain by tuning, using proper equipment. Any tuned circuit whose gain fails to change when tuned is an indication of a defective coil, defective tuning mechanism, or open capacitor across the tuned circuit (which can be either the small resonance-determining capacitor or the larger bypass capacitor, as for example, either C8 or C9).
Special Note 2: Oscillation in this stage is almost impossible due to the low input resistance, unless there is an open in an input circuit coil, or the 47 ohm resistor (R1) opens. For similar circuits without low impedance loading on the input circuit, oscillation may occur because of improper tuning, an open capacitor, or a defective transistor.

FET TV IF AMPLIFIER (Fixed Bias)

Characteristics of this circuit include low, medium, or high input impedance; high output impedance; no neutralization required; gain reasonably high; good noise figure; and the basic design may be used over a wide range of frequencies with suitable tuned circuits.

The circuit in Fig. 7-11 is a dual-gate MOSFET circuit similar to the AGC-controlled amplifier just described in Fig. 7-10. The main difference is the application of a fixed positive bias to gate 2 of about 4 volts developed across R2 in combination with R3.

Troubleshooting the Circuit

Because of the high frequencies, unless special equipment is available, the best check here again is by DC voltage or resistance readings. The current can be calculated by measuring the voltage across the source resistor (R4). Or you can also calculate the transistor current flow by measuring the drain voltage; here a representative +16 volts means that the voltage drop across the drain decoupling resistor R5 is 4 volts (20 - 16). Using Ohm's law and dividing the resistance of R5, 470 ohms, into the voltage drop of 4 volts, shows that the transistor current is 8.5 milliamperes.

Trouble Symptoms

Low or No Drain Voltage: Check for correct supply voltage. Drain resistor R5 open or changed value. L1 open. Shorted C4 or C3. Incorrect bias voltage, which might be caused by an open R2 or by a shorted or severely leaky C1.
Source Voltage High: Incorrect bias. R4 open. Defective transistor.
G2 Bias Excessive. R2 open. Defective transistor.
G2 Bias low: R3 open. Shorted C6. Defective transistor.

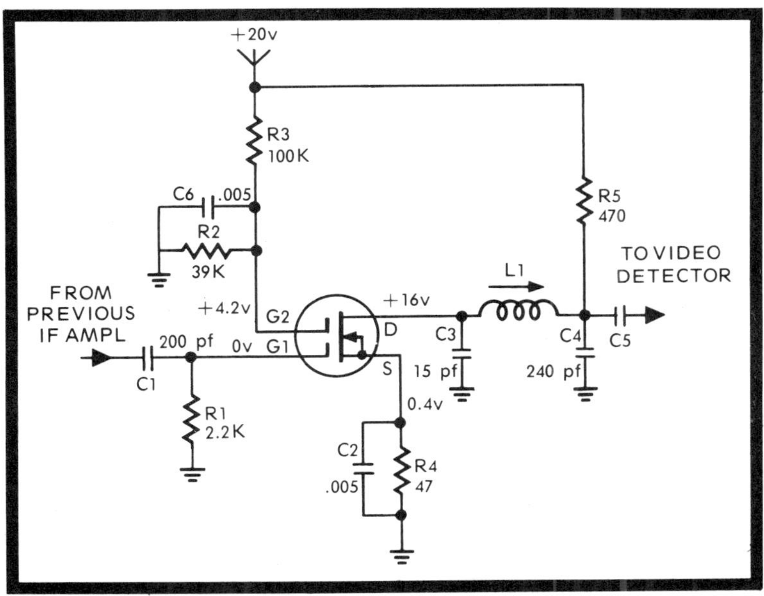

Fig. 7-11. Fixed-bias FET TV IF amplifier.

Source Voltage Low: Incorrect bias. Defective transistor. C2 shorted (unlikely). Drain voltage low.
Low Gain: Defective transistor. Incorrect bias or supply voltages. Source capacitor C2 open. Incorrect tuning. G2 capacitor (C6) open.

Special Note 1: When DC voltages appear normal, and gain still appears low, and you have temporarily bypassed the original bypass capacitors with known good parts, check for variation in gain as you tune the tuning slug(s) (if proper measuring equipment is available). If gain of the circuit fails to change as coils are tuned, check for defective coils, defective tuning mechanism, or an open fixed tuning or bypass capacitor, such as C3 or C4.
Special Note 2: Oscillation in this circuit is unlikely mainly because of the low input resistance, although in rare cases it might be caused by a defective transistor or by an open G2 bypass capacitor (C6).

AM-FM IF AMPLIFIER COMBINATION

Although most combination IF amplifiers are similar to those mentioned earlier in this section, Fig. 7-12 shows a circuit that is a bit different. Here the higher frequency IF input signal is fed to the emitter of a PNP transistor while the low frequency IF signal is fed to the base. This has several advantages, one of the major ones being that an emitter-fed amplifier does not require neutralization. Another advantage is that the secondaries of the two IF transformers are completely independent and thus neither can cause a signal loss in the other. The 100 pf base capacitor (which is not used in all similar circuits) acts as a signal ground for the 10.7 MHz signal while having almost no effect on the low impedance fed 455 kHz signal.

Otherwise the circuit is like other combination IF amplifiers; the primaries of the IF transformers are in series and the high-frequency transformer is connected closest to the transistor so that its leads can be short.

Troubleshooting the Circuit

If either the 455 kHz (AM portion) of the receiver is working or the 10.7 MHz (FM portion), then you can be reasonably certain that the transistor in a combination IF is NOT at fault. When one frequency or the other does not pass the stage, the fault is most likely in the transformer circuits themselves. However, you may get some false clues. You may be able, for example, to hear a strong AM station through the radio and not be able to get an FM station at all, or vice versa, and the cause can still be a combination circuit. This is because the strong signal may push its way through the internal capacity of the transistor.

Every IF stage should have gain and one way you can check for gain is to inject a signal from a signal generator through a .001 mfd capacitor to the COLLECTOR of the previous stage, and then to the collector of the suspected stage. The signal should be considerably stronger when injected at the previous stage collector when measured either by listening or by measuring the AGC voltage. (The signal generator should be coupled into the previous collector, and NOT into the base or emitter, since the difference in impedance of the base or emitter circuit can cause a false indication in output.)

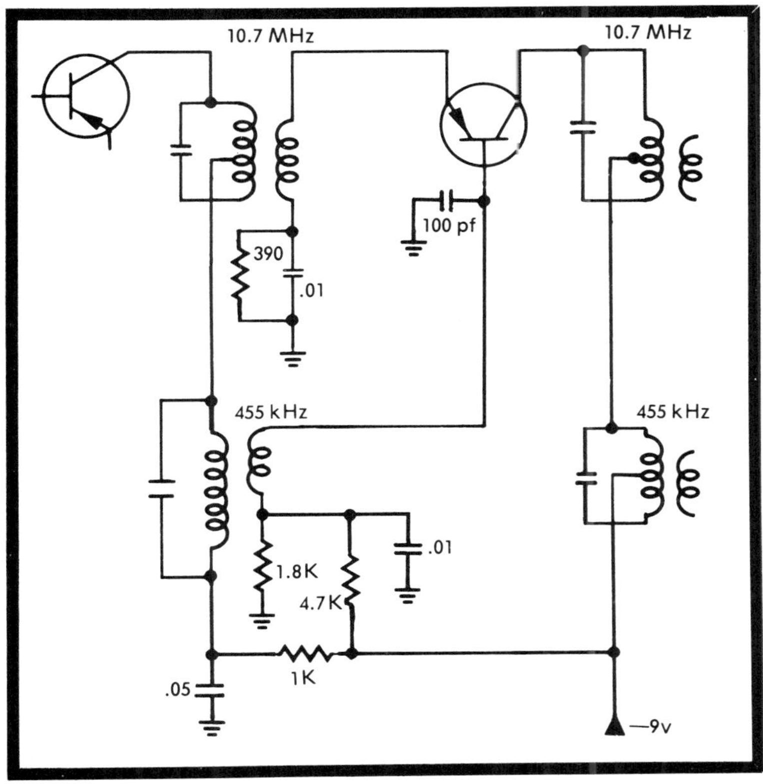

Fig. 7-12. Combination AM-FM IF amplifier.

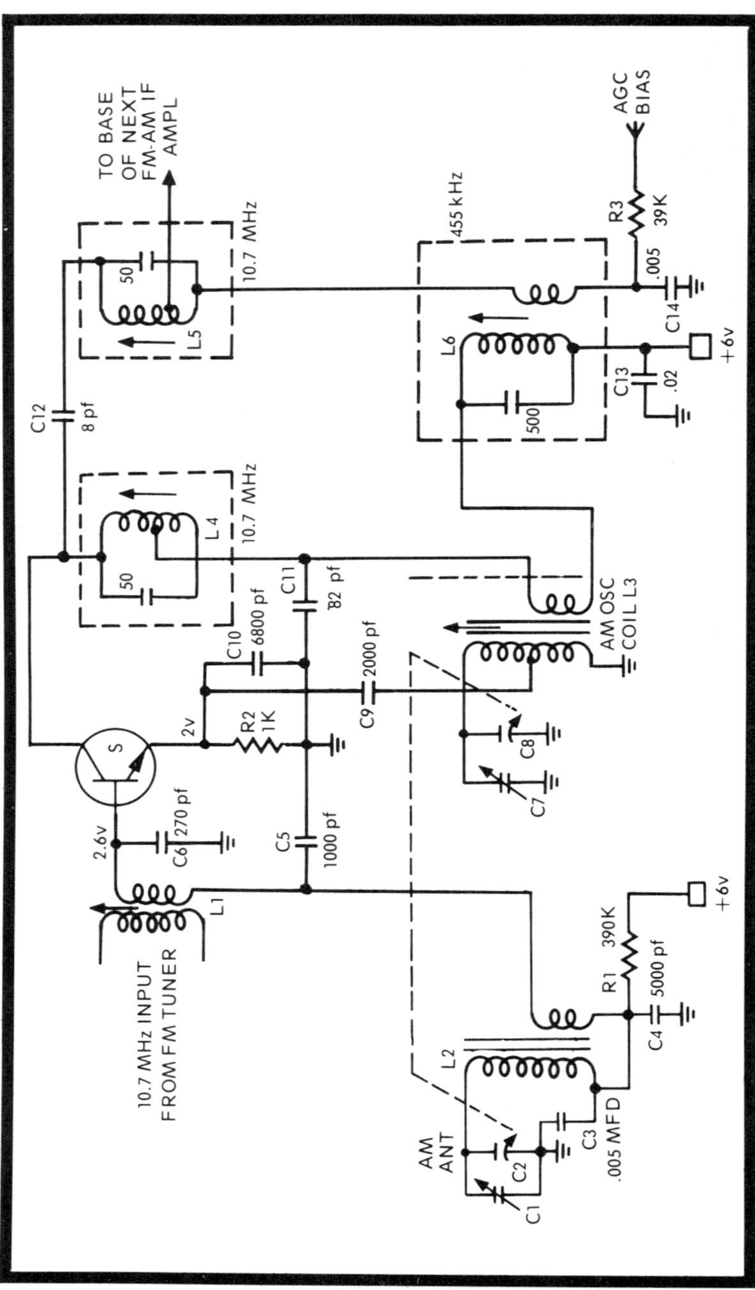

Fig. 7-13. Combination FM IF amplifier and AM converter.

Another method of checking for gain is with a wideband oscilloscope and a low capacity probe. There should be a noticeable increase in gain from one collector in the IF section to the next. If the oscilloscope seriously detunes the 10.7 MHz IF stages then measure from the input terminal of one stage to the input terminal (base or emitter) of the next stage. This low impedance will not be affected even by a direct probe.

FM IF AMPLIFIER AND AM CONVERTER COMBINATION

Because of the wide difference in frequency range for AM and FM it is quite feasible to use one transistor to do both jobs and many companies do it.

An NPN silicon transistor is used in this circuit (Fig. 7-13). The FM, 10.7 MHz circuits, being the highest frequency and therefore most affected by long leads, are connected directly to the transistor. But because the coils in the FM circuit are no more than a "long piece of wire" for the AM circuits, there is no problem of combining the two. To make the circuits even less sensitive to interaction, small capacitors are used to bypass the FM, such as C5, C11 which have little effect on the AM signals. Even the 1000 pf capacitor C5 has little effect on the AM signal because of the low impedance of the base circuit.

Troubleshooting the Circuit

Troubleshooting this circuit is similar to that discussed already for AM converter circuits. Obviously, if the FM section of the radio works but the AM converter section is not working, the transistor and the bias circuits can pretty well be eliminated as possible troubles.

The best method here is to simply treat the circuit as one type or the other depending upon which part of the circuit, AM or FM, exhibits trouble. If the stage does not work for both AM or FM then this is a good sign that the trouble is in the transistor or in the DC bias or supply circuits, and generally you could forget about individual coil or transformer trouble.

Never overlook the importance of DC bias and supply voltage measurements; these are often the simplest to take and also tell much of the story about whether the transistor is working as it should. For example, in this circuit the normal current for the transistor is about 2 ma. This is indicated because of the 2 volt drop across the 1K emitter resistor. If this voltage is zero or very low, then it is time to check the bias circuit. If the bias voltage is high, it indicates a defective transistor. If the bias voltage is low, check the bias resistor

R1, for leakage in C4, or even an open in L2 or L1 or leakage in C5 or C6. If the emitter voltage is significantly high, it is a good sign that there is a collector-emitter short in the transistor. Measure from collector to emitter; if the voltage is zero or nearly so, either the transistor is shorted or has excessive bias. Shorting from base to emitter should result in a large voltage across the transistor (C-E) otherwise the transistor must be shorted; assuming, of course, supply voltages are normal.

AM DETECTORS AND AGC

Detection of an amplitude modulated signal is basically a matter of rectification, because the AM envelope, so far as the audio in it is concerned, is self-cancelling (Fig. 8-1). As shown, the positive and negative portions of the envelope are of equal amplitude and so if this envelope were applied to a speaker, for example, the positive voltage trying to move the speaker cone in one direction would be cancelled by the equal negative voltage so there would be no output.

When the modulated signal goes through a diode, which allows the radio frequency to travel only in one direction, the negative (lower) half of the modulation envelope is sheared off. Using a capacitor then to bypass the higher radio frequencies, we end up with audio only.

It makes no difference whether we use the top or bottom half of the modulation envelope since they are identical. Reversing the diode in the circuit means that the negative half cycles can be passed on to the filter and audio amplifier, and the positive half cycles discarded.

Fig. 8-2 shows two detector circuits that are identical except for the polarity of the output. In Fig. 8-2A the DC voltage developed due to the rectification of the RF signal will be positive, and the amount of average positive voltage will be

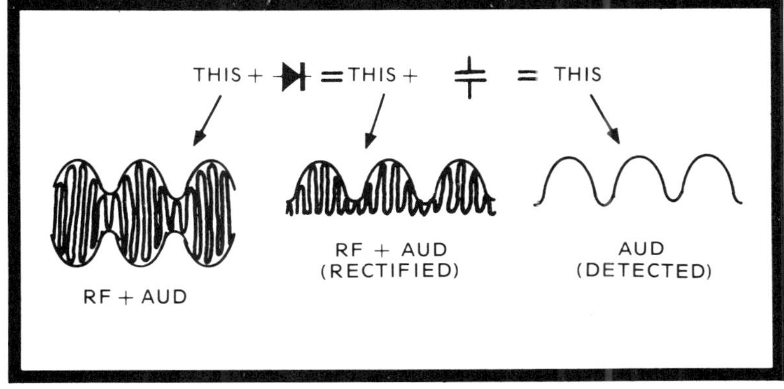

Fig. 8-1. Detection of audio from RF AM envelope.

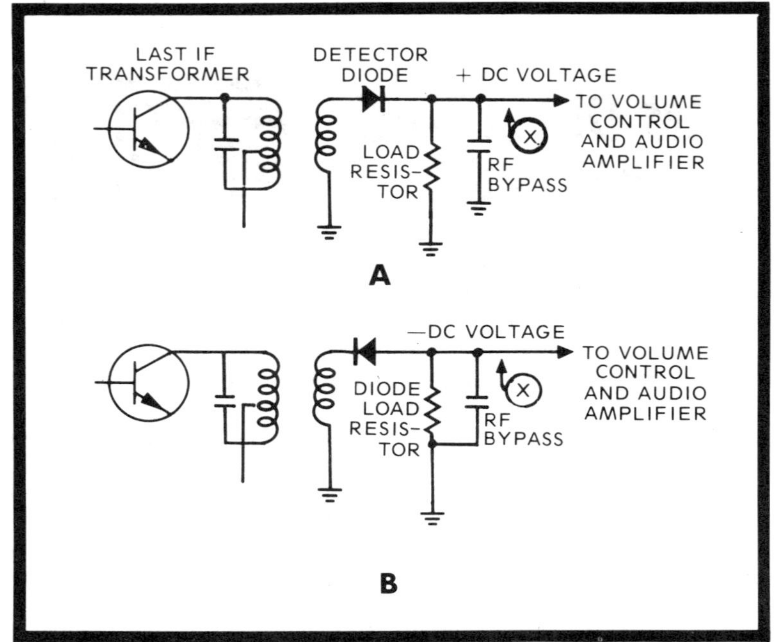

Fig. 8-2. AM detector circuits.

dependent upon the strength of the signal reaching the detector. So the output of the detector, in addition to the audio signal, also has a measurable DC voltage proportional to the signal. In Fig. 8-2B we again have audio output but because the diode is reversed, the DC output voltage is negative rather than positive, but again it is proportional to the signal input amplitude, at point X in both drawings.

Because the DC output of an AM detector is proportional to signal input, the filtered DC voltage (no audio) can be used for automatic control of the gain of a radio or TV (the video detector in a TV set is an AM detector, the sound uses an FM detector).

In Fig. 8-3 R1 and C1 make up the AGC filter circuit, and the DC voltage measured at point Y will be high if signal strength is high and low if signal strength is low. By applying this positive AGC voltage to preceding IF and RF amplifiers in such a way that added positive voltage reduces their gain, the circuit will be controlled so that a strong signal receives less amplification and prevents overloading the amplifiers, while a weak signal will receive more amplification to bring it up to near the level of the stronger signal.

AGC also prevents or greatly minimizes fading due to changing atmospheric conditions or as in the case of an automobile radio, minimizes fading due to changing location of the receiver and consequent changing of signal strength to its antenna input, such as when passing near or under steel structures, behind hills, etc.

If a negative voltage is required to reduce the gain of the amplifiers, simply turning the diode around in Fig. 8-3 results in a negative output voltage instead, and of course if C1 is an electrolytic capacitor, it too must be turned around so its polarity is correct. (If not reversed for negative output, the electrolytic acts pretty much like a short circuit.)

AM DETECTOR AND AGC CIRCUIT

The last IF amplifier of the AM radio (Fig. 8-4) feeds the diode from an untuned secondary of the last IF transformer. The diode is connected with the cathode toward the audio output side, so it passes the positive voltage pulses and rejects the negative ones.

A filter made up of C1 and C2 and R1 eliminates the IF from the audio and the audio is passed on to the volume control, R2, which is also the detector load resistor. The audio is fed from the center arm of the volume control R2 to the audio amplifier through DC blocking capacitor C3.

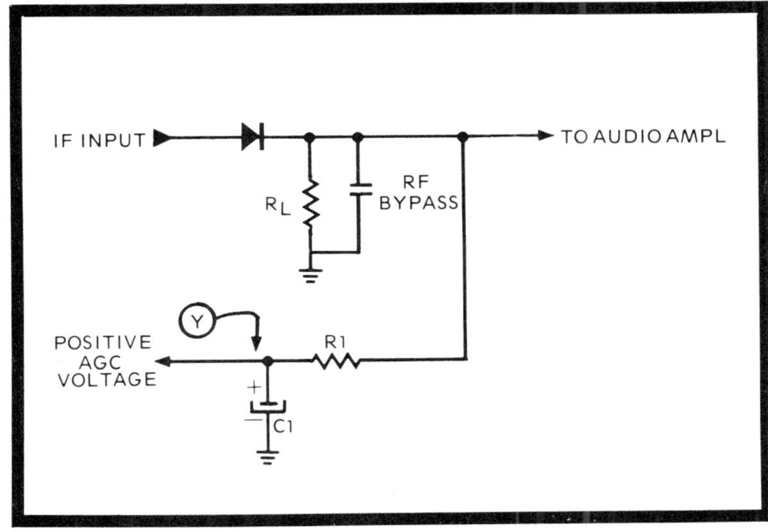

Fig. 8-3. AM detector with AGC filter circuit.

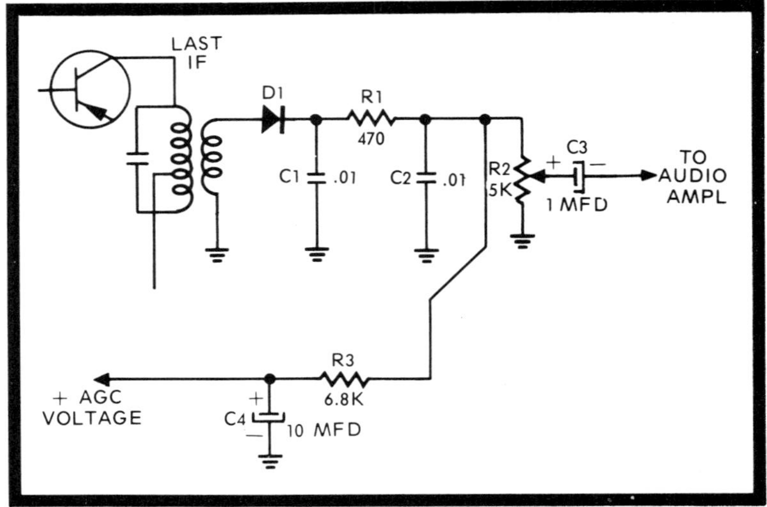

Fig. 8-4. AM detector and separate AGC circuit, auto radio.

R3 and C4 make up the AGC filter network which removes the audio from the AGC line but leaves the positive-going DC voltage developed by the diode.

Troubleshooting the Circuit

The simplicity of this circuit generally makes troubleshooting easy. If the diode should go bad, it can nearly always be checked accurately with an ohmmeter. A quick check for the diode and for the circuits preceding it is to measure the voltage across the volume control and see if it changes significantly when each station is tuned in—in this case, it should go more positive as stronger stations are tuned in.

A short in C4 will not affect the audio output directly but because it affects the gains of the preceding stages controlled by AGC, it will often result in overload and distortion, especially when strong local signals are tuned in.

If C4 opens the result is generally a "motorboating" effect because the circuit starts trying to correct for each audio change and then starts trying to correct for the changes it itself is making and thus a popping or sometimes a squeal develops. A quick check is to shunt the suspected electrolytic with a known good one, observing the correct polarity, and noting whether the radio or TV video performance returns to normal.

AM DETECTOR WITH SEPARATE AGC DIODE (Auto Radio)

The 262 kHz IF signal is detected by diode D2 (Fig. 8-5), the intermediate frequency is bypassed to ground by C3, while the audio signal is fed through R2 and C5 to the compensated volume control. A compensated control is sometimes called a loudness control and its purpose is to increase the bass response of the circuit at lower volumes since the human ear is less sensitive to bass frequencies when the volume is low. The 1K resistor R3 and 2 mfd capacitor C4 have the effect essentially of bypassing higher frequencies and so make the bass frequencies a larger ratio of the total signal.

The IF transformer here is dual-tuned, but the detector diode is tapped down on the secondary winding to provide a better match and reduce the loading on the tuned circuit so that selectivity (the ability to separate stations) is better—in other words the circuit tunes more sharply.

The AGC is taken off at the collector of the last IF transistor through a 150 pf capacitor, C2, and fed to diode D1. The diode passes the positive portion of the IF signal to ground, but not the negative pulses. So a negative DC voltage is developed and fed through R1 to the AGC line. C1 acts as the AGC bypass to smooth away any audio modulation.

Notice that the negative AGC voltage is applied through the 100K resistor to the base. The base is biased positive, by the 47K resistor from B+ so the NPN transistor will operate; therefore, the AGC voltage subtracts from this positive voltage to reduce the gain of the stage when signals are strong.

Troubleshooting the Circuit

As in similar circuits already discussed, the troubles in the detector can usually be found with an ohmmeter, or by shunting across a suspected electrolytic with one known to be good. The shunt capacitor need not be the same size but polarity should be observed. The effect of an open electrolytic which is in the signal path usually is not complete loss of audio but low volume and poor low-frequency response.

In auto radios or any other radio, if the set "blocks" when a strong station is tuned in but seems to play about normal on weaker stations, you can suspect trouble in the AGC circuit.

Open bypass electrolytics in the AGC circuit usually cause motorboating or squealing in the output of the radio because the unbypassed AGC circuit allows output signals from one amplifier to be fed into the input of a preceding one.

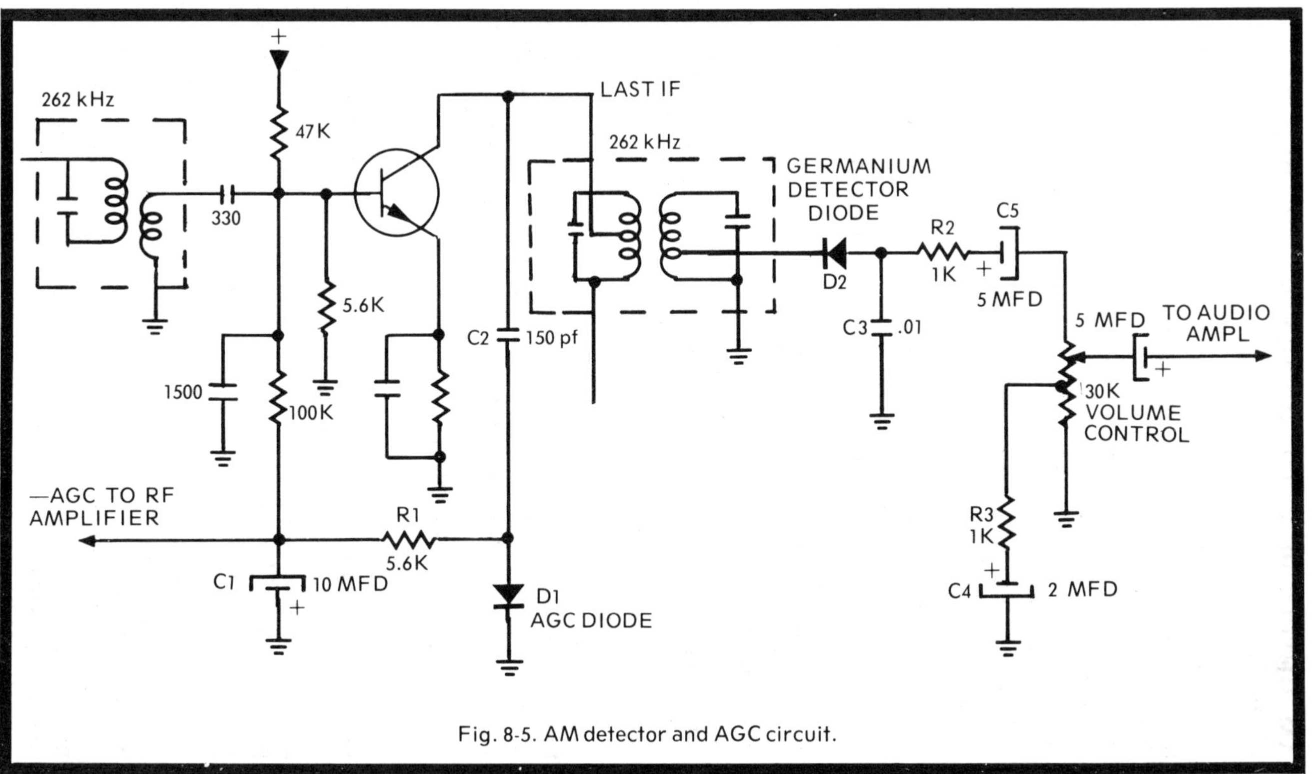

Fig. 8-5. AM detector and AGC circuit.

AM DETECTOR AND AGC AMPLIFIER COMBINATION

Any transistor is in reality two diodes and one of these diodes can be used as an AM detector, in fact, some designers have used a transistor with only two leads connected, or one lead grounded, instead of a regular diode.

In Fig. 8-6 the emitter-base junction of the germanium PNP transistor is used as the detector section. When the IF signal goes positive on the emitter, the transistor conducts to ground, and no current flows in the secondary of the IF transformer nor through the volume control. But on negative swing of the IF secondary, when the transistor conducts to the collector, not only does current flow in the volume control circuit, but also in the collector circuit of the detector-AGC transistor. The collector is connected through a 68K resistor to the negative supply voltage. When the transistor conducts, the collector stays negative—but goes somewhat less negative (more positive), and the amount of positive-going voltage is proportional to the signal arriving at the detector. By using

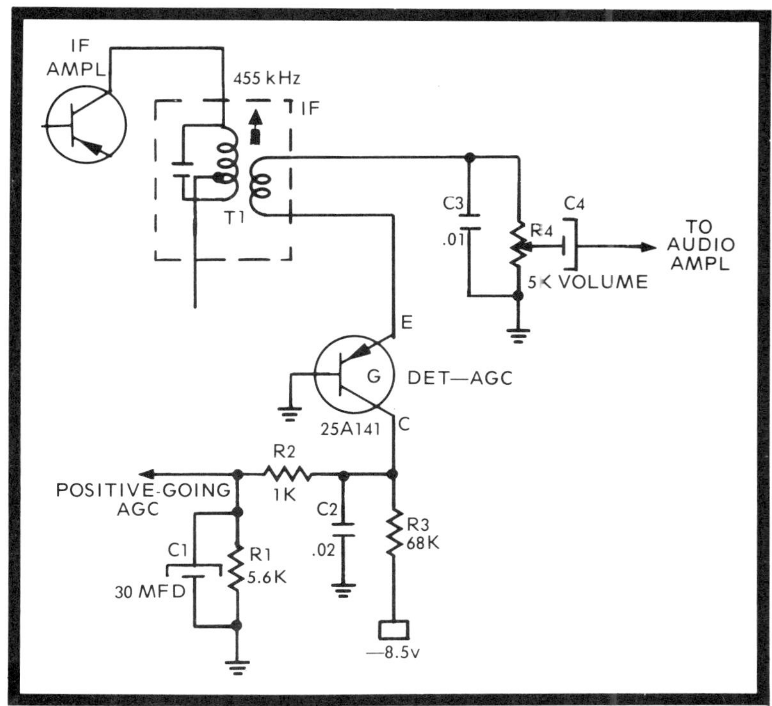

Fig. 8-6. AM detector and separate AGC circuit, auto radio.

this negative collector voltage for bias to one or more PNP IF transistors, when more signal arrives, there is less negative bias voltage and so the gain of the IF transistors decreases. But when less signal arrives at the detector, the negative voltage bias increases and so does the gain of the IF stages. Because this kind of AGC develops more voltage change than from a detector alone, it is called "amplified" AGC.

Troubleshooting the Circuit

This circuit generally can be checked with an ohmmeter as other types of detector circuits can. Measure between the base and emitter with the ohmmeter leads connected, then reverse the ohmmeter leads and read between base and emitter again; you should get one high resistance (about 5K if the transistor is left in circuit) and one low (in the neighborhood of 15 to 100 ohms). The same check can be made from base to collector.

Almost any germanium PNP transistor can be used as a replacement. A silicon transistor should not be used since it will not work well, especially when trying to receive weak signals.

FM DETECTORS

There are two types of FM ratio detectors in popular use, the balanced and the unbalanced. The balanced type is shown in Fig. 9-1. A complete analysis of how a ratio detector works is difficult in a short space because so much depends on the analysis of continually changing, instantaneous voltages. Basically, oversimplified, the theory of operation is that by careful coupling of the signals between the primary and secondary and by another coupling to the center tap of the secondary, this circuit can be made to shift more voltage to one side of the secondary when the frequency is high and more voltage to the other side when the frequency is low.

In the ratio detector, the diodes really aid one another so far as DC voltage is concerned. If the circuit is properly tuned, D1 will produce the same amount of negative DC output as D2 will provide positive output. If C4 were not used, this DC voltage would tend to vary in accordance with any amplitude modulation or noise in the signal. With C4 in the circuit, the voltage cannot change suddenly, and so most amplitude variations are "swamped."

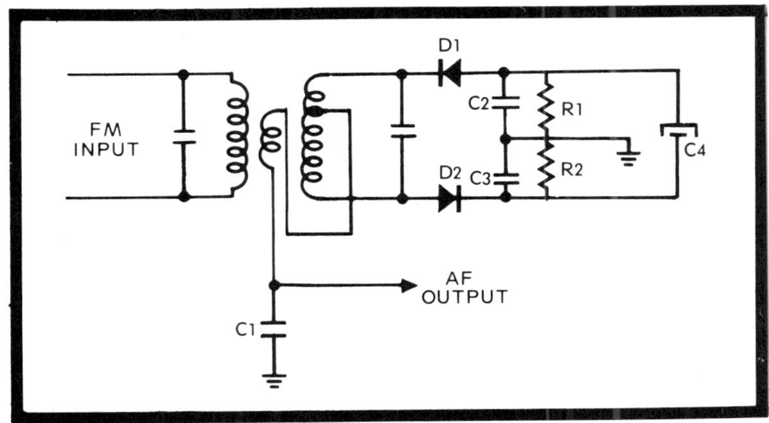

Fig. 9-1. Basic FM detector, balanced type.

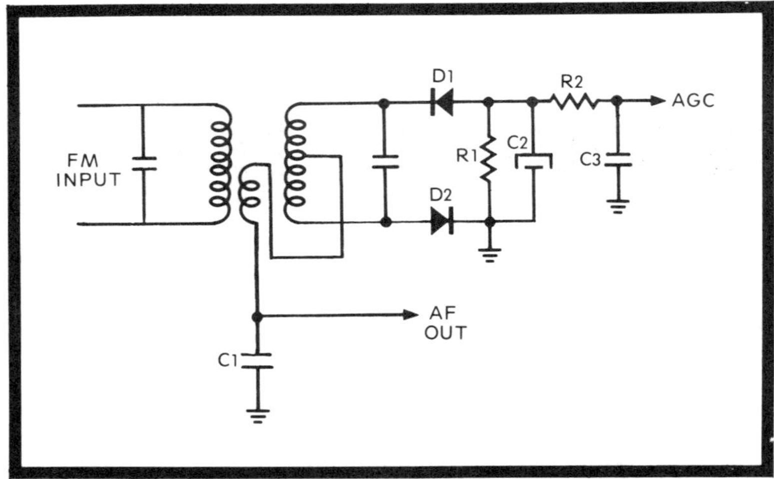

Fig. 9-2. Unbalanced FM ratio detector.

The audio output is taken from the centertap of the winding and the centertap of the diode outputs. This connection provides a voltage output that is the result of the ratio of the instantaneous voltages of the two diodes, thus the name "ratio" detector. For example, when the frequency is high due to a half cycle of modulation, one diode is conducting while the other is not, so the ratio of the two voltages is different. On the next half cycle of modulation, the other diode is conducting the same amount but in the opposite direction, so the ratio of the two is going positive to negative, depending upon the instantaneous modulating frequency.

The unbalanced ratio detector in Fig. 9-2 is nearly identical in operation to that in Fig. 9-1. The basic difference is that one of the diodes is grounded. This connection provides more negative (or positive if the other diode were grounded) voltage output for use in AGC circuits.

Considerable modification of these basic circuits has been the rule in actual circuits, which are discussed next. The most common modification is in the balanced circuit to provide an automatic frequency control (AFC) voltage varying around a zero axis. This voltage is used to control the local oscillator in the FM set so that if it starts to drift, the FM detector, sensing this frequency change, provides a voltage to be fed back to the oscillator which will "tune" the oscillator in opposition to the direction of drift. This keeps the radio tuned in to the station and eliminates the nuisance of having to retune the radio during use.

It is quite common practice now to use a complete integrated circuit (IC) for the sound detector in both radio and TV and especially in TV. Usually these circuits must be replaced as a unit when sound trouble occurs. About the only thing the technician can do is to make sure that the trouble is really in the integrated or module circuit and not a trouble from some external cause, e.g., a loss of DC supply voltage, a defective bypass, or a bad coupling capacitor.

FM RATIO DETECTOR, BALANCED

Fig. 9-3 shows a conventional balanced detector very similar to the basic circuit of Fig. 9-1. Note that the AFC voltage is taken off at the same place as the audio. Although the audio voltage here is moving positive to negative, the net voltage at this point is zero since the positive half cycle of audio is exactly the same size as the negative half cycle.

If, however, there is a detuning of the signal, as is caused by oscillator drift, the voltage here will go either positive or negative depending on whether the frequency change is to a lower or higher frequency.

Obviously we do not want to correct the local oscillator at the audio rate, since this would eliminate the audio output from the detector, so the voltage is filtered by R1 and C1, removing the audio changes and leaving only the DC.

The 820-ohm resistor R2 in the collector leg has an "unloading" effect on the detector transformer, as well as lowering the gain of the stage slightly to prevent any tendency toward instability and eliminating the need for neutralization.

Troubleshooting the Circuit

Normal DC voltage readings should be made on the IF transistor to determine if the transistor is working. If the emitter DC voltage is correct or close, you can be reasonably sure that the transistor is OK.

Tuning of this circuit is easy using a signal generator. Set the signal generator for the intermediate frequency (10.7 MHz generally in FM sets and 4.5 MHz in TV sets). Keep the generator output low enough so no more than about 2 or 3 volts is developed by the detector. Use a high impedance voltmeter and read the voltage from one side of the 5 mfd capacitor, C, to ground. Detune the slug in the secondary of the transformer T1 and then adjust both T1 IF slugs for maximum voltage.

Next move the voltmeter across C1 to read the AFC voltage. When the secondary of T1 is properly tuned, the AFC

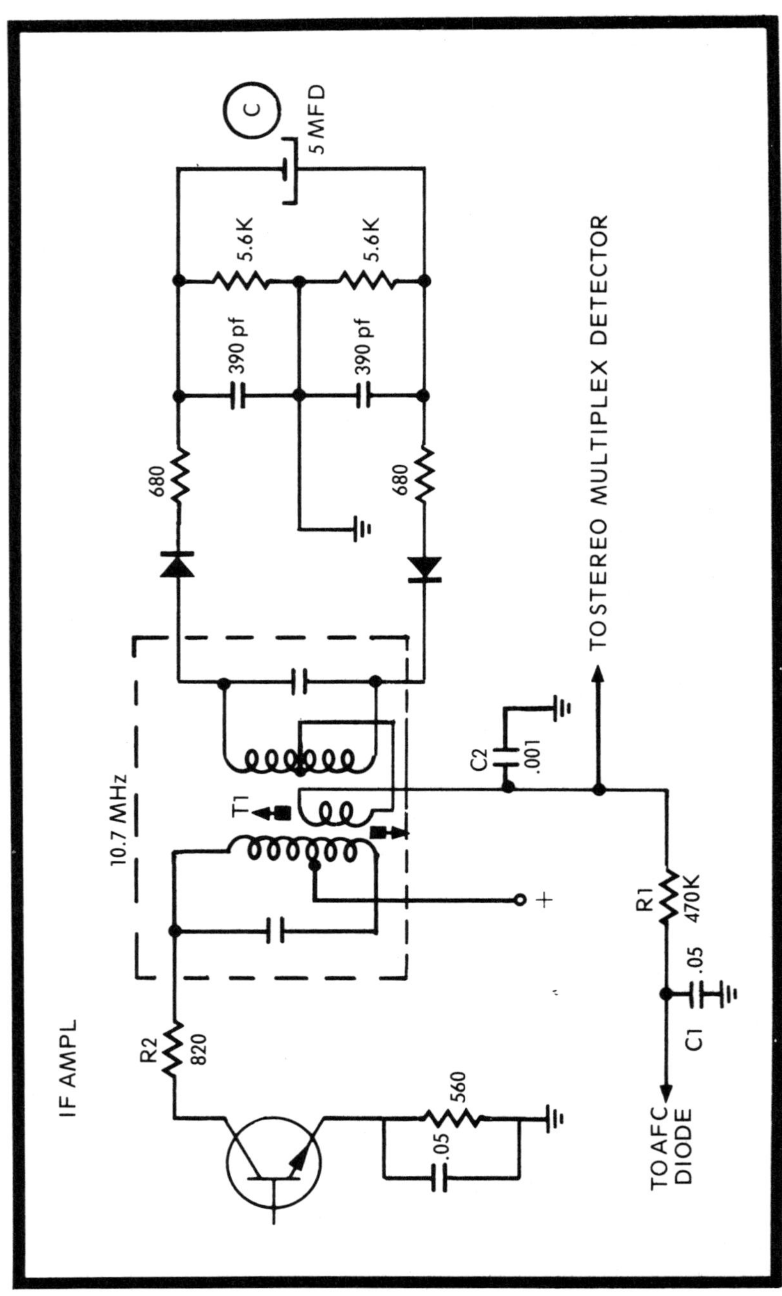

Fig. 9-3. Balanced FM ratio detector.

voltage should be zero. Tune the secondary slug back and forth and the AFC voltage should swing positive and negative if the tuning is correct.

If you have no signal generator and if you are reasonably sure that the other IF transformers are in tune, or even if you wish to tune them, you can do a fairly good job by measuring the voltage as above, from C to ground, and adjusting the primary of T1 to maximum voltage (you should have a station tuned in on the radio). Then move to the AFC voltage point, and without moving the radio dial, adjust the secondary of T1 for zero AFC voltage.

Note: If the radio has one, the AFC switch often shorts the AFC voltage to ground when the AFC is turned "off." And when tuning up the radio on a station signal the AFC should be turned off. Move the voltmeter to the other side of R1, in other words, across C2, while tuning the secondary slug in T1 for zero voltage.

BALANCED FM RATIO DETECTOR WITH TWO SHIELDED DETECTOR COILS

The circuit in Fig. 9-4 is nearly identical to Fig. 9-3 except for the coupling method in the detector transformers. This is a favorite method used in radios using small IF cans with top tuning.

A coupling winding inside L1 is connected with one end to the centertap of L2, and another winding inside L2 is placed in series with the winding in L1. Electronically, the circuit works the same as that in Fig. 9-3.

This circuit shown here is for a monaural radio because a de-emphasis circuit, R7 and C6 is used; however, if these two components were eliminated and the output across C5 taken directly, the output would be suitable for feeding a multiplex adaptor, just as in Fig. 9-3.

Troubleshooting the Circuit

Troubleshooting is almost exactly the same as for the previous circuit. In some ways the circuit may be easier to tune, simply because it is obvious which slug is the primary and which is the secondary. In combination cans, this is not always easily discernible, though many combination cans have both slugs adjustable from the top, especially in Japanese sets. American sets often have a hex hole in the slugs and you pass an alignment tool down through the top slug to reach one lower down. Usually, but not always, the top slug is the secondary.

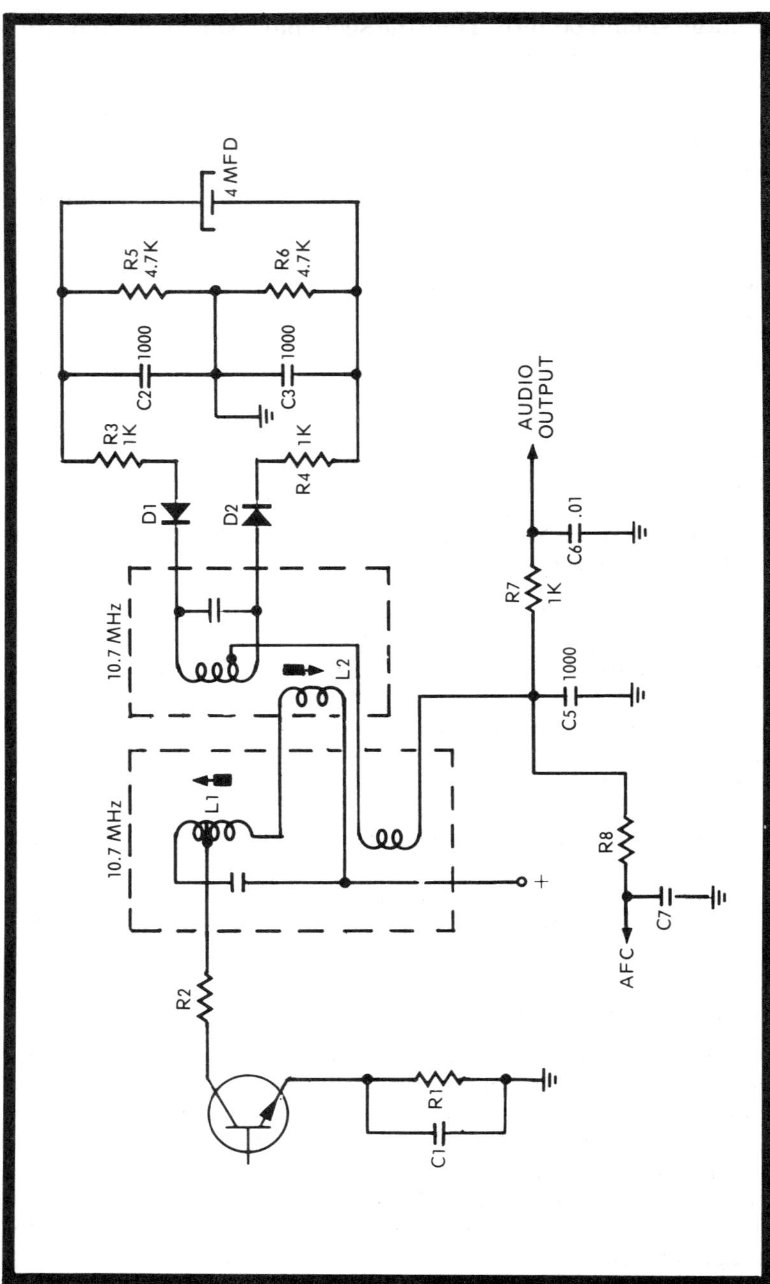

Fig. 9-4. Balanced FM ratio detector with shielded detector coils.

BALANCED RATIO DETECTOR WITH MODIFICATIONS

This circuit (Fig. 9-5) is pretty much the same as the previous two circuits. One difference is the 150-ohm resistor, R1, in series with the tertiary winding on the detector transformer. The resistor is selected to provide for the best performance of the circuit depending upon the coupling in the transformer, the diodes used, the load resistors, etc.

Shown here is an AFC switch that when turned "off" shorts out the AFC voltage. This has no effect on the detector audio performance since the 470K filter resistor isolates the "short."

Troubleshooting the Circuit

Refer to discussions for Figs. 9-3 and 9-4.

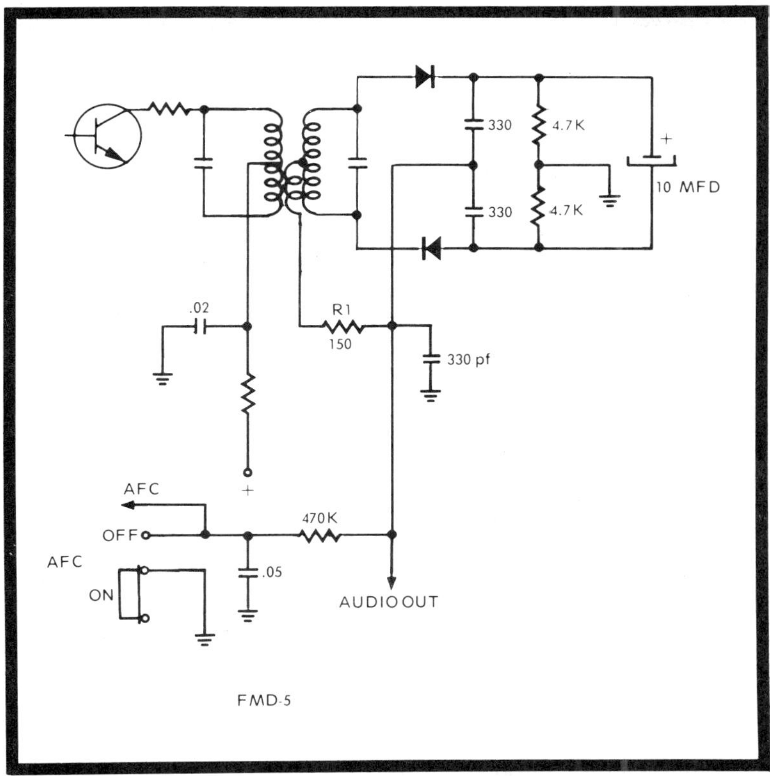

Fig. 9-5. Balanced ratio detector with modifications.

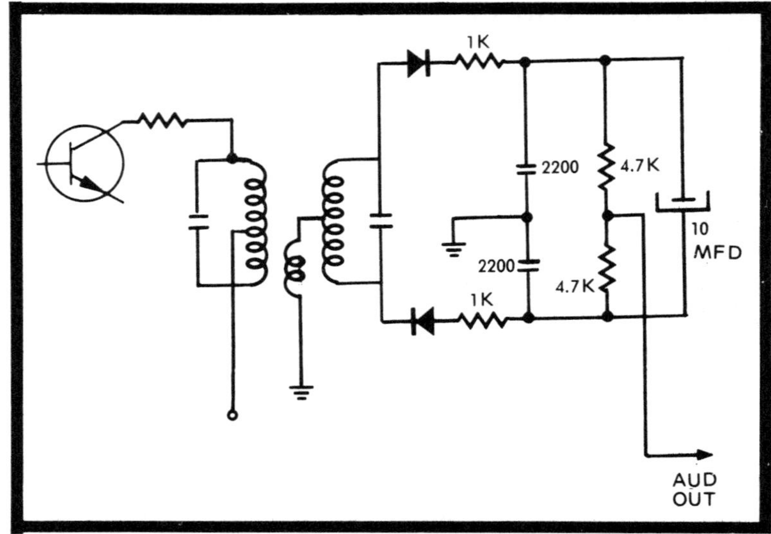

Fig. 9-6. Ratio detector with audio output at junction of load resistors.

RATIO DETECTOR WITH AUDIO OUTPUT AT JUNCTION OF LOAD RESISTORS

This is a modification of the other ratio detector circuits. Instead of taking the audio from the tertiary winding, the audio is taken from the junction of the two 4.7K resistors (Fig. 9-6). There is really no difference in this circuit except that the positions of the audio output and the ground are reversed.

Troubleshooting the Circuit

Refer to discussions for Figs. 9-3 and 9-4.

4.5 MHz UNBALANCED RATIO DETECTOR

This is a common type of circuit used in imported transistor TV sets (Fig. 9-7). AFC from the sound circuit is not used in TV; it is taken from the video IF circuit instead. This particular circuit uses the two separate shielded detector coils. A 2.2 pf capacitor is also connected from the primary to the base of the last IF amplifier for neutralization.

This circuit has a negative power supply feed, which for NPN transistors makes the emitter "hot" and the collector circuit at ground potential. It really makes no difference

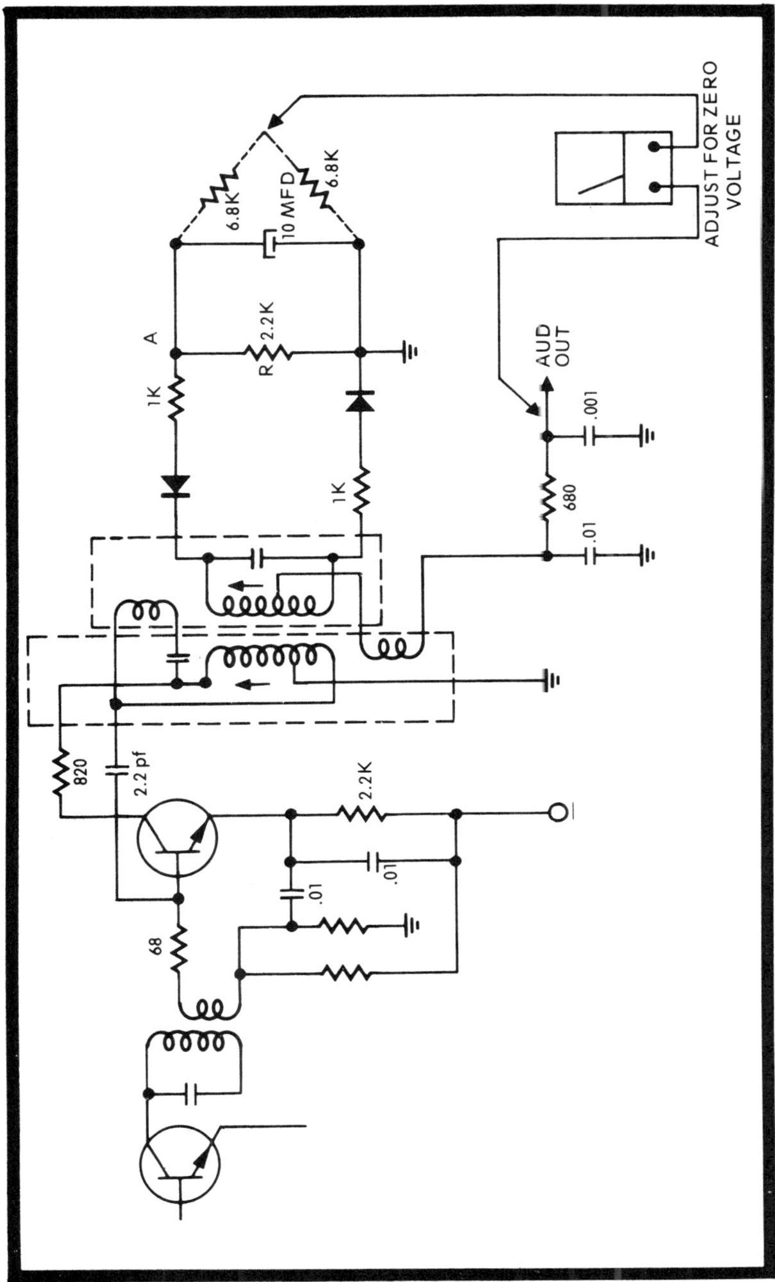

Fig. 9-7. Unbalanced ratio detector, 4.5 MHz.

which side is grounded so long as the technician repairing the circuit recognizes this when measuring the voltages. This is why it is recommended, if possible, that transistor voltages be measured to the emitter, especially bias and collector voltages. The emitter voltage is read across the emitter resistor.

Troubleshooting the Circuit

This circuit has no "zero" voltage point for checking the tuning; but fortunately, in TV sets, the secondary of the ratio detector can be tuned by ear generally just by tuning for minimum sync buzz in the audio output.

You can peak the tuning by measuring the voltage at point A in the circuit while adjusting the tuning of the IF transformers.

If you wish to tune the output of this circuit with a voltmeter, you can do so by taking two equal size resistors of around 6.8K and soldering temporarily (or even permanently) across the 10 mfd capacitor C. Connect the voltmeter (as shown dotted in the circuit) and adjust the secondary for zero voltage.

This latter measurement can be used for any unbalanced detector. The resistors selected should be as nearly matched for resistance as possible; matching is more important than the actual size of the resistors.

If the circuit, as used in a TV, cannot be adjusted so that the sync buzz disappears or is at least lowered to a non-objectionable level, check the 10 mfd capacitor C by connecting another capacitor across it temporarily. Also check to make sure the two detector diodes are okay. If one diode opens, it will be impossible to tune out the sync buzz.

STEREO MULTIPLEX

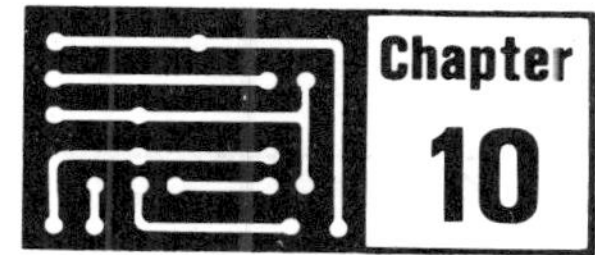

The process of obtaining stereo in an FM receiver is an interesting one since the same signal from which stereo is taken must also sound "normal" for people listening on monaural sets. To do this, the FM transmitter sends out a signal called L + R which is both the right and left stereo signals together, and these two together are the same as a monaural signal and will sound that way on a monaural set. (See Fig. 10-1.)

To obtain stereo, another signal is produced at the transmitter by running the +R signal through a phase inverter, making it a -R. This -R combined with the L signal becomes an L - R. An L - R signal sounds to the ear exactly like an L + R signal but if you combined an L - R and an L + R in the same circuit you would get L + L + R - R or, simply, 2L and no R. Remember this last point since it is very important later on.

The L - R signal, called a "difference" signal, is used to modulate a 38 kHz carrier called a subcarrier. Now when the subcarrier is modulated, in a real sense, we have a switch flipping back and forth from positive to negative at 38,000 times per second, meaning that on one excursion there is an L - R signal but when the 38,000-cycle oscillator reverses the signal becomes an -(L-R) or, without parenthesis, -L+R. So looking at it realistically, and without complicating the explanation with phase angles, etc., the subcarrier is producing first an L - R signal and than a -L + R signal **switched back and forth 38,000 times per second.**

Sending out a 38-kHz signal on an FM carrier would take up unnecessary bandwidth plus cause some interference to the L + R signal. Instead the 38-kHz carrier is suppressed leaving only the L-R and -L + R **sidebands** which are then used to modulate the FM carrier.

In order for stereo to work, though, we have to have some sort of signal to lock the receiver to the transmitter so that they are both switching at exactly the same time, that is, synchronized. Since the 38 kHz signal is suppressed and not sent out, we cannot use it. What is sent out is a 19-kHz "pilot" signal. This pilot signal is taken from the transmitter

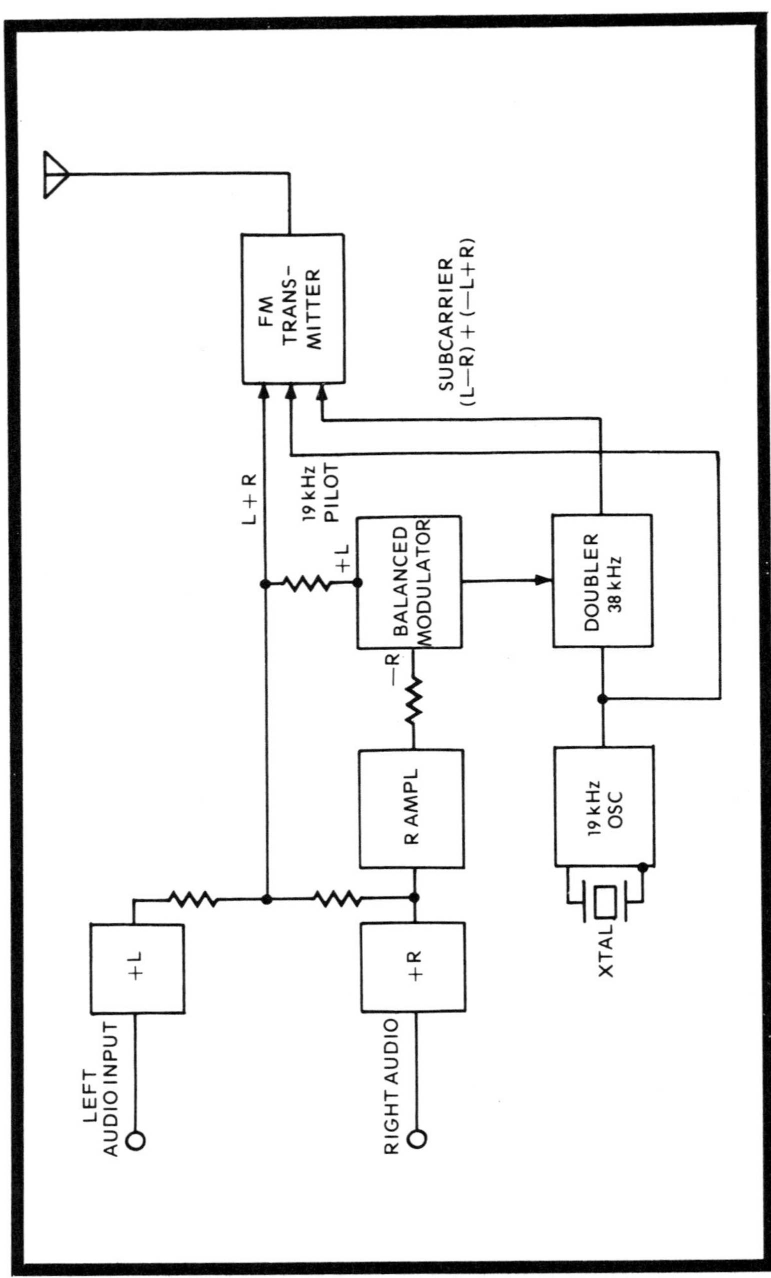

Fig. 10-1. FM stereo transmitter, block diagram.

oscillator which after doubling becomes the 38-kHz subcarrier. The 19-kHz pilot signal is high enough frequency so that it is not audible but low enough in frequency so that it can be sent efficiently by the FM transmitter. The pilot is limited to just 10 percent of the total modulation so as to minimize any interference it might cause in beating with the audio signals.

Fig. 10-1 shows a possible block diagram of a stereo transmitter. The left and right channels directly modulate the FM transmitter. The +R is then fed to an amplifier which inverts it, making it -R. The -R and the +L are fed into a balanced modulator which retains the sidebands but suppresses the 38 kHz signal. The sidebands are used to also frequency modulate the transmitter. And a small amount of the 19-kHz signal is fed also to the FM transmitter to be used as a pilot to lock in the 38-kHz "switch" in the receiver.

In Fig. 10-2 we have a block diagram of an FM stereo receiver. The audio taken off at the detector is channelled to an audio amplifier which in turn feeds the signal to the center tap of the 38-kHz transformer. And because the diodes are forward-biased, the audio will be fed with equal volume to both the left and right amplifiers.

But suppose there is a stereo signal being broadcast, what happens? The 19-kHz pilot is amplified and fed to a doubler, usually a simple full-wave rectifier circuit which is a natural doubler, and then into the 38 kHz amplifier. This amplifier builds up the signal so that there will be around 4 to 7 volts p-p 38-kHz signal across the secondary of T1. Without stereo both the diodes were forward-biased and passed the L + R signal without attenuation, but with a stereo signal, diodes D1 and D2 are turned off and on at a 38-kHz rate. Now the sidebands can mix with the L + R signal. On one half cycle, the L + R signal mixes with an L - R signal, the R's cancel (one is positive, the other negative) and the output from the diode is a Left channel signal. On the next half cycle of the 38-kHz switch, the other diode conducts and the first is cut off. Now the -(L-R) signal, which taken out of parenthesis becomes a -L + R signal, combines with the L + R and the L's cancel, leaving only the Right channel signal.

The resistive-capacitive circuit at the output of the detectors filters out the 38 kHz switching voltage, leaving only the stereo audio.

MULTIPLEX ADAPTER WITH DIODE BRIDGE DETECTOR

The input to the multiplex adapter shown in Fig. 10-3 is directly from the output of the FM detector. There must be no

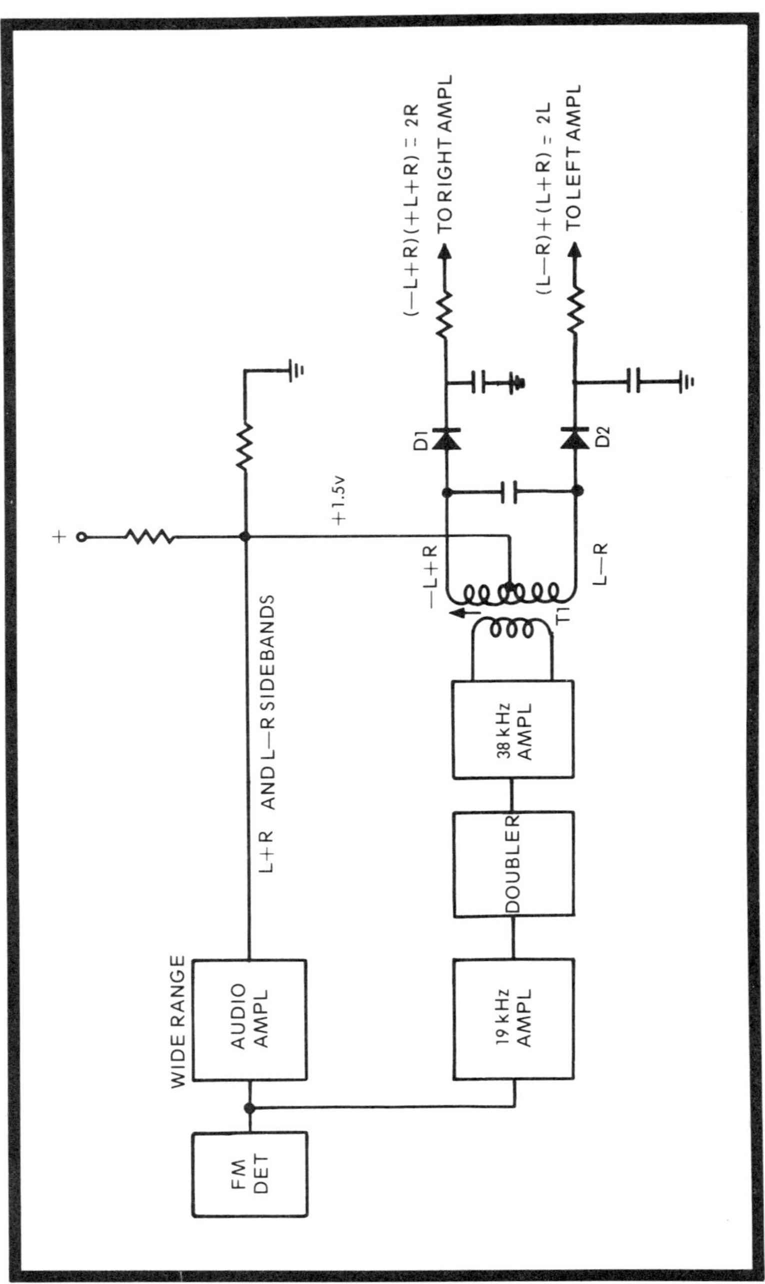

Fig. 10-2. FM stereo receiver, block diagram.

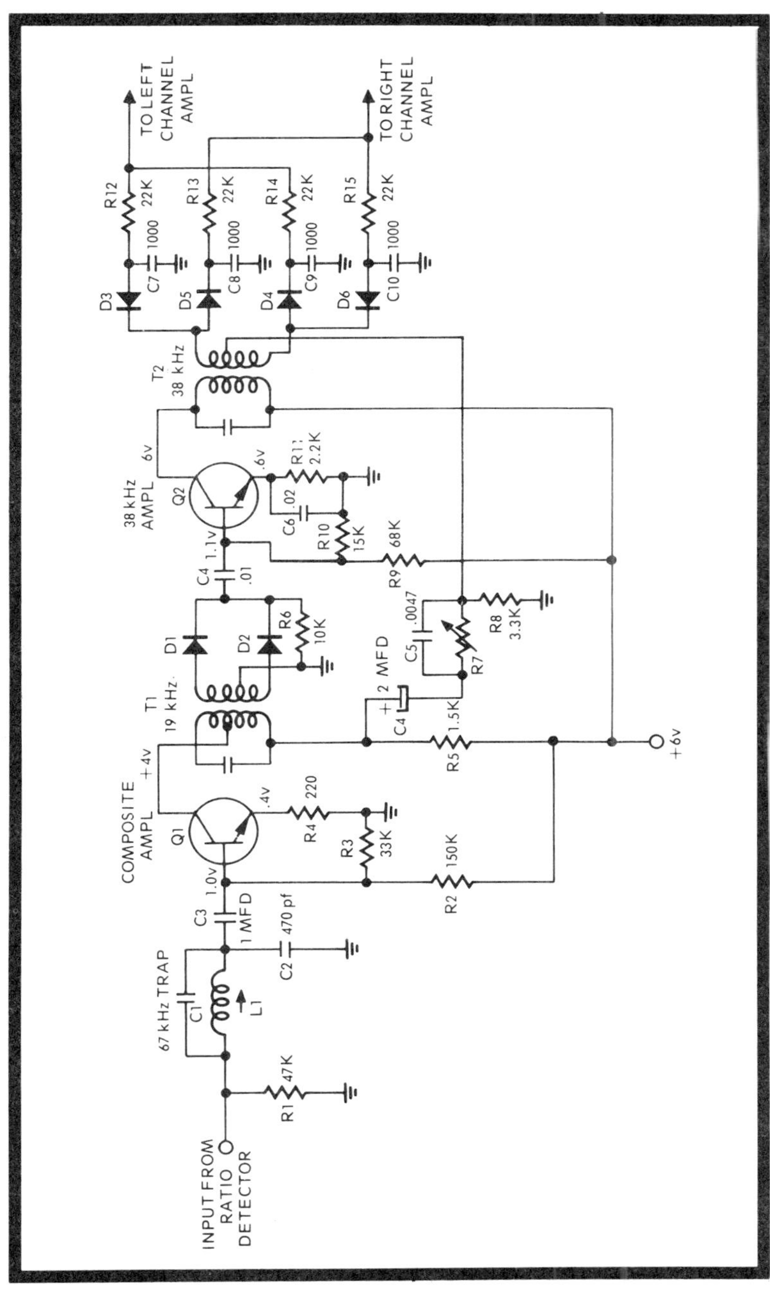

Fig. 10-3. Multiplex adapter with diode bridge detector.

de-emphasis circuit between the detector and the adapter otherwise the pilot and subcarrier sidebands would be lost.

The composite signal, including the 19-kHz pilot, the L + R and the L - R sidebands, is fed through a 67-kHz trap (L1, C1). This trap removes any SCA (storecasting) signals that might interfere with detection of the stereo. The signal then continues through C3 to the composite amplifier. A tuned circuit (T1) is the output impedance for the 19-kHz pilot, and the 1.5K resistor, R5, is the collector load resistor for the remaining parts of the signal which is coupled via adjustable R7 and C5 (.0047) to the centertap of the 38-kHz stereo detector transformer. The amount of L - R sidebands can be increased or decreased by adjusting R7 so as to exactly match the L + R signal, for perfect cancellation (or as nearly perfect as possible) of either the right or left signal, depending on which channel is active at any given instant. This is often called a "separation" control, since when the two signals are properly balanced the apparent separation between the signals is best.

The 19-kHz pilot signal is fed to a full-wave rectifier circuit, D1 and D2. As you remember, a full-wave rectifier in a 60-Hertz circuit has 120-Hertz ripple in the output—it is an automatic doubler and requires no tuning. In this full-wave circuit, the 38-kHz ripple output is fed to 38-kHz amplifier Q2 and then through T2 to the bridge or "ring" demodulator. (See Fig. 10-4, which is a very similar circuit but with a different schematic layout.)

When the signal goes positive on the upper half of T2 secondary, it will be negative on the bottom half. Diode D5 will conduct and so will diode D6. This balances the detector from a DC standpoint but acts as a phase detector combining the L + R with the L - R, cancelling the R's and leaving only the L's. When the signal goes negative on the upper half of T2, the lower half goes positive, and again the diodes balance the DC output but detect the phase between the L + R and the -L + R, this time cancelling the L's and retaining the R's. (Remember, of course, all this synchronous detection could not take place and there would be no stereo if the pilot signal were not in step with the 38-kHz switch at the transmitter.)

On a monaural signal there is no pilot signal so there is no 38-kHz switch to turn detector diodes D3, D4, D5 and D6 off and on. Instead the audio arriving at the center tap of T2 simply moves through the diodes to both channels equally.

Troubleshooting the Circuit

If the set is tuned to a stereo station but you hear only a monaural signal, though both left and right audio amplifiers are working, it is a good indication of trouble in the 38 kHz amplifier. The audio will continue to reach the amplifiers even if T1 is mistuned, diodes D1 or D2 are open, or the 38 kHz amplifier completely inoperative, since the audio is developed across R5 and fed (by C4, R7 and C5) directly to the centertap of the T2 secondary, then through the bridge detector diodes to the audio amplifiers.

Check diodes D1 and D2 with an ohmmeter. These are germanium types and will have around 100 to 500 ohms forward resistance, and should have 10,000 ohms reverse resistance (if connected in the circuit, due to R6). If disconnected for testing, both diodes should have forward and back resistances similar to each other and certainly no less than 100K reverse resistance. Check the emitter voltage for Q2. If it is high the transistor may be shorted or possibly the 15K resistor R10 from base of Q2 to ground is open. If the emitter voltage is low or zero, it can mean an open transistor, or it could be an open R9 which feeds base bias to Q2.

If DC voltages and components seem to be normal, yet there is no audio channel separation, it could be caused by mistuning or even defects in T1 or T2. Use an oscilloscope, tune the set to a stereo station, and adjust T1 for maximum signal across R6, or you can use a DC voltmeter here to do the same. To adjust the 38-kHz transformer, T2, use a voltmeter at the output of any one of the diodes across the companion 1000-pf capacitor and tune T2 for maximum DC voltage. To check for balance, measure the DC voltage at the left and right channel. In this circuit, both should be zero or very close to it.

If output is weak, try using a small eléctrolytic or even a 0.47 paper capacitor and couple between the input to the multiplex adapter and either of the audio amplifiers. If the signal increases or improves measureably in tone quality, there is trouble in the adapter circuit. Always check for open electrolytics which are used as coupling capacitors. Try shunting a 0.47 paper capacitor across a suspected one; if the signal improves you know the electrolytic is completely or partially open.

Do **not** adjust separation controls (R7) arbitrarily unless you have the equipment to reset them accurately. It is not likely that this factory adjustment will need changing. Most modern stereo adapters have no adjustment but use a fixed RC circuit. If you are sure that the separation control has been moved, and it often will be if an inexperienced technician has worked on the set, you should use a stereo generator that has either a left channel only output (or a right and left channel

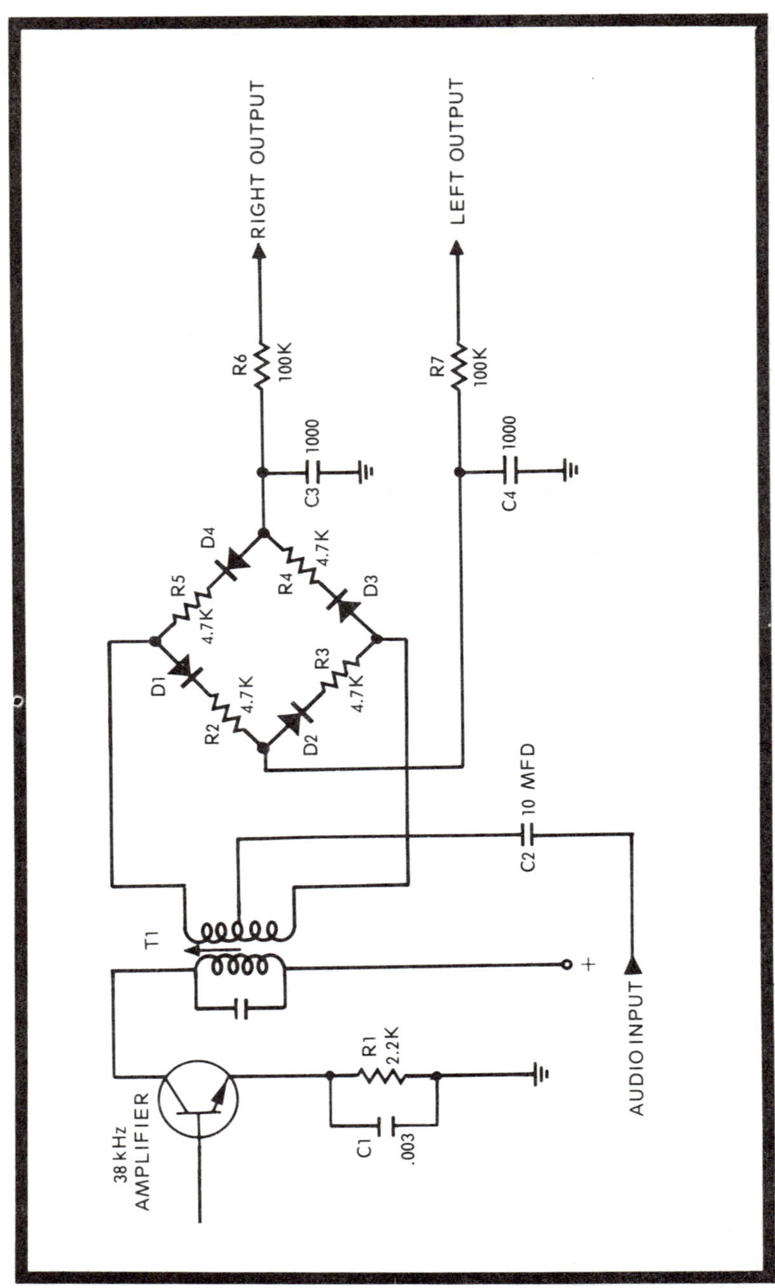

Fig. 10-4. Ring demodulator stereo detector.

switchable) then adjust the separation control until there is zero or at least a minimum output at the right channel.

If you have no equipment, and you know the control has been moved, you can set the adjustment by ear as a stopgap measure by listening carefully for the best stereo "feel" after you have carefully set the **balance** control and moved the speakers the same distance either side of you—assuming both your ears have about the same hearing level.

Distortion in either the right or left channel, which is heard on radio but not on the phonograph section, most likely will be caused by an open diode in the stereo detector output. If the unit does not have a phonograph so you can check the amplifiers, reverse the amplifier leads going to the detector (put the right on the left and the left on the right, or just parallel the distorted side with the undistorted side, which you can usually do by turning a function switch from "stereo" to "monaural") to see whether it is the audio circuit or the detector circuit.

A "tinny" distortion is often caused on both channels by an open electrolytic which feeds the center tap of T2 secondary (C4 in Fig. 10-3). This is because only the highs in the main channel (L + R) are getting through while the 38 kHz sidebands may get through with little or no attenuation.

In addition to other causes for poor separation of stereo, don't overlook mistuning of the 67-kHz trap. In some circuits more than in others, a mistuned SCA trap can play havoc with good clean stereo separation, even eliminating it altogether.

STEREO DETECTOR USING TWO DIODES

Almost every designer of early stereo multiplex adapters used a 4-diode detector circuit to divide the left and right channels. Later several manufacturers adopted the 2-diode system. The essential difference (see Fig. 10-5) is the forward biasing of the two diodes so that audio from a monaural signal travels through them without distortion. When a stereo signal is present, the diodes are alternately turned off and on by the 38 kHz signal, allowing the mixing of the L + R signal and the L - R, -L + R sidebands to produce individual outputs as explained in the beginning of this chapter.

The audio amplifier transistor shown here is actually also the 19 kHz amplifier in a circuit similar to that in Fig. 10-3. It is shown here without the tuned circuit for simplification.

R2 and C2 are fixed components selected to provide the proper matrix level between the main channel and the sidebands. C3 and C4 bypass the 38-kHz switching signal so it

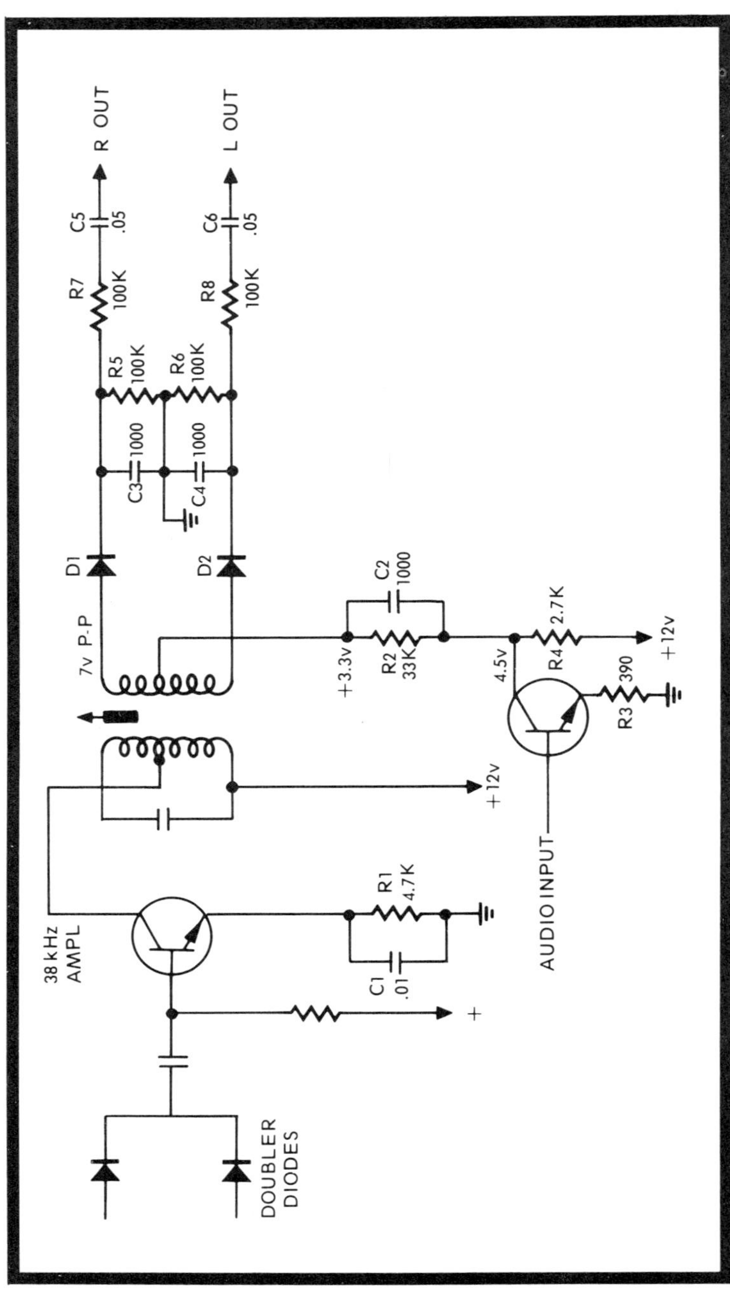

Fig. 10-5. Stereo detector using 2 diodes.

is not passed on to the amplifiers. The two 100K resistors, R7 and R8, isolate the detector and provide additional filtering (coupled with the shunt capacity of the left and right amplifiers). The .05 mfd capacitors, C5 and C6, block the DC voltage developed by D1 and D2 from reaching the audio amplifier inputs.

Troubleshooting the Circuit

Generally this circuit would have the same symptoms and generally the same problems as discussed for Fig. 10-3. Receiving good monaural signals but no stereo generally means trouble in either the 19 kHz tuning or in the doubler and 38-kHz amplifier. Lack of stereo could also be caused by some restriction in the high frequency response from the output of the detector to the multiplex circuit.

An oscilloscope with a low capacity probe is a good tool for signal tracing this circuit and also for adjusting the tuning, although DC voltages can also be used as tuning indicators. Tuning the 38 kHz transformer for peak, for example, can be done by measuring the DC voltage at the output of either D1 or D2 to ground. Adjust the transformer for maximum DC voltage. Using a scope you will check between the anodes of the diodes. Because this secondary is untuned and the frequency is low, almost any scope with a low capacity probe will result in low enough load that circuit performance will be unaffected. Adjust the transformer for maximum peak-to-peak voltage as indicated by the highest amplitude vertical scope waveform.

If the 19-kHz output appears to be good, DC voltages check okay but there is no 38-kHz output, check to see if one of the doubler diodes is either open or shorted.

"BI-PLEX" STEREO DETECTOR

At first glance the circuit (Fig. 10-6) seems to be unlike any other. In reality it is virtually identical to Fig. 10-5 except that a forward-biased transistor is used instead of diodes.

A transistor is by nature two diodes back to back and will so act when not in an amplifier circuit. Fundamentally the "bi-plex" transistor circuit is the same as that shown in the inset, using diodes.

Troubleshooting the Circuit

Troubleshooting techniques are similar to those described for other multiplex circuits. To check the transistor, use an

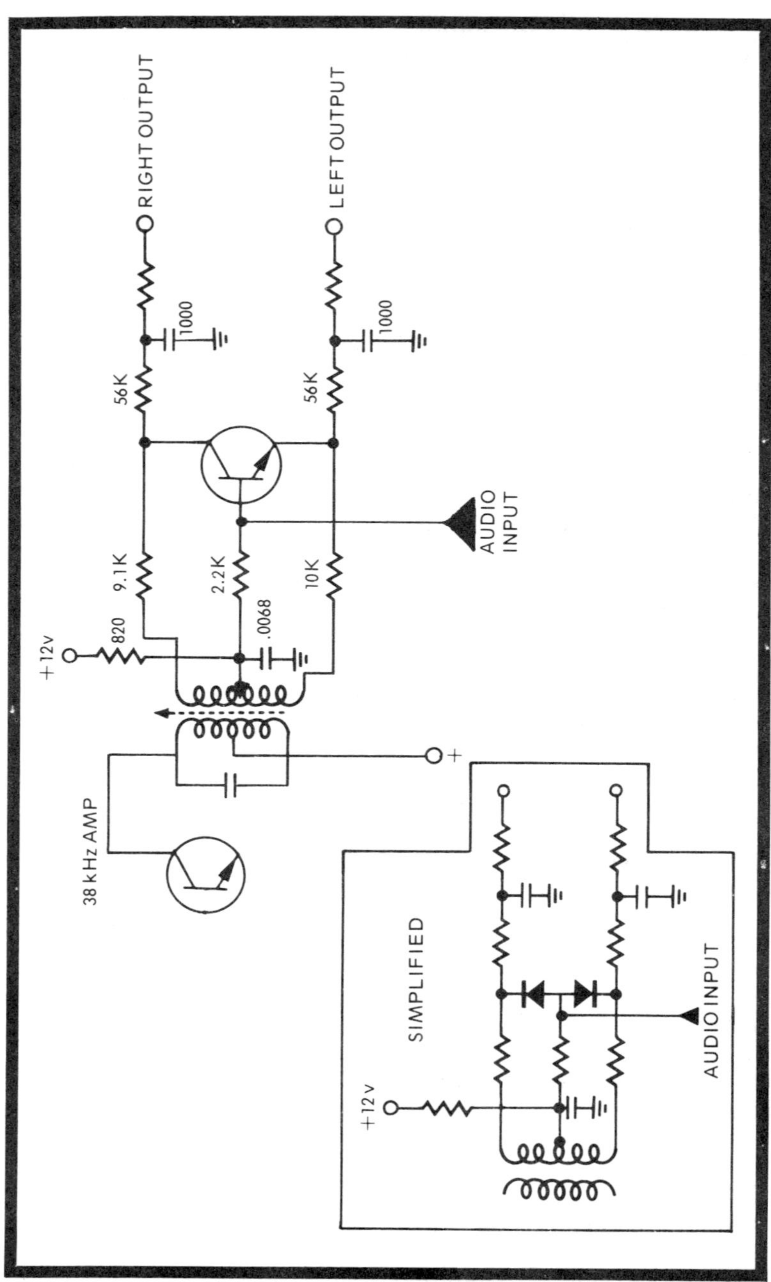

Fig. 10-6. "Bi-Plex" stereo detector.

ohmmeter, place the black lead (of most ohmmeters) on the base and then measure first to the emitter and then the collector. The resistance should be low and about the same. Now reverse the ohmmeter leads, putting the red lead on the base and using the black lead to check to both emitter and collector. This time, the resistance should be high in both directions (at least more than 11K or 12K, which represents the circuit shunt resistance).

VIDEO AMPLIFIERS

Transistor video amplifiers take on many different forms but basically they must consist of an amplifier that has relatively flat amplification from nearly zero Hertz to above 2.5 MHz at least and often up to at least 4.5 MHz.

The video amplifiers in black and white TV sets are not usually too complex and perhaps no more than two transistors are used. In color TV sets it is not uncommon to have four or five transistors and usually they are all direct-coupled. In color sets, the brightness control may in reality be a bias control for one of the video transistors, which in turn reflects through the entire video chain to change the bias on the picture tube. Often a brightness limiter control is used to establish the range of the brightness control. The brightness limiter is needed to compensate for slight variations in the transistors used, for even a slight variation in an early video stage can result in a significant change in the voltage shift across the final transistor.

Most direct-coupled video amplifier stages have a feedback circuit which tends to compensate for variations in transistor current so as to prevent drift and prevent a change in brightness as the set warms up.

It is not unusual for video amplifiers to not amplify at all, but simply act as isolation circuits for branching off to the sync, AGC, color amplifiers and the like, or for the application of blanking pulses to eliminate retrace lines and horizontal shading.

Sometimes a video amplifier will have outputs both from the collector and emitter circuits. Sometimes the amplifier will be emitter-fed (grounded-base circuit).

For amplifiers that are base-fed, the signal at the collector is 180 degrees out of phase with the input, that is, if the signal on the base is positive-going, the signal on the collector will be negative-going. In base-fed amplifiers, the signal at the emitter is in phase with the signal on the base and can never have more voltage gain than the input circuit.

For amplifiers that are emitter-fed (grounded-base), the output signal at the collector has the same polarity as the input signal.

The above information is important in tracing through a video amplifier circuit to find what kind of signal to expect at a particular video amplifier junction or test point. See example in Fig. 11-1. This is the signal path drawing. The direction of the video detector diode shows that the video output from it will be positive-going. The 1st video is an emitter follower; there is no phase reversal and no amplification; but it does provide a low impedance feed to the sync and chroma amplifier circuits and prevents them from loading the detector stage. The 2nd video is emitter-fed, and though there is no phase reversal, there is considerable amplification. The 3rd video is a base-fed (common-emitter) amplifier which reverses the phase of the signal and also amplifies the signal. The 4th video amplifier is another emitter follower which does not reverse the signal phase, and though it does not amplify the signal (voltage-wise), it does provide an increase in power and matching for the final video output transistor. The output transistor reverses the phase and there is a positive-going signal at the cathodes of the CRT, which is the polarity of video that must reach the cathode(s) of any CRT, so if in tracing through the circuits you find what appears to be a negative-going signal at the cathodes, you have made some mistake in assigning polarities somewhere along the line. If, however, the signal should be fed to the grid(s) of the CRT then the signal polarity must be negative-going.

The above is true for all sets built for American color or black and white TV because the strongest signal makes a "black" picture. For example, a strong signal makes the vertical blanking bar, which is black, thus it takes a positive signal on the cathode or a negative signal on the grid to reduce the CRT brightness and make a black picture. The sync signals, the part of the composite video above the "shoulder" of the blanking bar, are said to be in the "blacker than black" region.

FIRST VIDEO AMPLIFIER (COLOR TV)

The transistor is biased class A, that is, in normal operation, the current flow is constant regardless of signal input. See Fig. 11-2. Bias is provided through R1, R3, L2 and L3 from the 21-volt supply line to the base of the NPN transistor. Bias is also supplied by the output of the video detector diode via L1 and L2 primary.

The 4.5 MHz trap prevents a 920 kHz beat from appearing in the color picture. Peaking coils L3, L4, and L5 shape the output response of the amplifier. Resistors R4 and R7 broaden

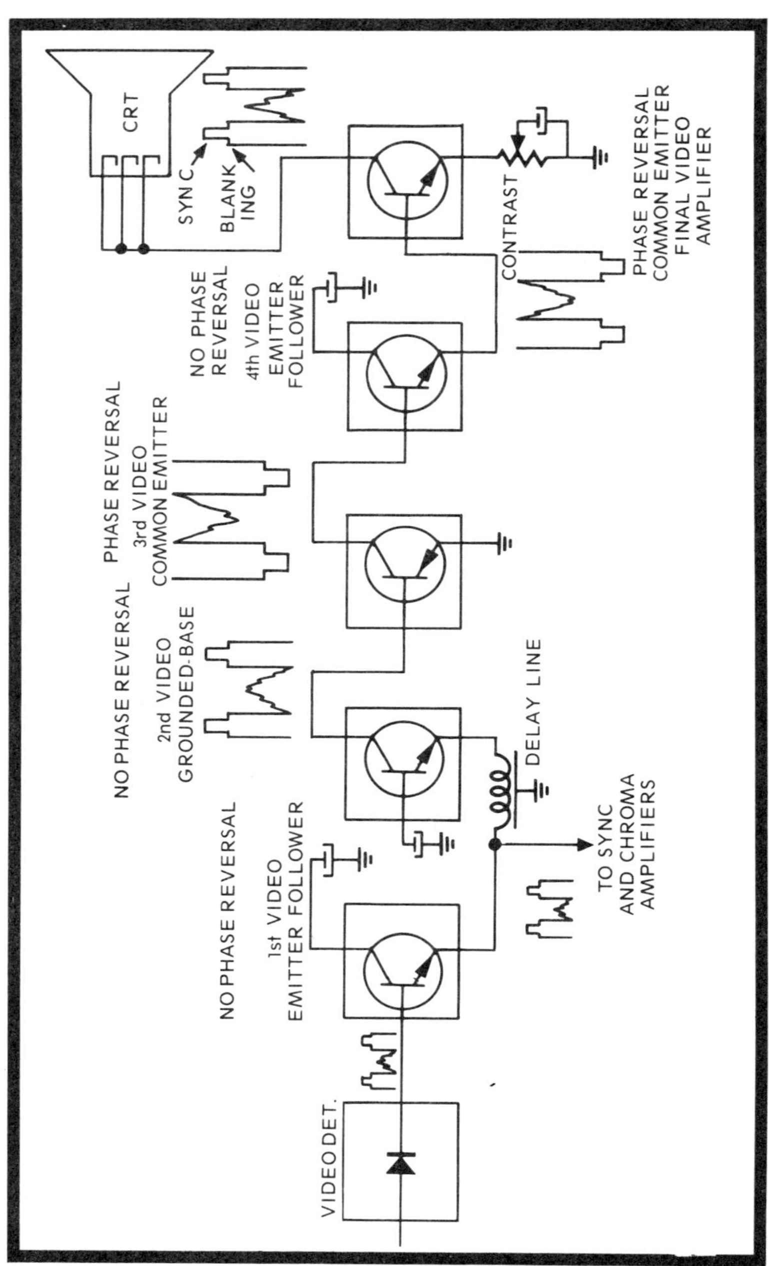

Fig. 11-1. A 5-transistor direct-coupled video amplifier, showing signal polarities.

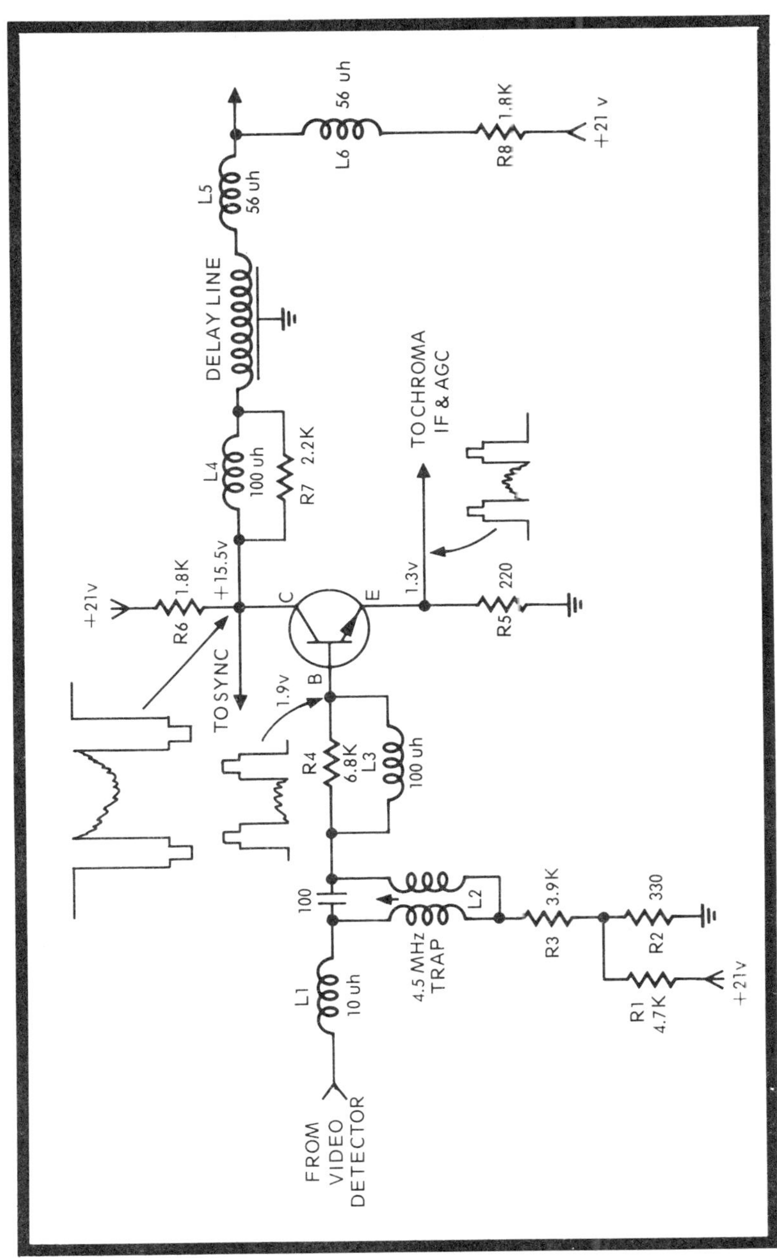

Fig. 11-2. 1st video IF (color TV).

out the peaking coil action to provide a wider response and also to prevent "ringing."

Two output signals are taken from this amplifier. The emitter output, which is not amplified but is decoupled by the transistor from the detector circuit, feeds the chroma IF circuits as well as the AGC in this particular arrangement. The video and sync outputs are amplified and reversed in phase in the collector circuit.

A delay line is used in the signal circuit of all video amplifiers of color sets. This "slows down" the "black and white" video to allow time for the color signals to pass through the chroma IF amplifiers, which results in the monochrome and color signals being in "register" when they arrive at the CRT.

Troubleshooting the Circuit

An oscilloscope can be used to follow the signal through this circuit. The oscilloscope should have good frequency response or at least "known" frequency response and should be used with a low-capacity probe to prevent undue loading of the circuit while testing. The polarity of the signal coming in will generally be positive-going; however some sets will have a negative-going signal into the 1st video. Whatever the polarity into the base, the polarity at the emitter will be the same. The amplitude at the emitter will be about the same as the input at the base or slightly less. The polarity of the signal at the collector will be opposite that going into the base; normally however, the amplitude of the signal at the collector should be at least 10 times that at the base.

Trouble Symptoms

Little or No Gain: Defective transistor. Before replacing transistor, check emitter voltage to ground. Typical current for this stage is about 5 to 10 ma. Use Ohm's law to determine if transistor current is within the expected range. If voltage is low across emitter resistor (R5), check transistor bias between base and emitter. Bias should be between about 0.5 and 0.7 volt. If bias seems close to correct, check to make sure that collector voltage is near normal; if it is high, the transistor is probably bad.

If bias voltage is low, check R1. If bias voltage is high, check for open R2. Another cause for high bias voltage could be a defective AGC circuit, allowing more than normal signal level to arrive at the video detector.

Fuzzy Pix Due to Poor High Frequency Response: May be

caused by open L3 or L4. Temporarily short across these coils with a short jumper, if picture quality improves, replace coil.
Ringing In Pix Due to Excessive High Frequency Response: May be caused by open R4 or R7. Again short across with a short jumper, if pix improves, place another resistor of the correct value across the coil.

Ringing can also be caused by an open ground wire to the delay line. Usually this is an external break and can be repaired rather easily. If break is not obvious, temporarily replace delay line to see if symptom is cured.
Low Collector Voltage (May be accompanied by a picture which is "milky"): Increase in value of collector load resistor (R6). Also can be caused by excessive transistor bias or by low supply voltage. Note that in this circuit the collector is fed through two different 1.8K resistors (R6 and R8). Depending on the remainder of the circuit, one of these resistors opening may not cause a completely significant change in collector voltage so as to make diagnosis easy using DC measurements. If either resistor opens, though, there will be a marked change in the response of the circuit. For example: If R8 should open it may cause ringing of the circuit due to an improper termination resistance for the delay line.

This circuit is direct-coupled to the next stage in most color sets. This means that any change of significance in the collector voltage will be reflected as a rather drastic change in bias on the following stage. Depending upon the number of stages following, this change in bias may cause either the screen brightness to go up or down. This is why, if a set comes in with either insufficient or excessive brightness, before readjusting brightness limit controls, you should thoroughly check the video circuits. Later in this section we cover a complete direct-coupled video circuit and give you hints for troubleshooting the overall circuit.

EMITTER FOLLOWER VIDEO AMPLIFIER (COMMON COLLECTOR)

The common-collector configuration (Fig. 11-3) is an excellent circuit for transforming impedance and, in the process, gaining power (though no voltage gain) for feeding a succeeding circuit. The input impedance of this amplifier is high, being roughly equivalent to the size of the emitter resistor times the transistor beta. For example, a transistor here with a beta of 75 would have an input impedance of about 75,000 ohms. Since here the resistive load on the detector circuit is about 4.7K ohms, the 75K ohm input impedance has

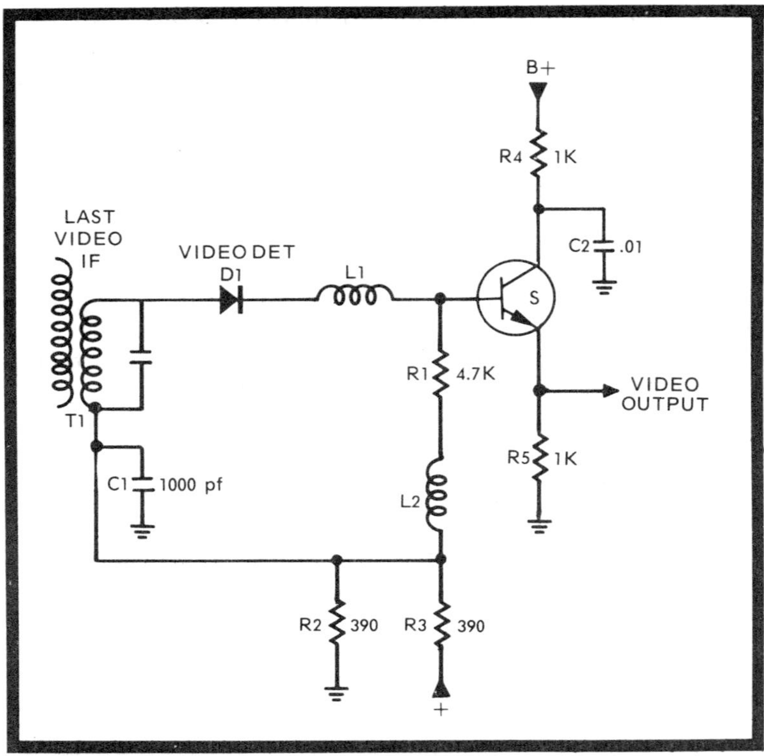

Fig. 11-3. Simplified circuit of an emitter follower (common-collector) video amplifier.

almost no effect on, that is, no load on the detector circuit. However, the voltage gain will be about 95 percent of that on the base, so if the signal is transferred from a circuit with 75K ohm impedance to a circuit with 1K or less of impedance, we have a power gain (due to current gain). For example, 1 volt across 75K results in a current flow of just .0133 ma, but .95 volt across 1K results in a current flow of .95 ma, a current gain of about 71 times.

The principal advantage of this circuit is that current is supplied to the following transistor stage for driving it, as well as current to sync and other circuits, with little or no effect on the detector circuit at all.

Capacitor C2 is the "collector ground" capacitor, which prevents any degeneration in the collector circuit from transferring all the available power gain to the emitter. The base bias is provided through resistor R3 with a bleeder to ground, R2. This "hard" bias (low resistance) circuit establishes the bias at a fixed level which is relatively unaffected by external influence. The transistor bias then becomes the result of this fixed bias plus the bias developed by the signal through diode D1 across the 4.7K resistor, R1. Peaking coils L1 and L2 compensate the amplifier and improve the high frequency response, but because they have a low DC resistance they have almost no effect on the DC bias voltages.

The current flow through the transistor is limited by both R4 and R5 so that even a shorted transistor, or a transistor with saturated bias, can have a maximum current flow of only 10 ma (assuming a 20-volt DC supply).

Troubleshooting the Circuit

This circuit should offer little difficulty for troubleshooting. Measuring the DC voltages alone should help you find almost any trouble, such as a shorted transistor, open transistor, lack of DC bias and the like. The bias for this silicon NPN transistor should be around 0.5 volt positive from base to emitter.

A trouble that could occur and not affect the DC voltages would be an open collector bypass, C2. With C2 open, there would be some tendency for feedback at higher frequencies due to the internal capacity of the transistor. Such feedback would reduce the high frequency gain of the stage and perhaps cause a degraded picture and a possible loss of the chroma signal. At the least, it would weaken the chroma signal. The actual result of an open C2 will vary with transistors, and you may sometimes find that the circuit appears to work almost as well without C2 as with it, though as a matter of good engineering practice, C2 should always be inserted.

When checking this circuit with an oscilloscope, see that the video output signal at the emitter is almost exactly the same size and shape and polarity as the signal at the base of the transistor, if not, check the amplifier circuit carefully. One problem that can cause an unusual condition that can vary from circuit to circuit and even from signal to signal is an open R1 or L2. Neither of these components is likely to open due to circuit currents but they can open due to physical stress, or they could be open due to an incorrect connection by a technician either at the factory or because of earlier service work.

DIRECT-COUPLED VIDEO AMPLIFIERS

Although Fig. 11-4 shows a simplified circuit, it should help to explain how almost any direct-coupled video circuit works. Let's follow the signal through it.

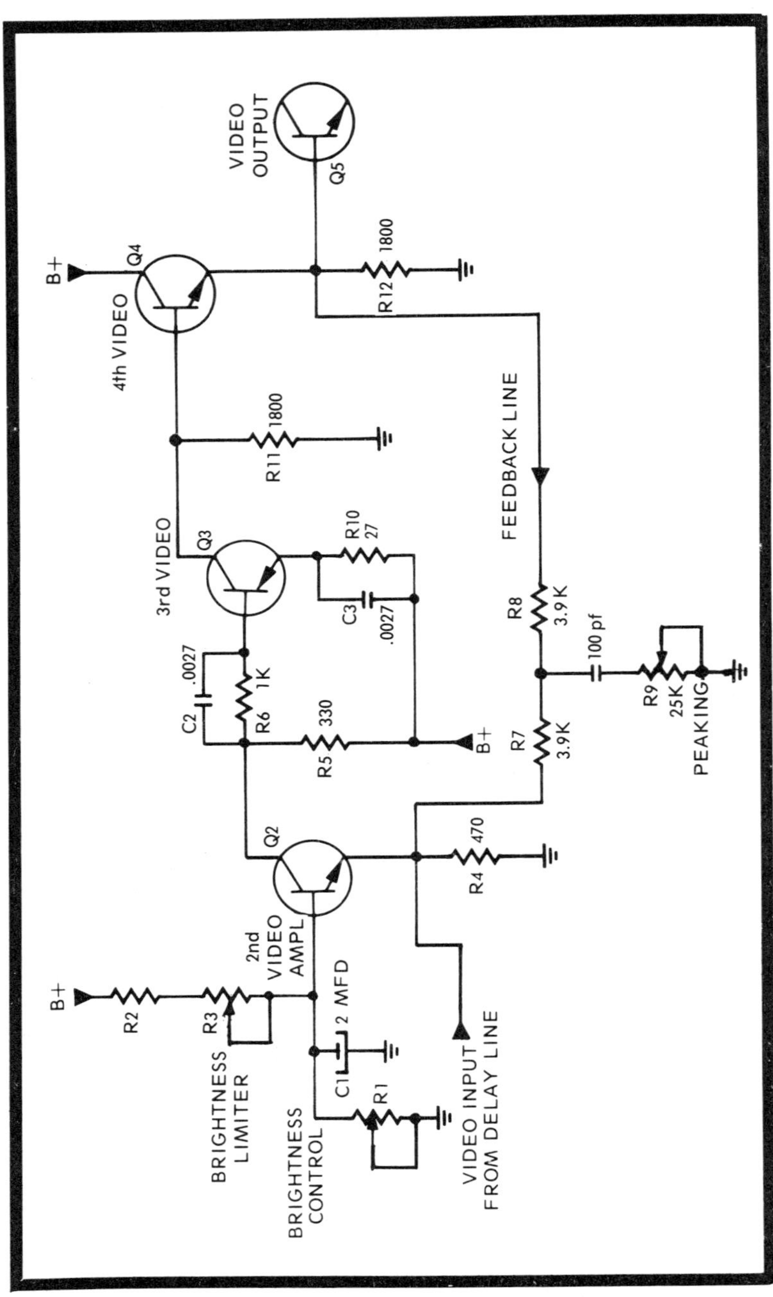

Fig. 11-4. Simplified 2nd, 3rd, 4th direct-coupled video amplifier.

Starting at the input of the amplifier at the emitter of Q2, the 2nd video amplifier, the signal is amplified to the collector. Then it goes through the RC network, C2-R6, to the base of Q3, then to the base of Q4, and finally to the emitter of Q4, which is connected to the base of Q5.

To show how a DC signal reacts on this circuit, let's suppose there's a positive-going bias at the emitter of Q2. The positive bias on an NPN emitter is the same as a negative bias of the same amount on the base (assuming the base cannot vary) and this reduces the collector current of Q2. With less current through R4, the voltage on the collector (to ground) goes more positive. The added positive voltage is transferred to the base of Q3 which is a PNP transistor. A positive increase at Q3 causes a decrease in its collector current, meaning less voltage drop across R11. With less drop across R11, the voltage to ground on the collector of Q3 will be less positive and since this voltage is direct-coupled to base of Q4, will result in reduced current through Q4. With less current through R12, there will be a less positive voltage on the emitter of Q4.

The feedback line sends the less-positive voltage at the Q4 emitter back through a resistance network to the emitter of Q2, where the voltage is positive-going. This results in a degenerative or self regulating feedback so that any decrease in current in Q2 results in a feedback voltage that tries to increase the current in Q2. If this were unity feedback, that is, if it completely cancelled any change in Q2 current, there could be no amplification so the feedback circuit must be selected by the designer to allow the most compensation without undue loss of gain. This circuit could be stripped of video and only allow a DC change to be reflected, but another use of this circuit is shown here. The video signal is fed back by the same circuit and tends to correct for "tilts" in the amplifier response, but a "side" peaking circuit can be adjusted to bypass more or less of the higher-frequency video signals. If more higher frequencies are bypassed then there will be less inverse feedback at high frequencies and so more gain at those frequencies. Adding high-frequency gain results in a "peaking" of the fine detail of the picture. Sometimes this peaking is desirable, especially if the picture sent out has some loss of detail. It is also desirable in weak-signal fringe areas to "depeak" the picture to reduce "snow" and noise.

Capacitors C2 and C3 both have the effect of improving the high-frequency response of the amplifiers. This does not mean that the amplifier has more high-frequency than low-frequency gain, it is simply a method of counteracting the natural loss of high frequency gain caused by residual capacity in the circuit due to internal transistor capacity and stray capacity around the parts.

The brightness control circuit varies the bias on the base of the 2nd Video Amplifier, and since this bias will reflect through the whole chain to the picture tube, any change of bias here controls the DC on the cathode(s) of the picture tube and consequently the brightness. A brightness "limiter" is in reality a designer's tool for setting the bias of the stage so that the brightness control will vary the CRT brightness in accordance with the specifications for a particular CRT.

The brightness control and brightness limiter could be in the cathode circuit of this transistor or in other video stages so that it would control bias. Or the brightness control could be in one bias-regulating circuit and the brightness limiter in another.

Sometimes a transistor is added in the brightness limiter circuit to detect a change in picture tube load and-or the high voltage and automatically shift the bias on the video amplifier to compensate for these conditions.

Troubleshooting the Circuit

When troubleshooting any direct-coupled circuit do not be overwhelmed by all the "wrong" voltages in the circuit. You must concentrate instead on how the circuit works and what can be expected from it when trouble occurs in any specific stage. The best place to start is at the beginning, since at the beginning any change in bias will get the most reaction at the other end of the video chain.

The collector and emitter voltages on the stages are important measuring points, more so perhaps in most cases than the base to emitter bias since this cannot be established at any "exact" optimum point—it may be 0.4, 0.45, 0.5, 0.55, etc., for the correct operating point, depending upon the transistor itself. But the current through R4, for example, as indicated by the voltage across R4, should be nearly correct and if it isn't, you need to find out why. If the voltage is high, it could be caused by a shorted transistor, or by a high bias, which in this case could be because of a misadjustment of either the brightness limiter or the brightness control or both.

If the voltage across R4 is correct, then chances are that the voltage at the collector of Q2 will be correct.

In this particular circuit, a reduction in current in any transistor results in a reduction of current all along the line. (It must be pointed out that not all circuits work like this, in fact many do not.) With this situation you can quickly check any suceeding stages starting with any transistor simply by zero-biasing that transistor (shorting between the base and the emitter).

If for example you short the base to emitter of Q2, the voltage drop across R5 should drop to zero, across R10 to zero, across R11 to zero, across R12 to zero, showing zero current flow through all the transistors. If, for example, you short the base to emitter of Q3, then the current for Q4 will also drop to zero; but because of the feedback circuit, the current through Q2 will increase since it is trying to compensate for the low current of Q4.

When you encounter trouble in a circuit such as this, and you are convinced the trouble is not caused by someone else having made an incorrect adjustment on it, you should check the transistors by measuring DC voltages on each transistor and then zero-biasing the transistor to see if there is a change—if there is none, then the transistor is defective. Do not try to check transistors in the circuit with an ohmmeter since the direct coupling will almost surely cause an erroneous conclusion. Instead, to check with an ohmmeter, disconnect either the collector or emitter temporarily from the circuit and then make the regular ohmmeter check, and if there is any doubt about the validity of the test, disconnect two terminals of the selected transistor from the circuit and remeasure either with an ohmmeter or with a transistor tester, or better still, tack in a substitute transistor.

COLOR TV VIDEO OUTPUT STAGE

The video output transistor has to be a different type transistor than the ones preceding it (Fig. 11-5). The main difference is that it must be able to operate with a high collector voltage, in this circuit around 200 volts. The reason the high collector voltage is essential is that the color CRT must have more than a 100 volt swing in voltage to drive it between full brightness and cutoff, so obviously a transistor with only 20 volts on the collector to start with cannot produce such a change. Thus, when a video transistor is found defective, you should always use an exact replacement if you are not absolutely sure that the replacement you wish to use will perform properly.

The contrast control varies the amount of gain but not the bias on the output transistor. If the bias was varied, the brightness of the CRT would vary with a change in the contrast setting. Instead, the contrast control varies the amount

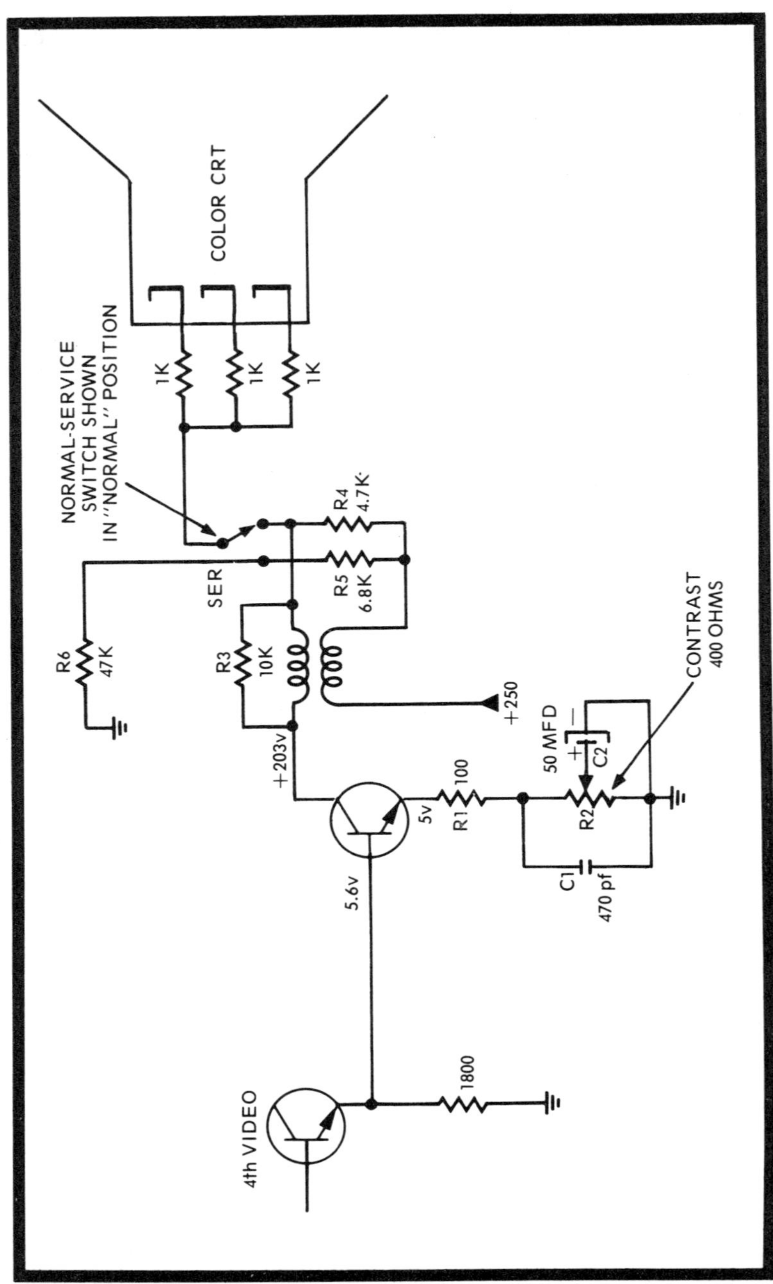

Fig. 11-5. Color TV video output circuit.

of signal bypassed around itself. With the center arm of the control at ground there is low gain from the video amplifier but there is full gain with the center arm at the junction of the contrast control and the 100-ohm emitter resistor. The 470-pf capacitor, C1, provides a high frequency bypass which tends to sharpen pictures set for low contrast and maintain a "visual balance" for all contrast control settings.

Troubleshooting the Circuit

If varying the contrast control does not affect the contrast, check for an open C2 (50-mfd electrolytic). The size of this component varies with different circuits, but almost any value of 5 mfd or more when shunted across a defective capacitor will make a significant difference in the gain or the contrast. Replace the capacitor with one of similar capacity, though usually any larger size that is no more than twice the size of the original will be satisfactory. CAUTION: Too large a capacity may cause a "lagging" effect when the contrast is changed, resulting in a momentary change in brightness and contrast which will then return to normal when the capacitor has had time to charge or discharge.

If the CRT brightness is high and varying the contrast control causes a change in brightness, then suspect a shorted 50 mfd capacitor, C2. If brightness is high and adjustment of the brightness control or the shorting of the base to emitter on the video output stage has no effect on brightness, this may indicate a shorted video output transistor. If brightness is low and the same tests produce no effect, it may be because of an open video transistor.

Disconnect the transistor from the circuit and make DC tests if an in-circuit test is inconclusive.

A "milky" or "bad CRT" appearance for the picture can be caused by an increased value of the 4.7K resistor, R4. An increased value here would increase the brightness but often this may have been compensated for either by the customer or by another technician by resetting of the brightness limiter.

Ringing in the circuit (outlines around sharp edges of a picture) could be caused by an open R3, or could be caused if someone inadvertently connected C1 from the emitter to ground rather than across the contrast control.

A NORMAL-SERVICE switch is shown in this circuit since one is often used in color video amplifier output stages. (Circuit simplified and incomplete.) The purpose of the switch is to establish a brightness level for the CRT which is not affected by the brightness control. Thus, when the switch is turned to SERVICE a fixed DC bias is applied to the cathodes of the CRT and the video circuit is removed. This brightness level is close to the low brightness position that would be established with the brightness control near minimum when the switch is in the NORMAL position.

Although this switch is intended primarily as a set up convenience, it makes an excellent quick check for video amplifier troubles that affect brightness. Turn the switch to SERVICE and if the normal set-up procedures produce the correct brightness level, then you can be almost sure that the brightness problem is caused by the video amplifier(s). If, however, you cannot establish the correct set-up brightness, you know the brightness problem is almost surely elsewhere, such as in the CRT grid bias circuit, or the screen voltage circuits, etc. The point is make a habit of using this switch not only for set up, but for a quick check for biasing problems in the video amplifier or picture tube.

SYNC SEPARATORS AND AMPLIFIERS

Synchronizing is the process of starting the TV picture scanning at the same time in the receiver as at the transmitter. If the synchronizing is correct, we say that the picture is "locked in." This means that it does not roll, tear, move sideways, or lean diagonally. The synchronizing pulses sent out by the transmitter occur after each horizontal line and at the bottom of the picture. These pulses, usually called sync (pronounced "sink") pulses, are sent with the video (picture information) but at about a 25 to 30 percent higher level. It is this higher level of the sync pulse that makes it possible for us to separate them from the video. (If the video does not get separated, the changing video signal will influence the vertical and horizontal oscillators and cause the picture to bend, tear, roll, streak, or otherwise be erratic.)

Fig. 12-1 shows a typical composite video signal. Note that the highest point of the video is below the sync pulse amplitude. To separate the sync signals from the video it is only necessary to bias an amplifier in such a way that it will respond only to high amplitude signals and not to those of less amplitude. To make sure that the "clipping" level is correct, the biasing must in some manner be automatic so that regardless of the overall sync pulse height, the clipping will still be only at or above the level of the sync pulse and not drop down into the video.

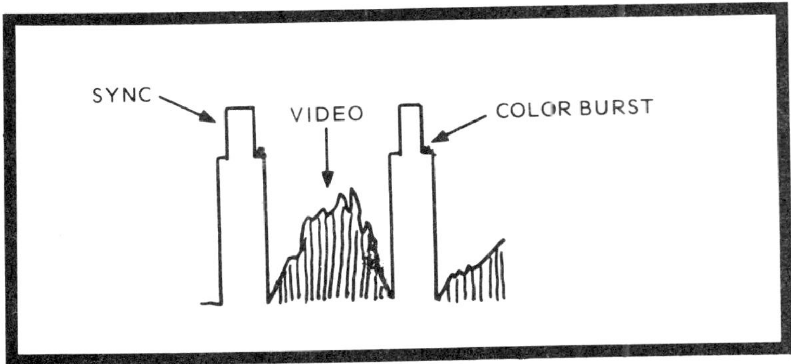

Fig. 12-1. Composite video signal including sync pulse.

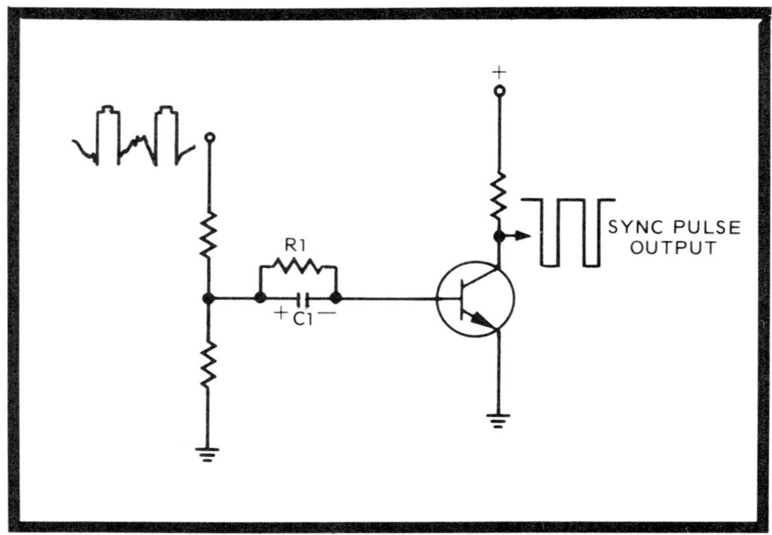

Fig. 12-2. Simplified sync circuit showing self-biasing method.

Fig. 12-2 shows a simplified transistor sync circuit using an NPN transistor. The positive-going input signal is fed to the base, which causes the transistor to conduct heavily in the base-emitter junction. Capacitor C1 charges as shown, making the base negative (which cuts off the NPN transistor). R1 is selected to hold the transistor at cutoff between sync pulses so that the video signal will not be amplified. C1 does discharge enough, though, so that the next sync pulse tip will again make the transistor conduct and also again charge up C1. This circuit is automatically self-adjusting since the capacitor will charge to a level determined by the sync pulse height, whatever it might be.

Solid-state sync circuit designs usually have at least two transistor circuits, the first to clip off the sync from the video and the second to produce a fixed-amplitude pulse regardless of input from the sync separator. This stage is often called a limiter. It is so biased that it will saturate or cutoff (or both) on a small sync signal and thus a larger sync signal can do no more, limiting the sync signal to a predetermined design level. Limiting the sync signal in this manner means a more stable control for the vertical and horizontal oscillators and prevents sync problems that might occur when either an extra weak or extra strong signal is tuned in.

A third sync stage that is often used in semiconductor sets is the sync phase splitter. Fig. 12-3 shows a simplified circuit.

The signal fed to the base is inverted in the collector circuit but remains in phase with the input signal at the emitter output terminal. There is no gain in this circuit, but this is a simple way of providing a two-phase signal which can be fed to a horizontal phase detector.

SYNC SEPARATOR CIRCUIT

The composite video signal is fed to the base of Q1 (Fig. 12-4) where the main purpose is to invert the signal so it can be fed to the sync separator Q2. But Q1 also serves as an isolation between the video circuit and the time constant circuits in the input of Q2.

The horizontal signals are fed to Q2 through C2, a .01 mfd capacitor which with resistor R4 makes an RC time constant circuit that holds the sync separator bias at the correct point for clipping. C2 however, does not pass the lower vertical sync signals too well but the leading edge of the vertical sync pulse does charge C2, causing D1 to be forward-biased. This forward-biased diode switches in the 0.22 mfd capacitor during vertical pulses. The added capacity holds the sync separator amplifier Q2 in saturation throughout the pulse interval.

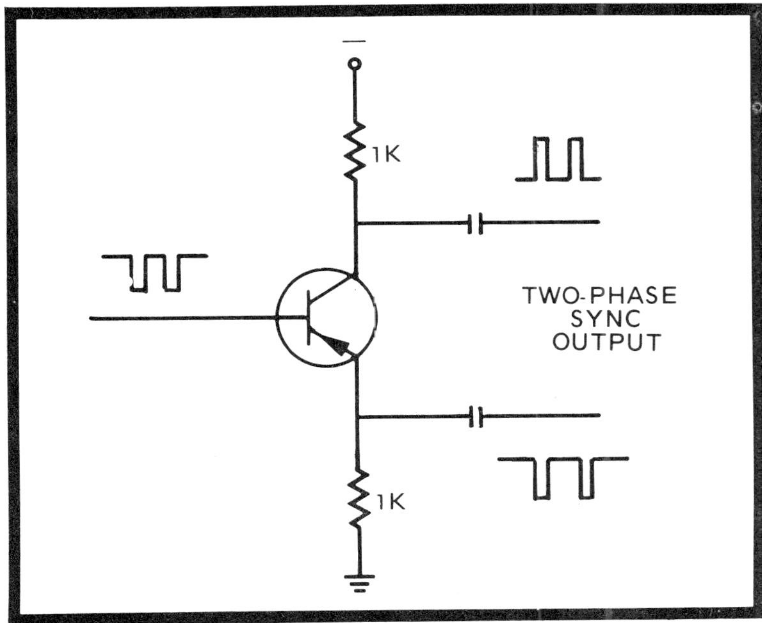

Fig. 12-3. Simplified sync phase splitter.

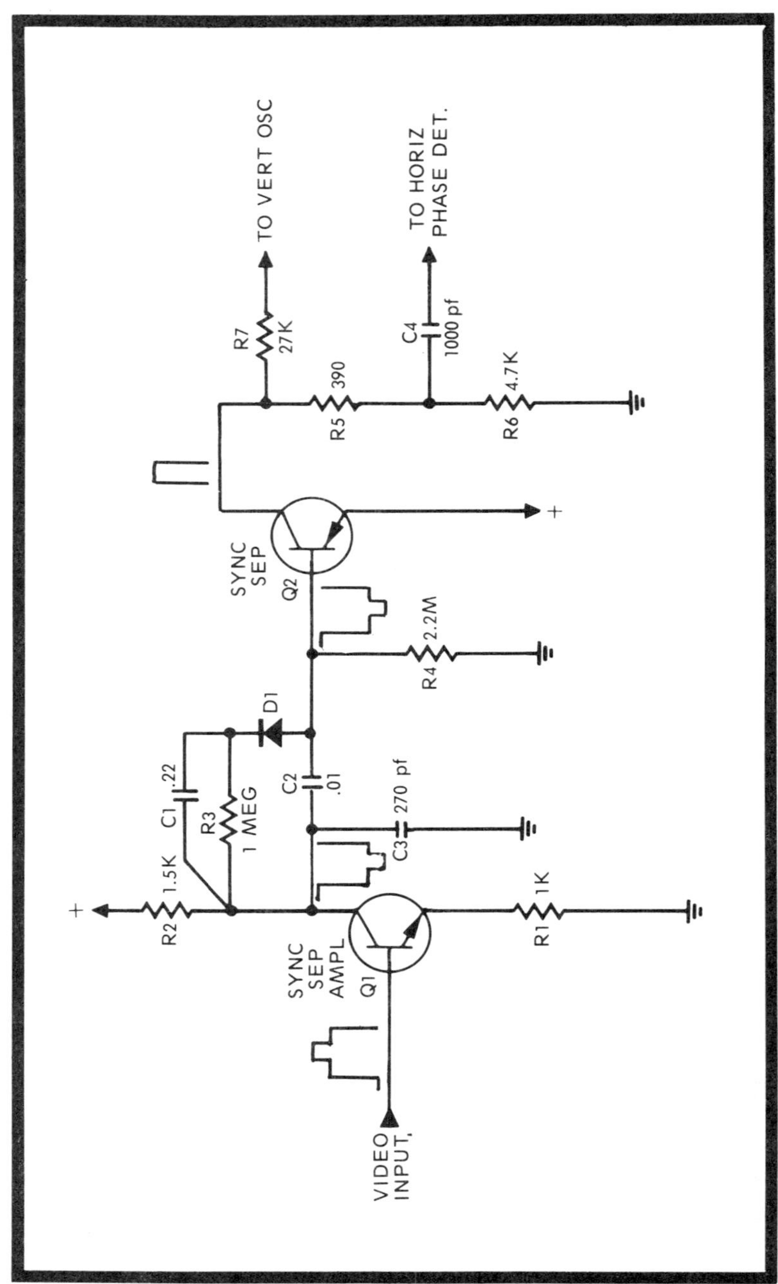

Fig. 12-4. Sync separator circuit.

Capacitor C3 (collector of Q1) bypasses some of the video and chroma high frequency "grass" to ground.

The output is fed through a resistor, R7, to the vertical oscillator circuit to prevent the input capacity of the vertical circuit from bypassing the horizontal sync pulses to ground. The horizontal pulses in this particular set are fed to a transistor phase splitter which in turn drives the horizontal phase detectors.

Troubleshooting the Circuit

It is difficult to diagnose trouble in a sync circuit without using an oscilloscope. The reason is that what appears to be a sync problem in a TV may in reality be an overload problem in the video or preceding amplifiers. Any overloaded amplifier will tend to clip the sync from the video and so if the sync amplifiers receive only a video input they cannot possibly strip the sync from it.

One of the major causes of preceding stage overload is a defective AGC circuit which allows one or more amplifiers to have too much input signal applied. But, to make matters worse, a defective sync stage itself can upset the AGC circuit so that earlier stages are overloaded. This is why, in any suspected sync trouble, it is a good idea first to "clamp" the AGC line with a fixed voltage. You can do this with any filtered power supply that is adjustable between about 0 and 22 volts.

CAUTION: The applying of a bias voltage to the AGC line is not to be taken without a bit of concern, especially in transistor circuits. It may be that the bias voltage is normally several volts above ground while on the other hand it may be only a volt or so above ground. Try to anticipate what the bias voltage should be when it is not near ground potential normally, and then set your bias supply near this voltage before making any attachment to the circuit. You can then juggle the voltage back and forth slightly for best results.

Connect the negative side of the power supply to the AGC line, or the positive side, depending upon which polarity is required. Start with zero voltage and increase it until the bias is at the value normally generated by the TV with a signal.

If the input signal to the sync amplifier is normal, that is, the sync pulses are riding clearly above the video by 20 to 30 percent, you know that the sync separators are at fault and you can continue tracing through the circuit.

With a positive-going video input, the collector of Q1 should have negative-going signals. The negative-going signals drive the base of Q2 into saturation and the coupling capacitors, C1, C2, charge up, forcing the base bias on Q2 to go positive, cutting off the transistor. The capacitors leak off some charge between pulses so sync pulses drive Q2 again into saturation, thus recharging the capacitors and again cutting off Q2. It is this saturation-cutoff cycle that supplies an output (on the collector of Q2) that is essentially an amplified replica of the input sync but not of the video.

The oscilloscope will show whether or not the sync separator is doing its job. If the sync output at the collector of Q2 has video in it (changes in size or shape with a change in picture), then the vertical and horizontal oscillators will be affected, depending upon the amount of video in the sync. With only a small amount of video, the sync may only be critical to adjust. With more video the picture may weave, bend, etc. With still more, sync will be lost altogether.

A common trouble in this circuit might be leakage in either C1 or C2, or an open or shorted diode D1 (check the diode with an ohmmeter). The capacitors may be checked by disconnecting one end and measuring the voltage from that end to ground—it should be zero after an initial charging indication. It may be difficult to disconnect either end in printed circuits. So for printed circuits you may find it easier to use a knife and CAREFULLY cut across the appropriate printed circuit to make the disconnection, REPAIRING the break after the check has been made.

If you pull the capacitor out of the circuit to make the test, do not rely on a leakage check using only an ohmmeter. Touch one lead of the capacitor to a source of voltage several volts above ground and then use your voltmeter between the other end of the capacitor and ground. A non-electrolytic capacitor should not allow any DC current through it and so the voltmeter should read zero after the first influx of charge current.

Transistors in this circuit can be checked by the ohmmeter method with reasonable success. Turn off power to the circuit. Measure between base and emitter, base and collector, and collector and emitter of each transistor, reversing the ohmmeter leads for each of the measurements. Between base and emitter you should have a high and low reading for each reversal of the meter leads. The same is true for the base to collector measurement. From collector to emitter, there should be a fairly high resistance (depending upon shunt resistances in the circuit) in both directions of meter lead connection.

When reading base bias on a sync separator, you will normally find a reverse DC bias when the TV is tuned to a station and a forward bias when it is not. This is because the sync pulses cause the average DC bias to reverse due to the charge on the base capacitor; this way only the high amplitude sync pulse itself is sufficient to drive the sync separator out of cutoff, but this pulse change in base bias is not indicated by the DC meter.

SYNC AMPLIFIER AND SYNC SEPARATOR

The sync amplifier is a class A amplifier (Fig. 12-5) which takes the video signal from the video amplifier and inverts and amplifies it. The output signal of PNP transistor Q1 is positive-going (assuming a negative-going input signal), and is applied to the base of the NPN sync separator Q2. The sync separator (Q2) has bias applied through R9. The large video signal appearing at the base of Q2 because of the output from Q1, is of sufficient amplitude to drive Q2 to draw considerable current due to the base-emitter diode action of rectification, which in turn makes the base go negative. With the base negative, only the most positive-going part of the signal causes current to flow in the collector circuit so only the sync signals are amplified and the video is ignored. The collector circuit of Q1, then, has a complete positive-going video signal, but the output of Q2 will (or should have) only negative-going sync pulses.

In this circuit, the supply voltage for the collector of Q2 is a higher voltage than normally might be expected in a solid-state circuit. This is because this circuit is driving a tube circuit which requires more voltage. If the circuit were controlling transistor oscillator circuits, the collector supply voltage would likely be no more than 20 to 30 volts.

Troubleshooting the Circuit

Note that sync amplifier Q1 is a PNP transistor, meaning that it requires a negative bias voltage between base and emitter. The transistor is biased by tying the emitter circuit to the +19-volt circuit and then direct-coupling the collector circuit of the video amplifier to the base. The video amplifier, though, may have no more than 15 or 16 volts on it, which would mean that Q1 would have too much negative bias (+16 from +19 would be a negative 3 volts) so a 1K resistor (R2) from the +19 volt source raises the voltage back up to the proper amount, along with the bleeder action of R3 from the base to ground.

The output of Q1, when checked with a scope, should usually show at least 5 times gain at the junction of R4 and R5

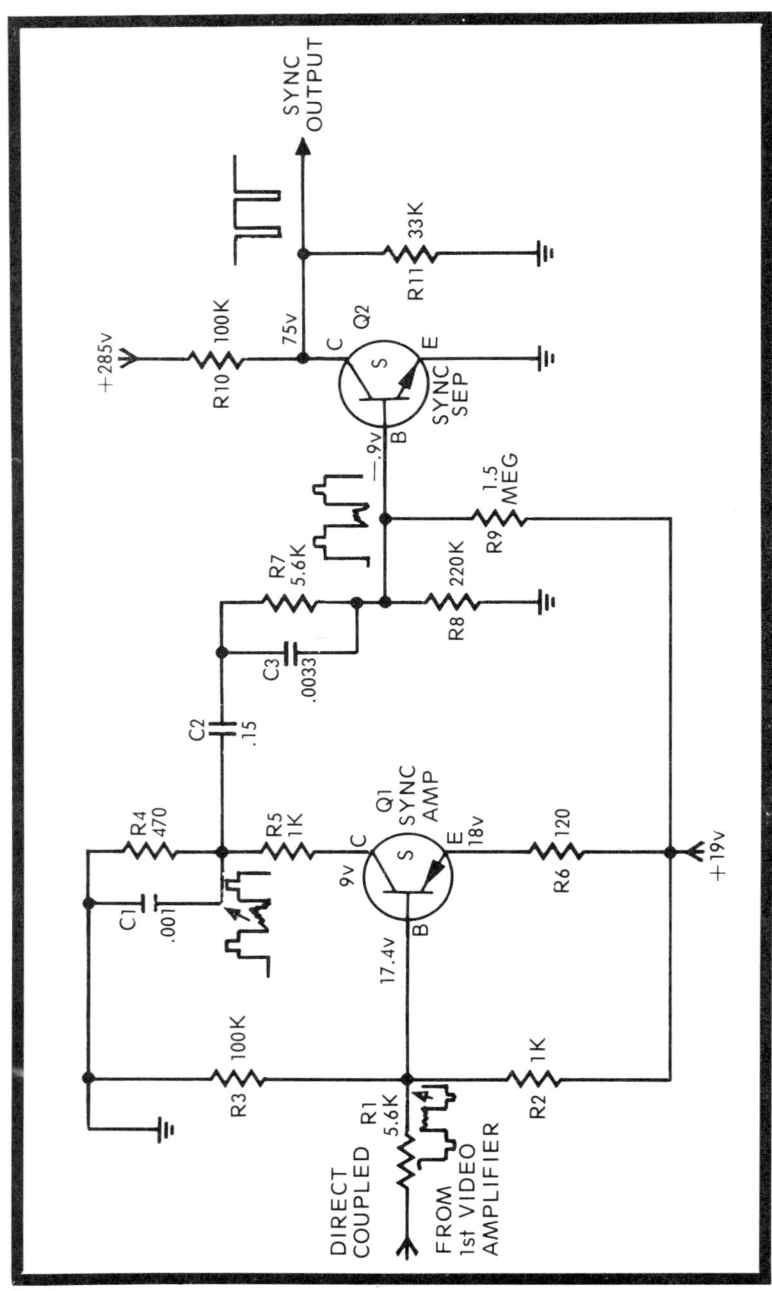

Fig. 12-5. Sync amplifier and sync separator.

as compared to the video at the base. The signal, now positive-going, is coupled through C2 to the shaping circuit of C3 and R7. The scope should show a positive-going signal at the base of Q2. At the collector of Q2, you should see no video but only strong negative-going sync pulses.

Once you have determined with the scope that the trouble is in one of these stages, you should make DC voltage checks to find the exact trouble.

Trouble Symptoms

Signal at Collector of Q1 Weak and Not Inverted from Base Signal: Transistor defective. R6 open. R2 open.

Signal at Collector of Q1 Distorted: Transistor defective. Check bias voltage between base and emitter; it should be near 0.6 volt. Check voltage drop across R6 and calculate transistor current. Current will likely be between about 4 and 7 ma if circuit is operating normally otherwise.

Signal OK at Collector of Q1, Weak at Base of Q2: C2 open. If C2 is open or any part of the circuit open so that the video signal cannot reach the base of Q2, the measured DC bias on Q2 will be **positive** between base and emitter. In normal operation, the sync signal will cause "reverse" bias on the NPN transistor Q2. Without signal input, collector voltage on Q2 will be **lower** than normal due to additional collector current flow.

Signal OK at Base of Q2, Little or No Output at Collector: Defective transistor. R10 open.

Transistor Replacements

General-purpose silicon transistors of most types will work okay in the Q1 stage. For Q2, because of the higher collector voltage, make sure that the replacement can withstand a collector to emitter voltage (Vce) of at least 90 volts.

NOISE INVERTERS, CLIPPERS, GATES, AND AGC

Many TV manufacturers provide some method of noise inversion or cancellation to minimize interruption to the horizontal or vertical hold during bursts of noise. These noise inverters, clippers or "gates" as they are sometimes called, do not reduce the amount of noise seen on the screen, but by clipping the noise pulses to around the level of the sync pulses or only a bit higher, the energy in the noise pulse is reduced to a small enough level that it generally will not cause false triggering of either the vertical or horizontal oscillators.

All noise clipper circuits embody the idea that the circuit will not respond to a normal level signal, but will respond to noise pulses (riding along with the signal) that are greater than the sync pulse amplitude. Once the circuit responds, it either inverts the noise pulse and applies this inverted pulse to the signal, cancelling the noise effect, or during the noise pulse, the sync amplifier is cut off to prevent it from passing the noise pulse on to the vertical or horizontal oscillators. These "holes" in the output of the sync signal, even if they occur during the regular sync pulse, have little effect on the overall sync lock, since sync is established by the regular passage of a number of sync pulses. Noise, however, being in a random order, will not regularly occur at the same time the sync pulse arrives; thus, the cancellation of noise pulses normally will not affect the sync lock of the TV.

Noise clippers can cause sync trouble if they get out of adjustment and start clipping on lower pulse levels, thereby clipping the sync pulses themselves.

NOISE INVERTER

The noise inverter in Fig. 13-1 is fed a small positive signal from one of the video amplifiers. The normal video signal is fed to the sync amplifiers through the 470-ohm resistor, R4, and all the circuitry below the dotted line could be eliminated without affecting the TV performance except during noise interference.

This is because transistor Q2 is normally not conducting. Q2 has no DC base bias applied, and since it is an NPN silicon transistor, it requires about 0.5 volt positive bias before any current flows from the collector to emitter. The video signal applied through D1, R2 and C1 has a sync tip peak voltage of about 0.2 volt so there is no conduction and no affect on the video in the collector circuit. However, if a noise pulse that has a peak of 0.5 volt or more occurs, the transistor amplifies that pulse and because of the natural inversion, the positive pulse becomes a negative-going pulse in the collector circuit. This negative pulse cancels the positive pulse and so the composite video to the sync amplifier is "cleaned up."

The 10K resistor (R5) in this circuit provides a threshold bias for diode D1, allowing it to conduct only during the positive portion of the video signal, holding the p-p voltage level to a point below the 0.5 volt level necessary for the transistor to conduct. However, any noise pulse, which would be higher than the video level, is fed without attentuation to the base of the noise inverter.

Troubleshooting the Circuit

Finding out whether a noise inverter is working is sometimes more a problem than finding out if it is working

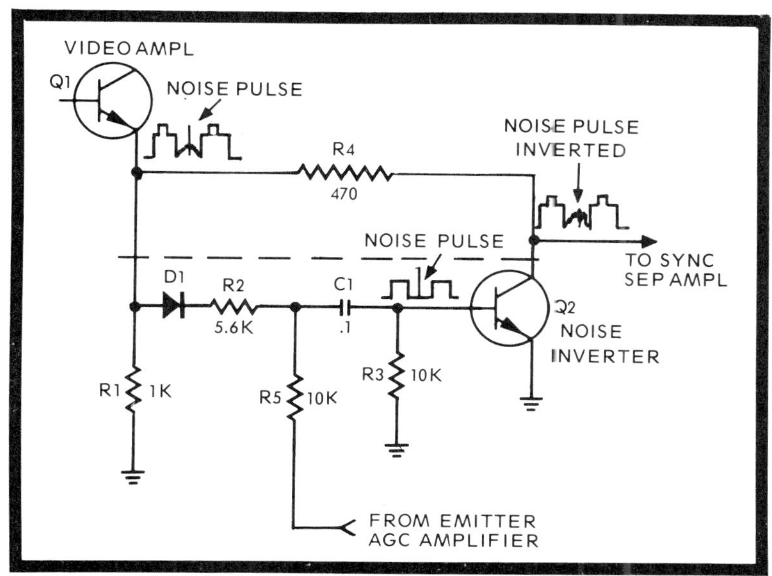

Fig. 13-1. Noise inverter.

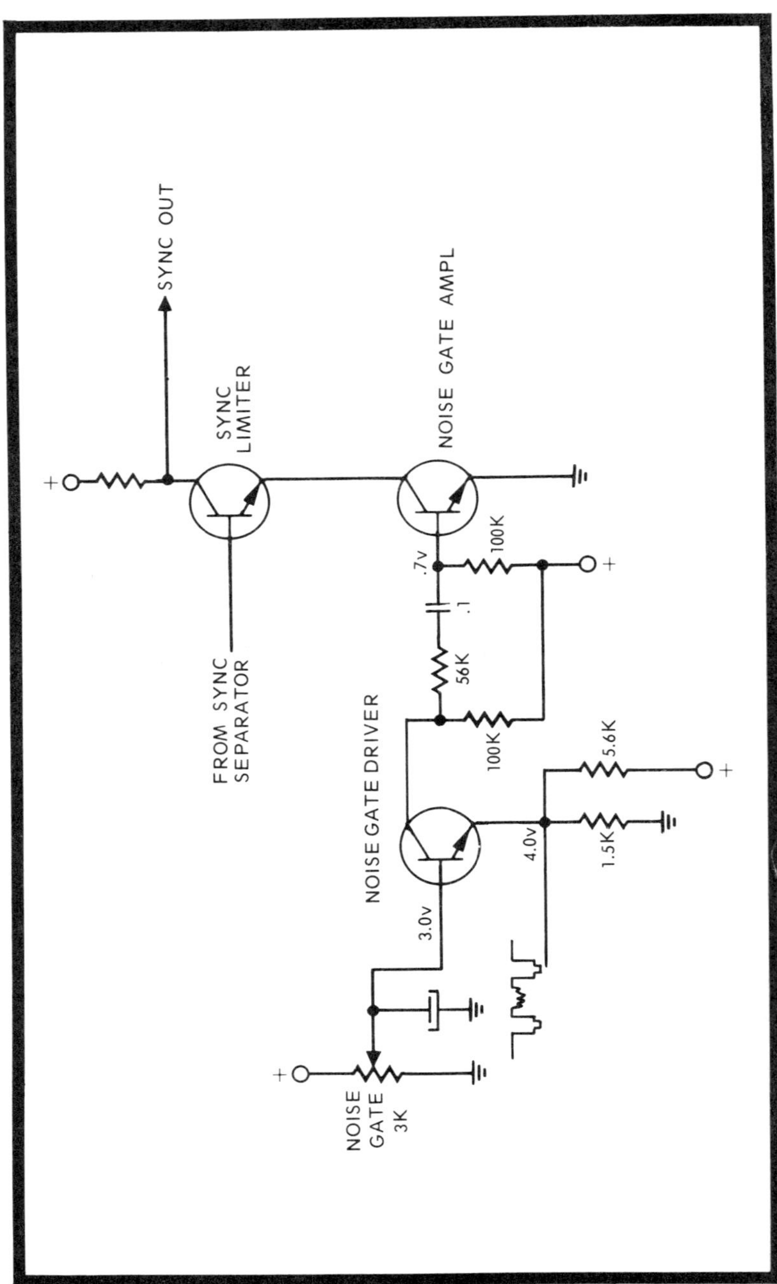

Fig. 13-2. Noise gate in series with sync limiter.

TOO well. The reason that the noise inverter works only when there is noise interference and so if the set is not being disturbed by interference there is no sure way of making sure the noise would be minimized. But by its very nature, if the noise inverter is misadjusted so that it starts clipping the video as well as noise, the first thing to go will be the sync pulses and vertical and horizontal lock will become critical, erratic, or non-existent.

If you suspect the noise inverter is causing sync trouble, you can simply disable its operation and see if the sync trouble clears up. You may be able to do this by a "Noise" adjustment usually located on the rear apron of the set—just turn it to its extreme in both directions and see if in one direction the sync trouble clears. If there is no noise adjustment, or if it also affects the AGC voltage as in this circuit, you can either disconnect the collector or the emitter from the circuit and if the sync clears you know that the noise inverter has either a transistor or a transistor bias problem.

NOISE GATE

In this circuit (Fig. 13-2) the noise-gate amplifier transistor is biased so that it is normally at full (saturated) conduction and this means a low resistance between collector and emitter and also a low resistance between the emitter of the sync limiter and ground.

A composite video pulse is fed into the emitter circuit of the noise gate driver. The DC bias on the noise gate driver is reversed, so that for the regular video signal there is no conduction. But a strong noise pulse will drive the transistor to conduction and produce a negative pulse in the collector (there is no phase inversion since the noise gate driver is a grounded-base amplifier). The negative pulse on the collector is fed to the base of the noise gate amplifier. Remember, a negative pulse to an NPN transistor cuts off the transistor and "opens" the emitter circuit of the sync limiter, so that during the noise pulse the sync has a "hole" in it rather than a large noise pulse which could falsely trigger the vertical and horizontal oscillators in the TV.

Troubleshooting the Circuit

Since the normal condition for the noise gate is conducting to saturation, if you suspect trouble in the noise circuit is possibly causing a sync problem, you can easily find out. All you need do is attach a temporary clip jumper from collector to emitter on the noise gate amplifier. If the trouble clears, then you know the trouble is in the noise gate circuit itself, either the transistor or the 100K bias resistor. Trouble in the noise gate amplifier circuit could be a misadjustment of the noise gate control, allowing the video pulses on the emitter to cause the noise gate amplifier to conduct on sync tips which in turn would put "holes" in the sync signal for every sync tip and result in a partial or complete loss of sync.

As with other noise circuits, it is hard to be sure that the noise circuit is really working since it only goes into operation when there is noise interference. One way you can check here would be to provide yourself with a clip jumper to short across collector to emitter of the noise gate amplifier transistor, then turn on some sort of interfering signal strong enough to make the sync unstable, such as an old electric razor, then remove the clip from across the noise gate transistor and see if the sync is significantly improved.

Noise controls should always be adjusted so that there is a sync instability and then backed off until the sync is completely stable on strong signals.

KEYED AGC CIRCUITS

The basic idea of a keyed AGC circuit is to eliminate or at least greatly reduce AGC response to noise pulses, and to develop AGC voltage on the average of the sync pulse amplitude rather than on the average of composite video.

If the AGC is the "average" video type, that is the kind that is dependent upon the composite video signal, the TV set may overload on signals with high levels of modulation such as commercials often have, while operating normally for most other pictures.

Circuit Description

The keyed AGC amplifier can be called a coincidence amplifier since it responds only when two signals arrive at the amplifier terminals at the same time. In Fig. 13-3, the two signals are the sync pulse and a pulse fed back from the horizontal sweep circuit in the TV. This means that the AGC amplifier conducts during sync time, but any noise pulse occuring at any other time has no effect on the circuit. This also helps to eliminate "airplane" flutter caused by signals reflected from airplanes because the sync pulse from the reflection arrives later than the direct signal pulse therefore the AGC is not affected since the horizontal pulse does not coincide with the reflected pulse. (This does not mean that the picture will not show interference due to the reflected signal but it does mean that the AGC should not fluctuate. AGC fluctuations would add a change in contrast to the other interference.)

Fig. 13-3 is not a practical circuit for several reasons but it does show the basic premise of a keyed AGC amplifier. An NPN transistor receives a composite video signal (positive-going) to its base. The collector circuit needs a positive voltage in order to conduct; but, instead, resistor R2 is returned to negative the same as the emitter. Under these circumstances, even with a large positive pulse to the base, the collector cannot conduct because there is no voltage difference between the collector and the emitter. But now if we add a positive-going pulse from the horizontal circuit through the .001 mfd capacitor, C1, and if that collector pulse is going positive at the same time as the sync pulse on the base is going positive, the transistor conducts. The only return path for the DC current from the collector to the emitter is through resistor R2. A voltage drop develops across R2 which is negative at the collector end.

Since the amount of conduction in the transistor is determined by the amplitude of the pulse on the base, the negative output will be in proportion to the size of the pulse. So if the signal input is weaker, there will be less negative AGC (or vice-versa) and the gain of the AGC-controlled amplifiers will increase to compensate.

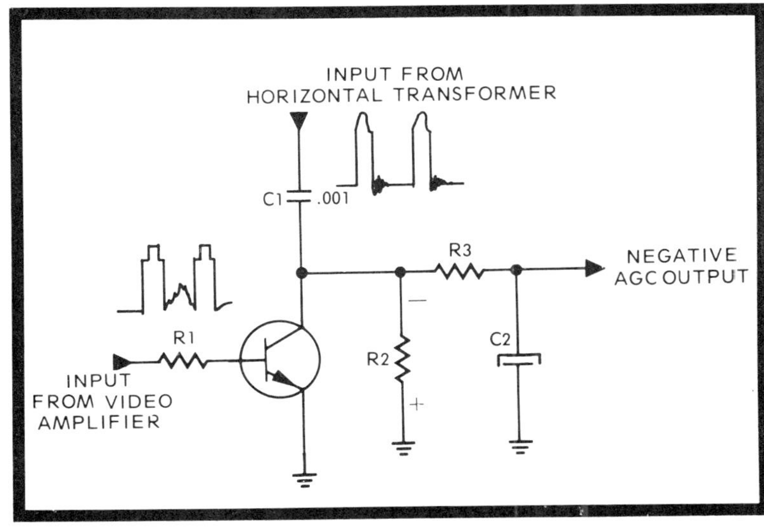

Fig. 13-3. Simplified keyed AGC.

R3—C2, the RC network, filters out the horizontal pulses and prevents the AGC from changing too quickly such as might occur during sudden fades, but still allows the AGC to change quickly enough to compensate for longer fades or to compensate for different signal strengths when changing channels.

As stated before, the simplified circuit of Fig. 13-3 is not practical for more than one reason. First, there must be some method of setting the bias on the transistor otherwise the transistor would not only respond to the sync pulses but the video as well, so an AGC adjustment is necessary to allow the amplifier to be triggered only by the sync pulses. Another problem is that pulses arriving at the collector tend to have a slight negative excursion, not only because of the "tails" on the signal itself but also because of passing through a capacitor and losing a bit of DC reference. A negative voltage on the collector of an NPN transistor causes the collector-base junction to be forward-biased, and this can damage the transistor. To prevent this possibility, a diode is placed in series with the amplifier to prevent any negative voltage from reaching the collector.

Fig. 13-4 illustrates a practical circuit showing only the "delayed" negative voltage output terminal. (The delay will be discussed below.) The composite video is taken from the collector of a video amplifier transistor which is at +15 volts, therefore this DC bias is passed to the base through R1 along with the video. R1 here does two things; (1) it limits base current flow in the event the AGC control is misadjusted, and (2) it also isolates the input capacity of the keyed AGC transistor from loading the video amplifier and reducing its high frequency response.

The AGC control adjusts the emitter voltage of the keyer and so establishes the point at which the AGC amplifier will conduct. Diode D1 prevents any possible forward-biasing of the collector-base junction of the keyer transistor.

The 12 megohm resistor R4 is used to "delay" the AGC action since here the circuit is supplying a tube type RF amplifier. The tube type RF amplifier to have the most gain should operate without bias, but without some sort of delay, even a weak signal will produce some AGC output. The 12 megohm resistor connected to the AGC line from the +150v line overcomes this difficulty, applying a positive "bucking" voltage on the line that cancels out any small negative voltage. To prevent the line from possibly going positive when there is no or little negative voltage, diode D2 will conduct, shorting any positive voltage to ground. When the signal input is stronger, however, the negative voltage from the AGC circuit will overpower the positive voltage and so the tube will receive a negative bias to reduce its gain. This preventing of the negative voltage until the signal strength rises to a predetermined threshold level is called "delayed AGC" and is used in many TV circuits and some radio circuits.

Troubleshooting the Circuit

The most common trouble with any AGC circuit is misadjustment. If the AGC control is rotated too far in one direction the transistor will not conduct at all and so no AGC voltage is developed. This allows the set to overload on strong signals, usually blanking out the screen, and on less strong signals causing sync instability. Depending upon the circuit design, a complete loss of AGC may still allow weak TV signals to be received, or signals to be received when no antenna is connected, though such reception is usually quite snowy. A loss of AGC may also be indicated if the set will receive a snowy picture (when the fine tuning is adjusted) on the channel adjacent to the transmitter channel, for example, you may be able to tune in Channel 3 on Channel 4. The additional loss through the tuner RF circuits may be enough to allow a snowy picture to be seen even though the AGC is inoperative.

If the AGC control is rotated in the opposite direction, the keyer transistor will conduct too vigorously and this will produce excessive AGC and reduce the gain of the RF and IF amplifiers to zero or nearly so. Then there will be no snow on the screen and no picture, but you may be able to hear some audio.

The second most probable cause of AGC trouble is a defective keyer transistor. Usually it shorts, and if it does, diode D1 should be replaced when the transistor is replaced (actually D1 should be replaced any time the transistor must be replaced for whatever reason), and D1 should be of the same type as the original, having a high reverse breakdown voltage.

Other troubles that occur in AGC circuits include a lack of pulse from the horizontal circuit. Usually this pulse is taken from a tap on the horizontal output transformer (H.O.T.). An oscilloscope is the best check for a lost horizontal pulse, but make sure that you are not just picking up a radiated pulse through your scope probe as can sometimes happen if the probe is not too well shielded and is set for the low capacity position. With transistor circuits, a direct scope probe is

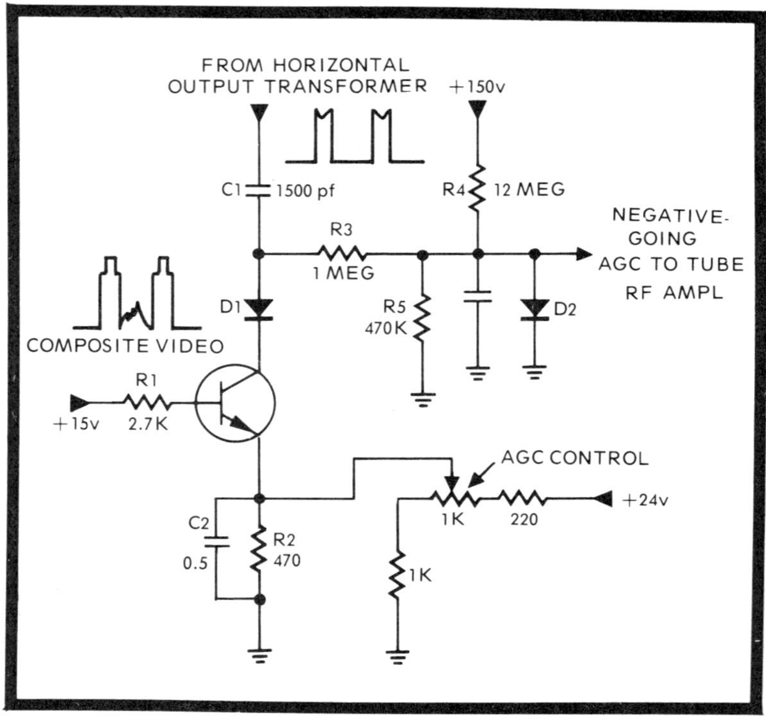

Fig. 13-4. Practical keyed AGC providing delayed negative AGC output.

probably best since the load of the probe will not seriously alter the waveform as seen on the collector.

Sometimes the pulse is fed from a separate tap on the H.O.T. and if so, even if the winding opens, the only thing affected will be the AGC.

Another trouble that can cause AGC trouble is capacitor C1 either shorted or breaking down under pulse voltage. This provides a DC path for the collector other than the AGC load resistor. If the capacitor returns to a highly positive or negative DC voltage on the H.O.T., this voltage is fed directly into the AGC line and may either cause (depending upon design) excessive gain, or deficient gain, which in either case usually means no picture and perhaps no sound.

You can usually determine if the problem is AGC by simply measuring the DC voltage on the AGC line, such as at the junction of R3, R4, R5, and then turning the AGC control to see if there is a significant change in voltage (the set should be tuned in to an active channel).

AGC KEYER WHICH VARIES PLUS VOLTAGE ON FET IF AMPLIFIER

Although the output of a keyed AGC amplifier increases in a more negative direction for an increase in signal, it still can be used to vary a positive voltage. In Fig. 13-5 the circuit is similar to Fig. 13-4 but the maximum gain for a MOSFET IF amplifier is with several volts positive on the base, with less gain as the gate is made less positive, finally going negative on very strong signals where low IF gain is desirable.

The bias for the FET is through the 1 megohm resistor (R4) which, with resistor R2 as a bleeder to ground, provides

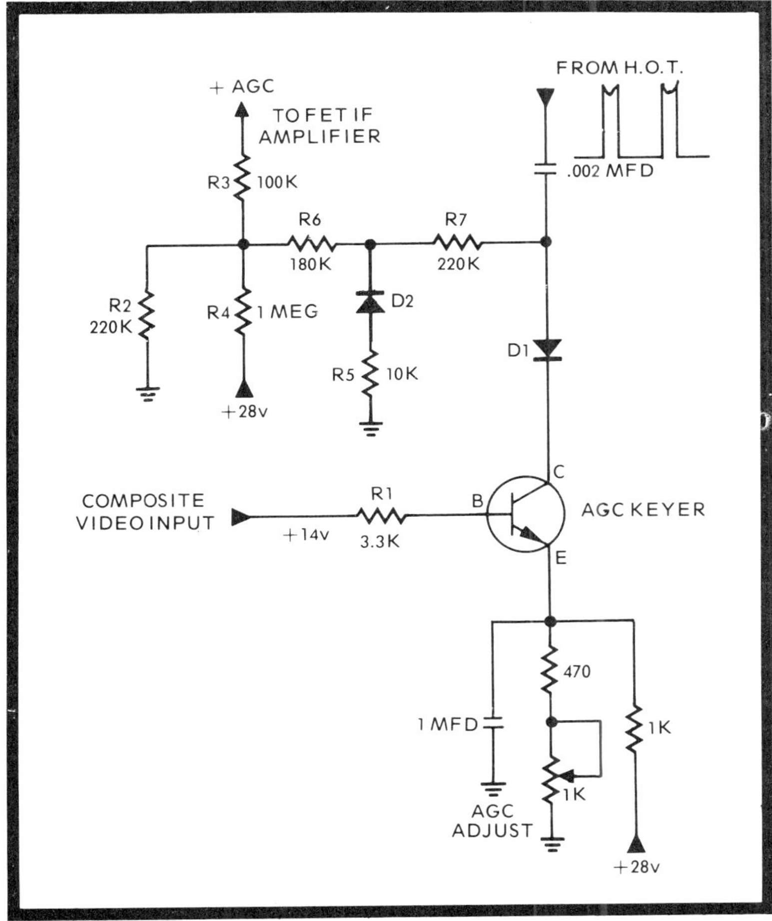

Fig. 13-5. AGC keyer which varies plus bias on FET IF amplifier.

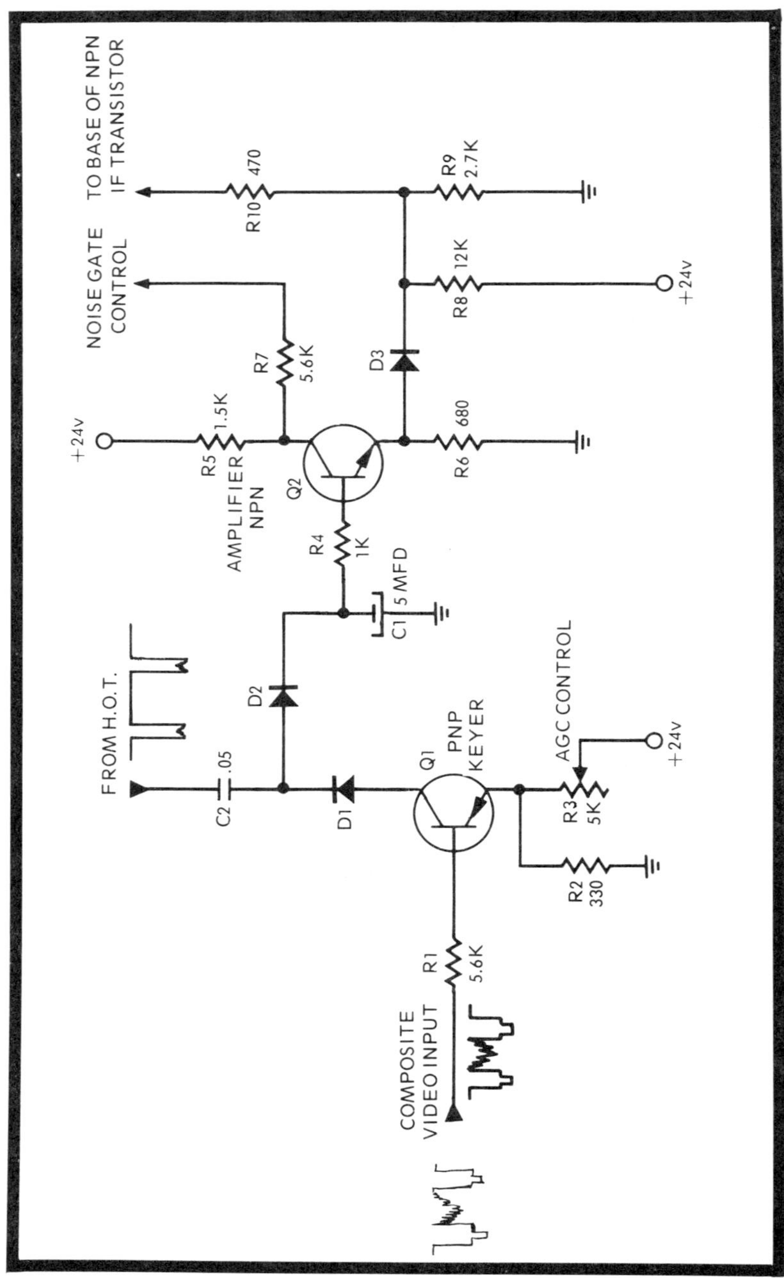

Fig. 13-6. Keyed AGC circuit and amplifier.

around +5.5 volts with zero AGC voltage. This positive voltage provides maximum IF amplifier gain. With a stronger signal, however, the AGC starts cranking out a negative voltage which is fed to the junction of R2 and R4 through R6 and R7. This negative AGC voltage subtracts from the positive voltage and so the bias on the FET amplifier is reduced and so its gain.

On very strong signals, the AGC voltage can completely overcome the positive bias and drive the FET gate voltage negative. When this happens, diode D2 starts to conduct. D2 is in series with a 10K resistor and so effectively the 10K resistor starts "bleeding" the AGC line. The net result is that the AGC line cannot be driven too far negative. This is a designer's trick to provide better tracking between the RF AGC (taken from another network) and the IF AGC when signal input is extremely strong.

Troubleshooting the Circuit

Generally the same troubles can occur in this circuit as discussed for Fig. 13-4. Here an electrolytic is used as an emitter bypass and electrolytics must always be suspect when in a circuit. If the electrolytic opens, the gain of the keyer is greatly reduced and AGC output is dropped. Depending on other circuit factors, with the 1 mfd capacitor open or partially open, you may be able to adjust the AGC control to re-establish AGC control, but it will be erratic and critical and the set will tend to block or blank out when changing from channel to channel. You may even have to reset the AGC for each channel to get any sort of picture at all.

KEYER AND OUTPUT STAGE

If a transistor is used as an AGC keyer and if considerable current change is required to bias the IF or RF amplifiers, such as when bipolar transistors are used in the IF and RF, an AGC amplifier or output stage is normally used.

Fig. 13-6 shows one such circuit. This one uses a PNP keyer transistor, Q1, that must be triggered on with a negative-going signal. The bias for the keyer is manually preset by the AGC control. No bypass is used here because of the relative low impedance in the emitter circuit and because not bypassing the circuit gives an additional degree of linearity to the keyer.

Note that diode D1 is reversed from that shown in Figs. 13-4 and 13-5 because of using the PNP keyer, and the PNP keyer must also have a negative-going pulse fed to the collector.

When the keyer conducts, it produces a positive DC output which is fed through D2 and smoothed by C1, and fed through R4 to the base-emitter junction of Q2. Q2 is an NPN transistor, so it conducts in direct proportion to the positive AGC voltage. This voltage is taken from the emitter circuit of Q2, which gives a power though not a voltage gain and prevents loading of the keyer.

Diode D3 allows the positive AGC voltage to be fed to the junction of R8 and R9 while preventing the bleeder circuit from feeding back to the emitter should the emitter voltage be lower than the voltage at the junction of R8 and R9.

The AGC amplifier or "output" as it is often called, is pressed into double duty here by taking a negative-going DC voltage and feeding it to the noise canceller circuit. This way the noise canceller tracks (depending upon the strength of the input signal), and there is less chance for the noise canceller to cause clipping problems (see "noise cancellers" elsewhere in this book).

Note that the output of this AGC circuit (Fig. 13-6) is such that an increase in signal produces a more **positive** output. This more positive output is fed to NPN IF transistors, not to cut them off, but to cause them to saturate. A transistor that is saturated cannot respond to a signal on the base any more than a transistor that is cut off, so the effect of reducing the gain of the stage is much the same whether you increase or decrease the transistor bias. Increasing the transistor bias to lower the amplification is called "forward AGC" and it is almost universally used in TV IF amplifiers using bipolar transistors. The reason is that cutting off a transistor removes the load from the IF transformer and in turn this has a considerable effect on the tuning of the transformer. Conversely, saturation increases the load on the transformer but not nearly in the ratio that cut-off decreases the load and so there is less "tuning" effect with AGC change. Additionally, an extra load on the transformer has a tendency to broaden the response which also lowers the stage gain, while removing the load will narrow the response, and the gain will try to increase to some extent.

Troubleshooting the Circuit

This, like other keyer circuits, must be properly adjusted if performance is to be optimum. Normally, an AGC circuit is set for as much contrast as possible without instability when the set is tuned to the strongest available signal.

When diodes are used in a circuit, they, like electrolytic capacitors, are usually the most suspect. Checking diodes can generally be done with an ohmmeter, without taking the diode(s) out of the circuit. Check the diode to see that it measures a fairly low resistance in one direction of the ohmmeter leads across it, and a fairly high resistance in the reverse direction. If there is a question about the in-circuit readings, clip one diode lead and remeasure with the ohmmeter. On rare occasions a diode may check perfect with an ohmmeter, especially in a pulse circuit, and yet fail to operate correctly due to break down with a higher voltage than supplied by the ohmmeter. In this case, either use a higher voltage diode checker or temporarily replace the diode to see if the trouble is corrected.

As with all other transistor circuits, don't overlook the importance of DC voltage readings. If, for example, the base voltage reading on Q2 is zero or nearly so, trouble is indicated in the keyer circuit.

A high positive voltage on the base of Q2 might indicate an incorrect setting of the AGC control, or depending upon the circuit, could mean leakage in C2.

The most common trouble in keyer transistors is shorting between collector and emitter. If a short occurs in the transistor, and you replace it, be sure also to replace diode D1 with a type similar to the original.

Chapter 14 VERTICAL DEFLECTION

Transistors are well suited for deflection systems in TV sets since they can supply high current at low impedance. This makes it practical to operate the vertical deflection system without matching transformers.

Fig. 14-1 shows an output stage in its basic form. A sawtooth of current is required in the deflection yoke to smoothly push the vertical scan from top to bottom and then quickly return it to the top after the scan is complete and start a new scan.

Note that the output voltage waveform (which an oscilloscope would reproduce if connected from collector to ground) is not a pure sawtooth; it shows the effects of the yoke

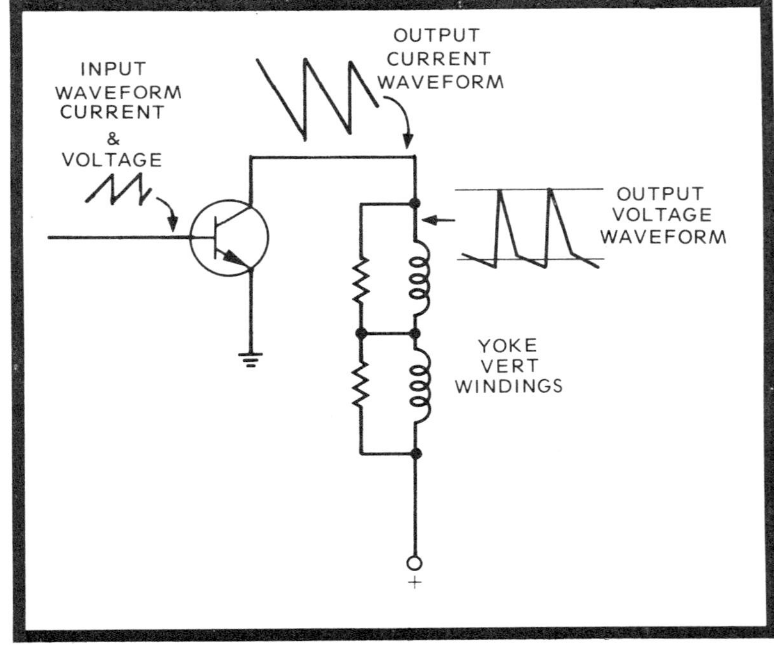

Fig. 14-1. Simplified vertical output stage.

inductance. To see the sawtooth of current, insert a small resistor in the collector circuit and connect the scope across this resistor.

The resistors across the yoke provide some "damping" on the circuit, reducing any slight tendency for the inductive circuit to "ring" and create speed changes in the sweep which might cause nonlinearity, especially at the top of the picture.

A vertical amplifier, unlike a horizontal amplifier, is generally operated class A, that is, average current flow remains constant and the transistor is not cut off during any part of the input cycle.

The yoke inductance in transistor circuits must be kept rather low to reduce the height of inductive spikes which might cause transistor breakdown. Even then, sometimes these spikes will break across a defective transistor, creating vertical sweep problems which can be cured by installing a new transistor, but generally the old transistor will check good on any transistor tester. This is why in vertical sweep circuits especially (and in horizontal sweep circuits, also), substitution of transistors is the only sure method of testing.

Connecting a yoke as shown in Fig. 14-1 is not usually practical because the DC flowing in the yoke produces a steady magnetic field which offsets the picture from center. To eliminate this problem, the yoke may be transformer-coupled to the transistor, Fig. 14-2A or connected through a large capacitor (B), or sometimes connected by a parallel inductor which has low DC resistance but high impedance to the 60-Hz sawtooth (C).

The vertical oscillator may be a self-sustaining oscillator such as the simplified blocking oscillator in Fig. 14-3, or it may be a vertical "switch" which receives a feedback pulse from the output stage to sustain the oscillation.

A sawtooth is formed by allowing a capacitor to charge up to a fraction of the voltage applied and then quickly discharging it. The reason for only a fraction charge is that the first part of the charge applied to a capacitor causes an essentially linear voltage rise but the rise tapers off exponentially as the charge builds.

Conversely, of course, a sawtooth can be formed by discharging a fraction of the voltage from a fully charged capacitor.

The blocking oscillator circuit in Fig. 14-3 uses the discharging principle to form a sawtooth. The circuit works this way: when first turned on, the base bias is supplied by the positive voltage at the center tap of the vertical hold control. This starts the transistor conducting, and the current through

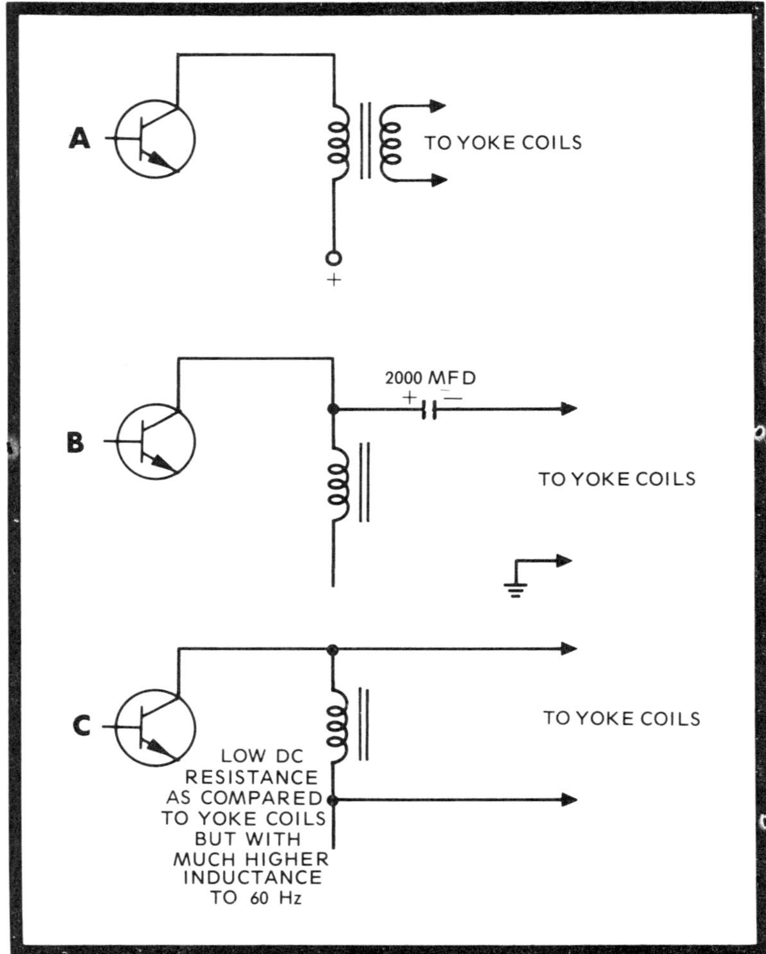

Fig. 14-2. Practical vertical deflection couplings.

the primary of the blocking oscillator transformer induces an even larger positive pulse on the base of the transistor, forcing the transistor quickly to saturate or "block." Meanwhile, capacitor C1 has charged due to the high current through R1. When the transistor blocks, however, the pulse in the transformer stops, because current has ceased to flow in the primary. But now the transistor cannot conduct, because capacitor C1 has charged the emitter highly positive, and the transistor remains cut off. Capacitor C1 starts to discharge through R1, and it is this discharge that forms the linear sweep part of the vertical signal. When the capacitor has discharged to a certain level, the transistor again starts to conduct, again a pulse is induced in the base circuit, and the cycle repeats.

The circuit can be locked in by a small positive sync pulse which comes along at the right time to drive the base of the transistor positive at the time the emitter voltage has dropped to a more negative voltage. The vertical hold control has changed the oscillator frequency to some extent because it sets the DC bias of the transistor. R1 and C1, in addition to forming the sawtooth, also have considerable effect on the oscillator frequency. If R1 has too low a resistance, for example, C1 will discharge too quickly and bring the transistor back into conduction before the sync pulse arrives. If, on the other hand, the resistance of R1 is too large, C1 would not be discharged quickly enough and so the oscillator transistor would not come out of cut off even when the sync pulse arrived.

This means that if R1 is too low a resistance, oscillator frequency will be high, if too high a resistance, oscillator

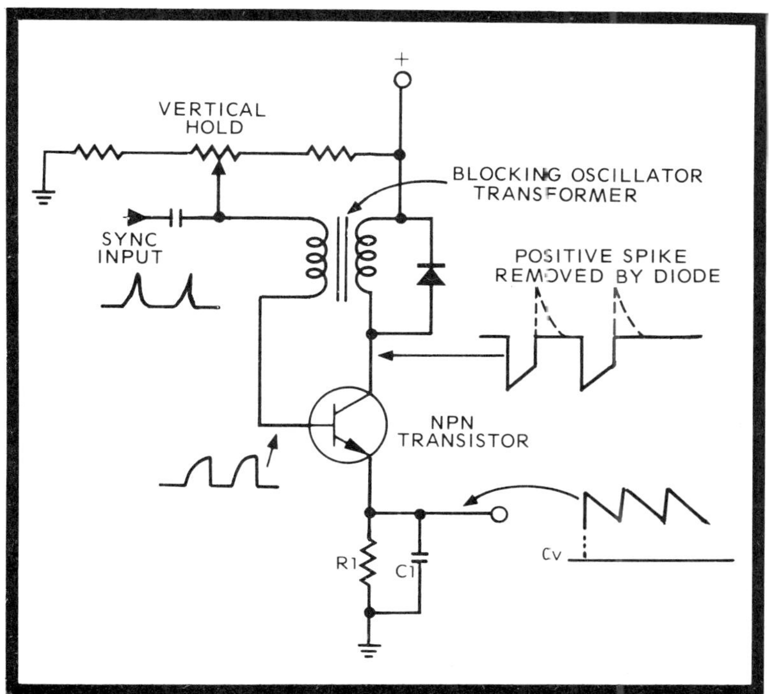

Fig. 14-3. Simplified blocking oscillator with vertical sawtooth output across emitter resistor.

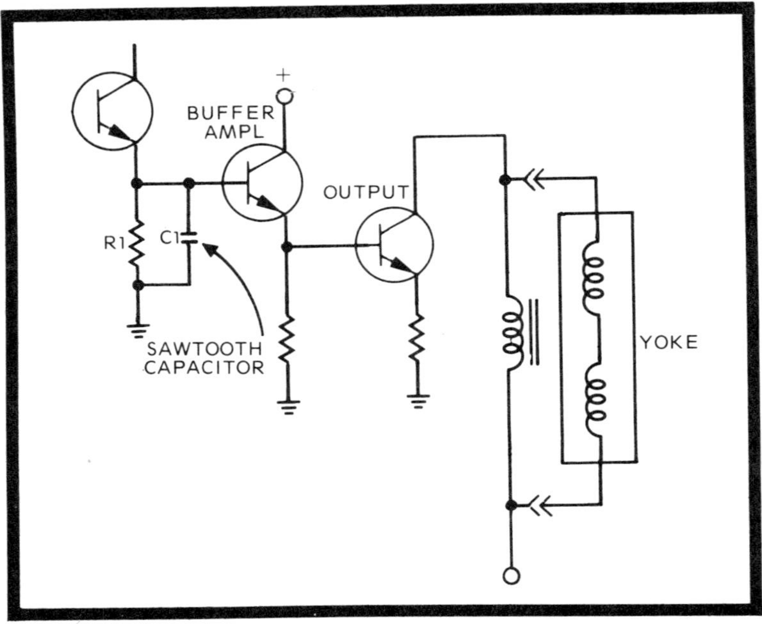

Fig. 14-4. Buffer amplifier driving the output stage.

frequency will be low. Leakage in C1 will have the same effect as a too small resistance but because leakage is usually not a stable condition, this may cause picture roll as the set warms up. This warm-up instability can be adjusted for awhile by readjustment of the vertical hold control but eventually the hold cannot recapture the sync lock. If trouble occurs in the vertical hold which resembles this symptom, check capacitors for leakage.

Now let's look into buffer amplifiers in a vertical stage. The problem of developing a sawtooth is complicated when an attempt is made to amplify the pulse, especially with solid-state circuits. The reason is that solid-state circuits require current in the input of the amplifier, and any current drawn by the amplifier affects the charging or discharging time of the sawtooth capacitor. Transistor circuits can be designed so they have little current loading but when this is done they have smaller power output also. To get around this problem, TV designers generally use from three to five transistors in a vertical circuit. This means one or more buffer amplifiers are needed, amplifiers whose main purpose is to isolate the output from the input and to provide considerable current drive for the output stage without upsetting the charging current in the oscillator stage.

Fig. 14-4 shows one simplified way this can be done. A transistor used as an emitter follower (common-collector circuit) has a high input impedance and an output impedance which is rather low, permitting it to amplify the sawtooth with almost no loading and at the same time providing a high current to drive the output stage.

Establishing and maintaining good linearity and fast retrace time is a considerable problem in any vertical deflection circuit and becomes even more of a problem as stages must be added. It is for this reason that a vertical deflection solid-state circuit often looks overly complicated.

Troubleshooting the Circuit

In servicing these circuits, the most common problems are electrolytic capacitors, and the transistors. Transistors in these circuits cannot be indiscriminately substituted and therefore exact replacements are often worth the extra effort that may be needed to obtain them; depending upon the circuit, however, you will find that substitute transistors often work surprisingly well. If you use a substitute and find that the circuit will adjust normally, and the transistor does not overheat, then the substitute probably will work reliably.

HORIZONTAL OSCILLATORS, DRIVERS AND OUTPUT STAGES

Every TV set must use some system of deflecting the electron beam horizontally across the picture tube face, but although that is the basic function of the horizontal circuit, it is by no means the only one.

The horizontal circuit also is the source of the high voltage applied to the CRT anode. This voltage may run from 10KV to 25KV or more depending upon the design of the TV set and upon the picture tube used.

The high voltage is developed by a winding on the horizontal output transformer, which is popularly called a "flyback" transformer. The high voltage winding has many turns and develops a high voltage alternating current which in turn is rectified by either a tube or high voltage solid-state diode to produce the DC kilovoltage. Taking the high voltage from the horizontal circuit has several advantages, not the least of which is that the circuit is less lethal in case of accidental contact than a 60-Hz power supply. Besides this, because of the high frequency of the horizontal (about 15,750 Hz), the filtering is simple, in some cases no more than the metallic (aquadag) coating on the inside and outside of the glass picture tube, one side connected to the high voltage and the other side to ground, forming a small capacitor.

Besides the high voltage, pulses are taken from the horizontal circuit for keyed AGC, for keying of burst amplifiers in color sets, and for convergence correction in color sets to produce good color purity and register even at the picture edges.

Fig. 15-1 is a block diagram of a typical horizontal sweep circuit as used in a transistor TV set. The horizontal oscillator is free-running at about 15,750 Hz, and it can be adjusted close to the correct frequency by a horizontal frequency control, which may be either a resistance-type control that varies the voltage on the oscillator or AFC circuit, or may be an adjustable slug in an oscillator coil, or both.

The exact frequency of the oscillator is determined by the synchronizing pulses from the sync circuit. These sync pulses

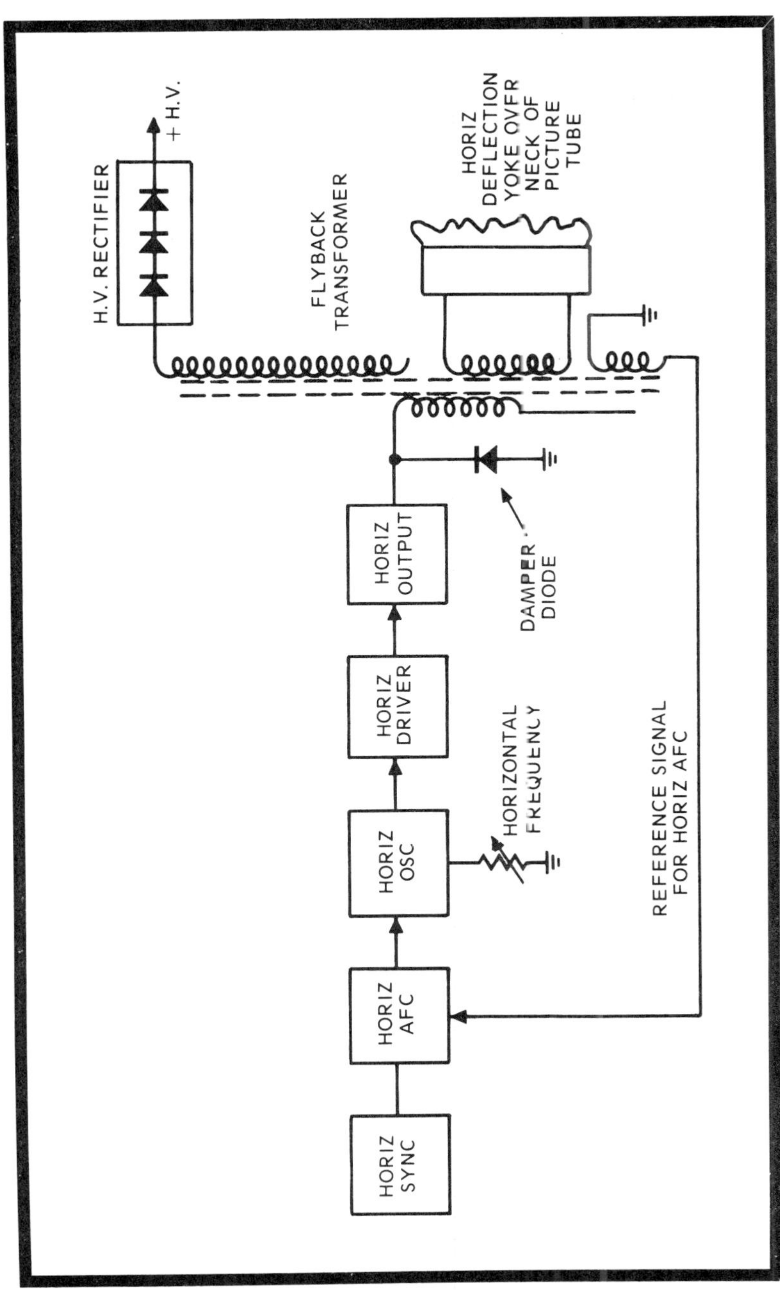

Fig. 15-1. Block diagram of typical horizontal sweep circuit.

are sent out by the TV transmitter. They are processed by the set and fed to the horizontal AFC circuit where they are compared to the actual frequency of the horizontal oscillator. If the two are different, the horizontal AFC circuit puts out an error voltage which "pulls in" the horizontal oscillator so that it is in step with the sync pulses. If the two are not locked together, the TV picture will have either right or left slant and appear to have diagonal black bars in it.

The horizontal driver is usually used in solid-state circuits to provide enough current to drive the output stage without unduly loading the oscillator. (If the oscillator is too heavily loaded, it may fail to start or may operate erratically.)

The output stage is a power type transistor usually mounted on a heat sink or bolted directly to the chassis with only a thin piece of insulation between. It not only must supply power to drive the horizontal deflection yoke but also to provide high voltage current.

The damper diode is essential in a horizontal deflection circuit. The reason is that the current in the deflection yoke and flyback rise slowly, then when the raster line reaches the right side of the picture tube, the current suddenly reverses, thereby causing the spot to "flyback" to the other side. The flyback time is much faster than the forward trace time and this sudden reversal at the right side and then again at the left side produces a "shock" to the flyback system. This "shock" will start the circuit ringing on its own at its natural resonant frequency which is around 70 or 80 Hz. One half cycle of this is useful since this provides the flyback current which returns the spot to the left of the screen at about 5 times the speed of the forward trace, as indicated above. But once the retrace is made this ringing must be stopped to prevent it from interfering with the forward trace. This is the function of the damper diode. When the ringing starts to reverse polarity, the damper diode conducts and produces essentially a short circuit across the transformer, killing the "ring" at the natural frequency.

HORIZONTAL OSCILLATOR AND DRIVER (Blocking Oscillator)

Because of the limitations on peak-to-peak voltage output from transistors using low voltage, transistor horizontal circuits generally use one transistor operating at lower voltage to act as the oscillator and feed another driver transistor operated at higher collector voltage.

The circuit in Fig. 15-2 is a blocking oscillator type using emitter feedback. A stabilizing circuit (L1-C3) is tuned to slightly above the 15,750-Hz horizontal oscillator signal. The purpose of this circuit is to make the oscillator insensitive to noise pulses which might occur near the sync signal time, by providing a sharp rise in the signal to the base at the sync pulse time. Note the waveform shown at the junction of L1 and R3. This is the same familiar waveform seen in synchroguide tube circuits. The ringing waveform is superimposed on the horizontal waveform, dropping the voltage on the base and then bringing it to a sharp positive peak when the next sync pulse is due. The 1K resistor, R2, lowers the "Q" of the L1-C3 circuit to prevent its taking over of the oscillator frequency rather than just shaping the base voltage.

Diode D1 acts to some extent like a damper by placing a 1K load on the primary of T1 when the signal reverses and this helps to shape the signal properly. Diode D2 also provides shaping as does L2 and R7.

Troubleshooting the Circuit

One problem that can occur in this circuit, as with tube circuits, is a tendency toward erratic frequency control, usually caused by improper adjustment of the horizontal stabilizing (waveshape adjust) coil, L1.

An oscilloscope can be used to set the waveform (point A) but if an oscilloscope is not available then a reasonably good adjustment can be obtained by adjusting the horizontal hold control (which is in the phase detector circuit and sets the DC bias to the junction of R1, C1) to about midrange. (All adjustments must be with a station properly tuned in.) Short circuit the stabilizing coil. Remove the sync input from the circuit by connecting a .05 mfd capacitor from the base of the sync output stage to ground. Adjust the **vertical hold** so picture rolls as slowly as possible. Remove the short from across the stabilizing coil. Adjust the stabilizing coil until the picture moves across the screen slowly. Disconnect the .05 mfd capacitor from the sync. Picture should lock in. Check another station to make sure that there are no spurious streaks in the raster between stations and that the horizontal locks cleanly on each active station.

Any distortion of the raster, such as nonlinearity, vertical light streak, etc. can be caused by defective diodes in these circuits. Check the diodes, preferably by replacement, though a defective diode in these circuits can usually be found with an ohmmeter.

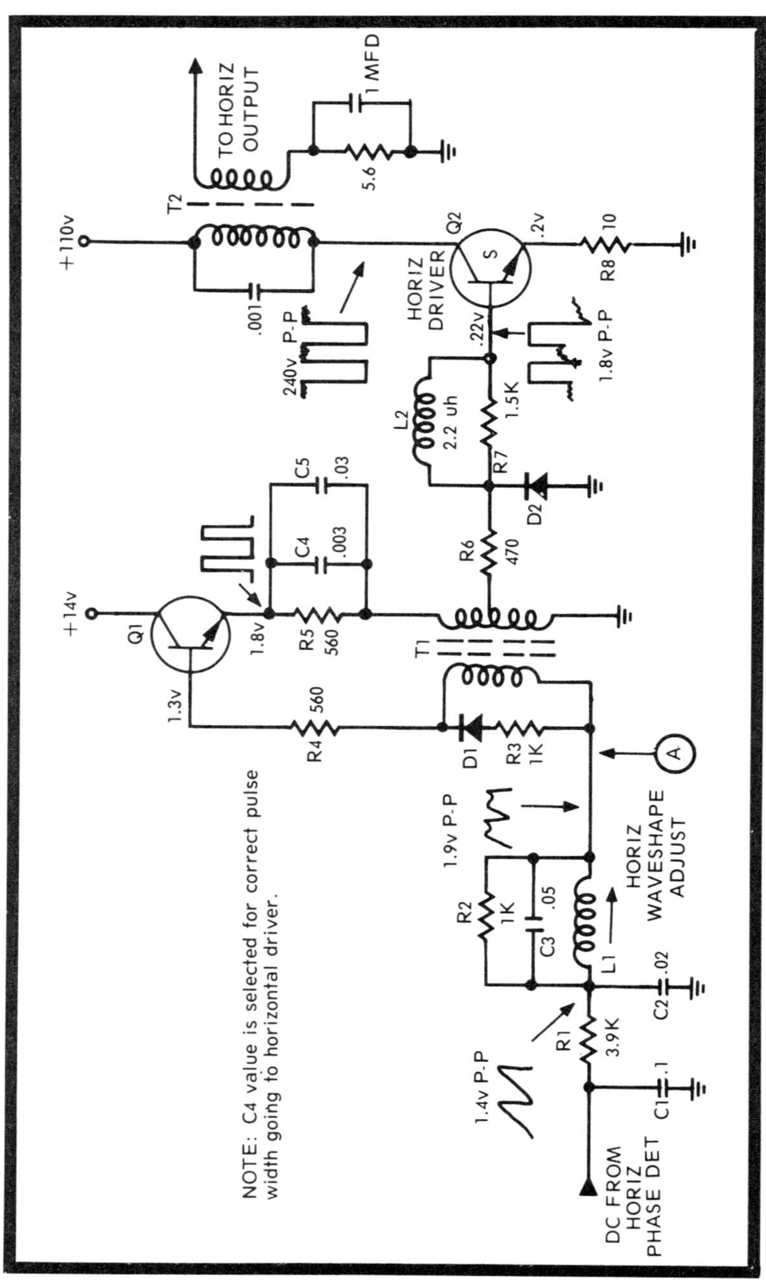

Fig. 15-2. Horizontal oscillator and driver.

Note the DC bias on Q2 is low for a silicon transistor. This is normal because the transistor is made to conduct by the input pulse rather than by a fixed DC bias. The only bias provided otherwise is due to rectification by D2 of the negative excursion of the pulse. The current through Q2 though, as indicated by the emitter resistor voltage, is 20 ma. There is also high peak-to-peak voltage on the collector of this transistor, making it more susceptible to breakdown; in other words, Q2 is more apt to short between collector and emitter than is Q1. For this reason, Q2 must be replaced with a transistor designed for this service and for high DC collector voltage as well—do not replace this transistor with a low voltage type!

HORIZONTAL OSCILLATOR AND DRIVER (Hartley)

Fig. 15-3 is a transistor Hartley oscillator which provides basically a sine wave output. Feedback for Q1 is by the tap on oscillator coil L1 to the emitter. Tuning for the oscillator is by C2, plus the capacity of C1 in series with the AFC transistor. A DC voltage on the AFC transistor provides for more or less conduction and makes the effect of C1 felt more or less across the oscillator coil.

DC bias for the oscillator is provided by the bleeder, R1 and R2. The oscillator signal is mixed with a signal from the flyback to produce the needed waveshape to drive Q2. The output of Q2 (collector) is essentially a square wave. The waveshape to the output transistor is a square wave which takes up about half of the deflection cycle. The width of this waveform is basically a function of R7 and C6.

Note in this circuit also that the DC bias on Q2 is less than would cause the transistor to conduct, which means that the transistor only conducts on the peak of the input signal.

R5 and C5 across T1 are selected to provide proper output waveshaping and when transistor Q2 is replaced, if not with an exact replacement, resistor R5 might have to be changed for optimum waveform output.

Troubleshooting the Circuit

If the TV set develops no high voltage due to a lack of horizontal drive, the trouble may be back in the oscillator or driver stages. An oscilloscope is the best instrument to use for a test since you can look at the waveforms or check for the absence of them. But DC voltages often give enough information for you to determine the trouble spot. For example, if Q1 has 25 volts on the collector instead of 20v, it is evident

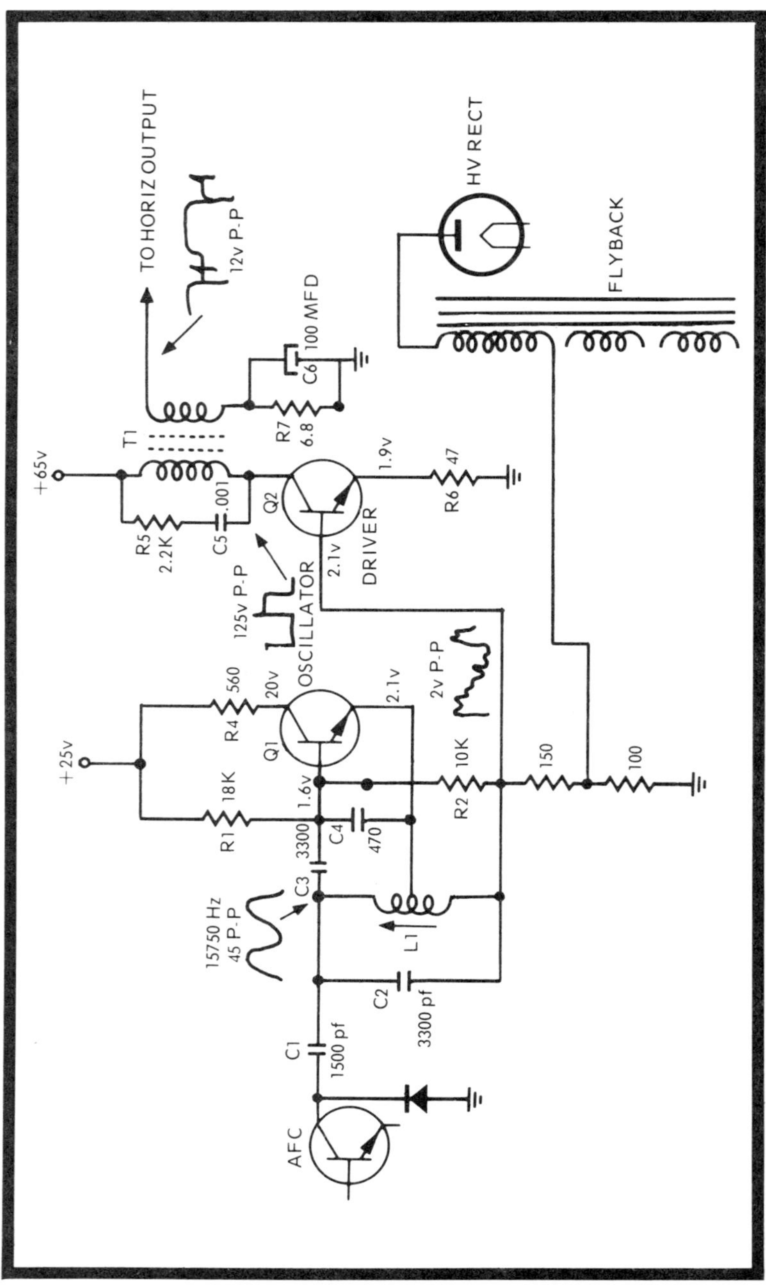

Fig. 15-3. Horizontal oscillator (Hartley) and driver.

that the transistor is not drawing any current. This could be caused by an open transistor, or no bias due to an open R1.

If on the other hand, the collector voltage of Q1 is significantly low, it could mean a shorted transistor, possibly an open R2, low 25-volt supply, or a changed value R4.

If the horizontal oscillator is not operating at the correct frequency, it could be because of a defective AFC circuit. The transistor might be shorted, or possibly the diode. One way to check whether the trouble is in the AFC is to disconnect the AFC end of the 1500-pf capacitor (C1) and connect a variable resistor of about 0 to 10K to ground. If the oscillator can be brought to the point where a picture floats by sideways, the trouble is in the AFC circuit and not in the oscillator.

If the trouble is in the collector circuit, it sometimes happens that oscillator coil L1 develops shorted turns. If adjusting the slug in the coil has little effect, the coil itself may be bad. The only sure check is with a substitute coil. Also check capacitors C1, C2, and C3 for leakage. Even slight leakage here can drastically affect the oscillator frequency.

The driver stage will not cause a significant change in the horizontal oscillator frequency even though it were operating abnormally.

Remember that any change in DC bias on the oscillator has an effect on the oscillator frequency, with higher bias causing an increase in oscillator frequency.

The driver stage can be checked, as other transistor circuits, by making DC voltage checks but this will show up only DC troubles such as an open, leaky or shorted transistor, an open emitter resistor, or an open T1. If transformer T1 develops shorted turns, or if C5 should short, the DC voltage may not change at all. If the input to Q2 appears to be okay but the output of the collector is severely distorted, the trouble may be the transistor, but it also can very well be T1 or C5, or, in rare cases, an open R5.

Note that Q2 has higher DC collector voltage than some other transistors in the set and also a higher peak-to-peak voltage. It is imperative when this transistor is replaced to replace it with an exact replacement or one designed for the same type of circuit. Replacement of Q1 is generally not too critical but again it is wise, if possible, to use an exact replacement.

HORIZONTAL OUTPUT

The output transistor driving the flyback deflection circuits, even in a small screen set, delivers considerable power.

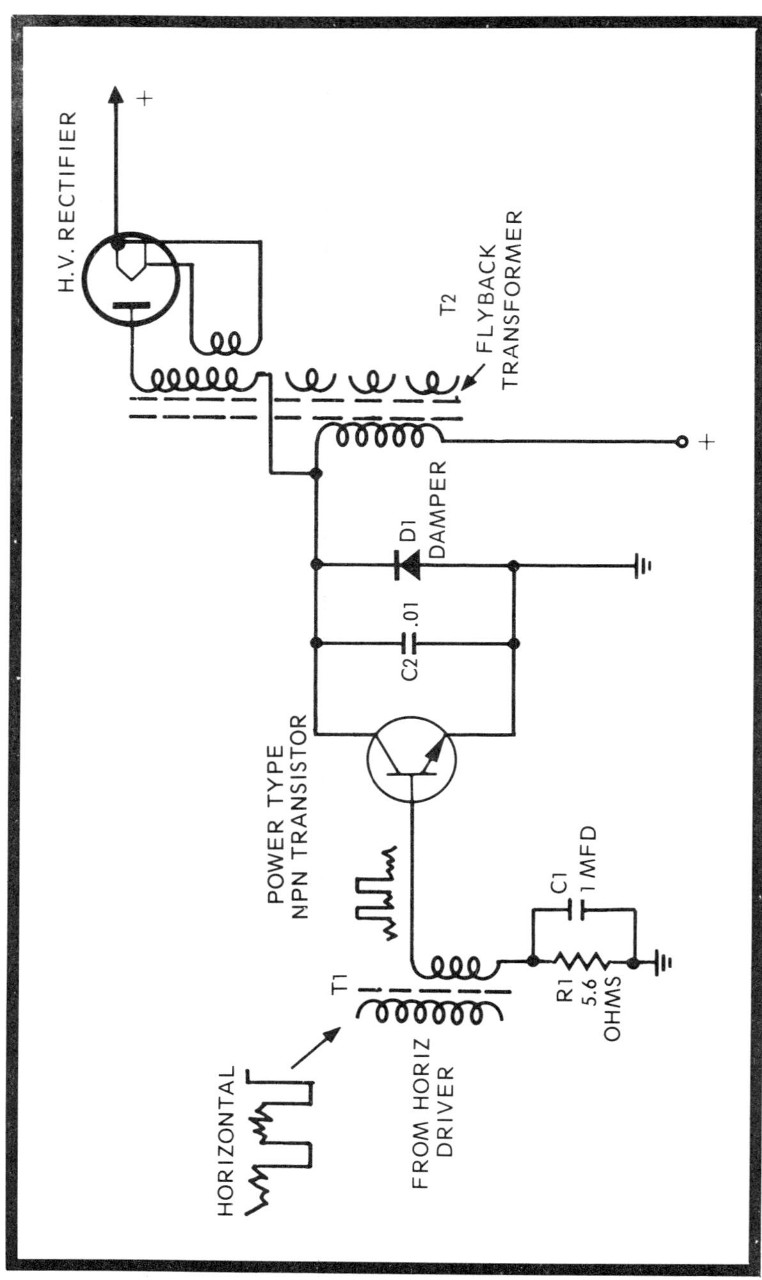

Fig. 15-4. Transistor horizontal output stage.

The transistor used is of the larger power type (Fig. 15-4) and will be so mounted as to use the chassis or some other large metal surface as a heat sink. In this circuit, a horizontal signal is fed from the horizontal driver stage to the horizontal output through an impedance matching transformer, T1. The horizontal pulses cause the output transistor to conduct and drive the flyback transformer T2. R1 and C1 is a self-biasing network of sorts which prevents excessive loading by the output transistor due to normal changes in pulse level, and which assures that the transistor conducts on the pulse tips.

The damper diode D1, like its tube damper counterpart, acts as a short circuit for the "ringing" voltage developed when the flyback is not being driven by the transistor. The diode also prevents the transistor from being forward-biased between collector and base during the normal ringing reversal of the flyback voltage. Capacitor C2 is in a sense a "tuning" capacitor which establishes the ringing time and consequently the flyback time of the deflection. This capacitor also acts as a bypass for spurious pulse voltages which might damage the transistor, and also reduces the "crossover" interference in the damper diode at the instant it goes from non-conduction to conduction and back again.

Troubleshooting the Circuit

The most common trouble here is a defective damper diode or a defective output transistor. The damper diode cannot normally be checked with an ohmmeter unless it happens to be "dead" shorted. High-voltage diodes often develop trouble only at higher voltages and to check these diodes you should have some sort of high voltage test, or substitute the diode with one known to be good and of the same general type.

Fig. 15-5 shows one way a high voltage diode may be tested. A DC voltage source is connected through a resistor to the diode. The diode is tested, connected in the circuit both in the forward and reverse direction. In the forward direction the voltmeter should read the same or nearly the same as the voltage of the supply used. In the reverse direction, there should be no voltage reading. Any significant reverse reading means that the diode is breaking down. If there is neither forward or reverse voltmeter reading, the diode is open.

Insufficient drive (insufficient raster width) may be caused by an open C1, or R1 increased to a high value. Insufficient width can also be caused by an open C2. Sometimes, there will be no high voltage developed when C2 is open.

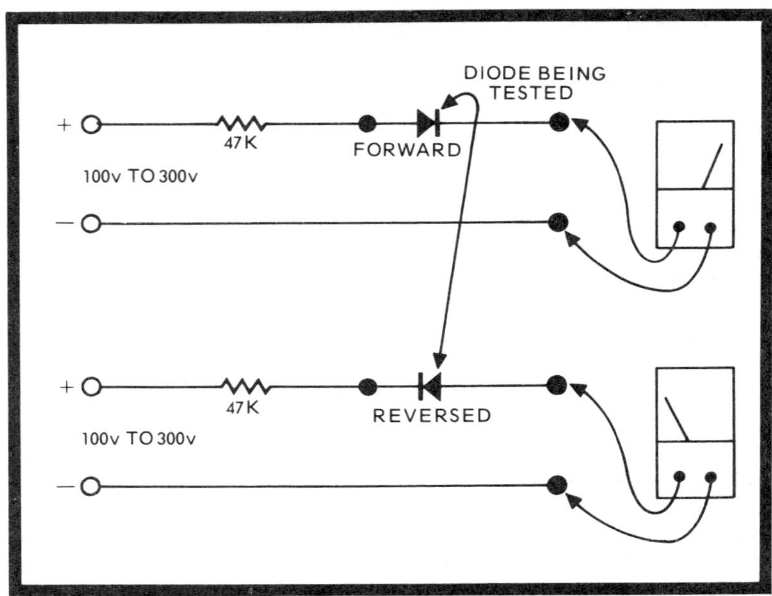

Fig. 15-5. Testing a high voltage diode.

One fortunate thing about transistor horizontal outputs is that a loss of drive does not hurt the transistor as it would a tube. The transistor without drive has no bias since all the bias is provided by the drive signal, and with no bias the transistor does not conduct.

The transistor should be replaced by exact replacement type. Often transistors which appear to be similar in characteristics, often even those listed in substitution handbooks, will not work correctly. The incorrect replacement can result in insufficient raster width, poor horizontal linearity, overheating of the transistor, etc.

Besides incorrect replacement, overheating of the transistor can be caused by an excessive load of some sort on the deflection circuit, such as a defective flyback. (A defective flyback will not always cause overheating of the driving transistor but can be a cause.)

HORIZONTAL OUTPUT AND DEFLECTION CIRCUIT

The horizontal output circuit in Fig. 15-6 is similar to that in Fig. 15-4. Ferrite beads are used on the leads to the input of the horizontal output to reduce radiation and also reduce the tendency toward spurious oscillation. Damper diode D1 is of the high voltage type which must be checked as explained for Fig. 15-4. The horizontal deflection coils, L1 and L2, are paralleled and connected through a 1 mfd capacitor, C3, directly to the collector of the horizontal output transistor.

The flyback transformer T1 is also driven by the horizontal output, and B+ is supplied through the primary winding. Four B+ circuits are taken from the flyback circuit:

(1) Diode D2 rectifies the 510-volt p-p horizontal pulse at the collector of Q1, deriving about 485 volts for the focus circuit. Since the current drawn is small and the frequency is high (15,750 Hz), the small 1000 pf capacitor, C4, is adequate as a smoothing filter.

(2) Diode D3 rectifies a lower p-p voltage and supplies +24 volts to operate other circuits in the TV. The 10 mfd filter is necessary because of considerably higher current drawn here.

(3) Diode D4 provides a +150-volt source for the video amplifier by rectifying a pulse voltage and adding to the +70-volt source which is tied to one end of the flyback winding.

(4) The HV rectifier tube supplies about 20 kilovolts for the anode of the picture tube.

Troubleshooting the Circuit

Troubleshooting of the horizontal output section is very similar to that described for Fig. 15-4. Be sure to test diode D1 with a high voltage or better still, check by substitution.

If the set has a vertical line at the center of the picture tube, check to make sure the yoke plug is not disconnected, then check C3 to see if it is open. Since this is a parallel yoke, one open yoke coil will **not** cause a trapezoidal raster as in sets using a series-connected yoke.

A loss in high voltage will occur if diode D3 or D4 shorts due to the extra load on the circuit. A shorted D2 will reduce the focus voltage to around 70 volts but probably may not cause a loss of high voltage due to the light load.

If either C6, C4, or C8 shorts, there will be a loss of high voltage.

If high voltage is low and the picture blooms (dims out and widens as brightness is turned up), check the high voltage rectifier tube then go back and check the peak-to-peak voltage on the base and collector of the output transistor.

It is not too unusual for the horizontal output transistor to check good on any transistor tester but fail to work correctly in the circuit. This occurs because no tester will subject the transistor to the high peak voltages of this circuit. Replace the transistor with an exact replacement if at all possible,

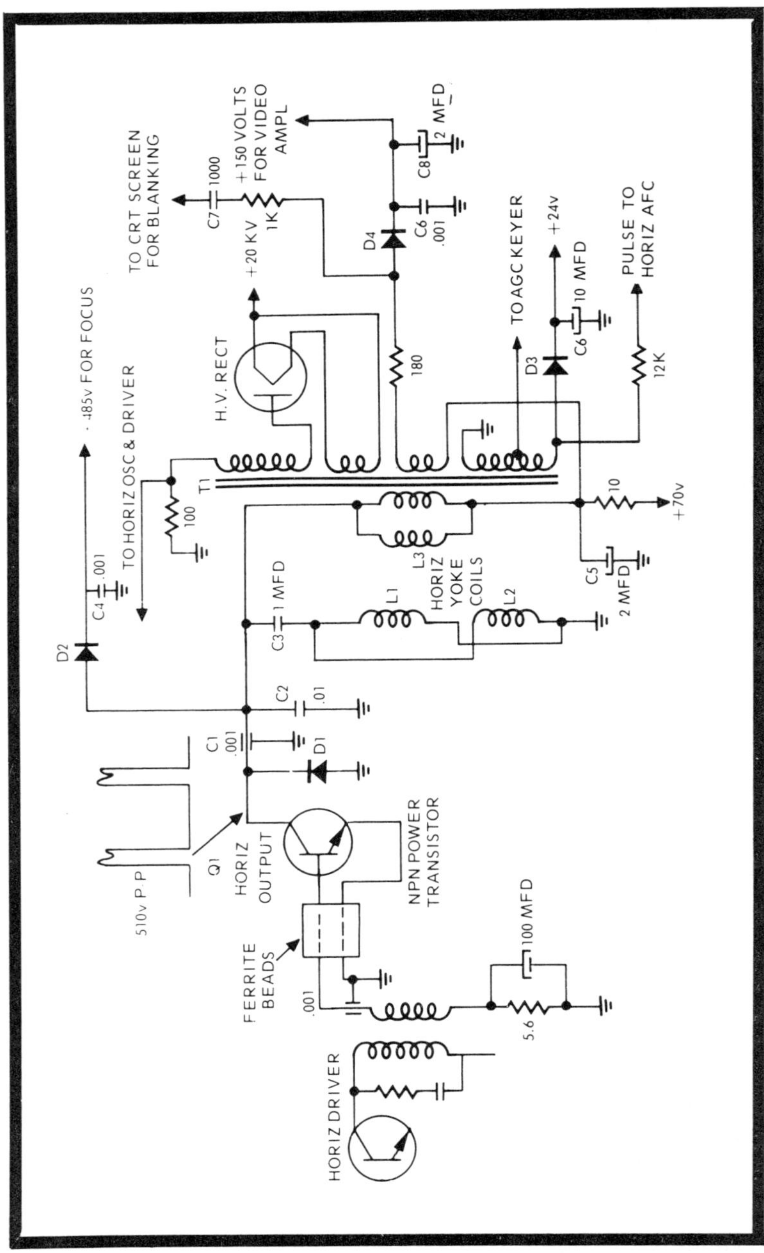

Fig. 15-6. Horizontal output and HV circuit including deflection coils and auxiliary power sources.

otherwise you may have poor linearity, vertical bars in the picture, and frequent failure of the transistor.

The diodes in this circuit are special, especially D1 and D2 which must have high inverse breakdown voltage ratings. Do not attempt, for example, to replace either D1 or D2 with a regular power supply silicon diode—it will short almost immediately, especially in the D1 location.

If C2 must be replaced, use a capacitor with a rating of at least 1000 volts. C3 in this circuit is a special non-polarized capacitor and any other type capacitor may give trouble if used as a replacement.

L3 is a special coil for matching; use an exact replacement if it should be damaged.

As a general rule, horizontal circuits are the result of careful design by engineers so that each part complements all others, and any attempt to use substitute parts except for such things as low voltage capacitors and resistors in non-critical areas, is normally an exercise in frustration.

Chapter 16 SPECIAL COLOR TV CIRCUITS

A burst amplifier is necessary in a color TV set to recover and amplify the color sync signal. The color sync signal is sent on the "back porch" of the horizontal sync signal and consists of 8 or so cycles of 3.58-MHz signal used at the transmitter as the color subcarrier.

BURST AMPLIFIER CIRCUITS

To recover the color sync signal (Fig. 16-1), the burst amplifier (Fig. 16-2) must be tuned to near 3.58 MHz, but this is not enough because the color sidebands are also on either side of this frequency and unless the burst amplifier is keyed on only during the horizontal pulse, it will amplify all the color sidebands and this will upset the color sync.

Fig. 16-2 shows basically how any burst amplifier operates. A video signal which includes the sync pulses with the color burst signal is fed into the color burst amplifier through a small capacitor. A keying pulse, also applied to the amplifier, biases the amplifier on and permits it to amplify only during the horizontal sync pulse time interval. The burst is amplified in the collector circuit, but the keying pulse is rejected due to the tuned circuit in the burst transformer.

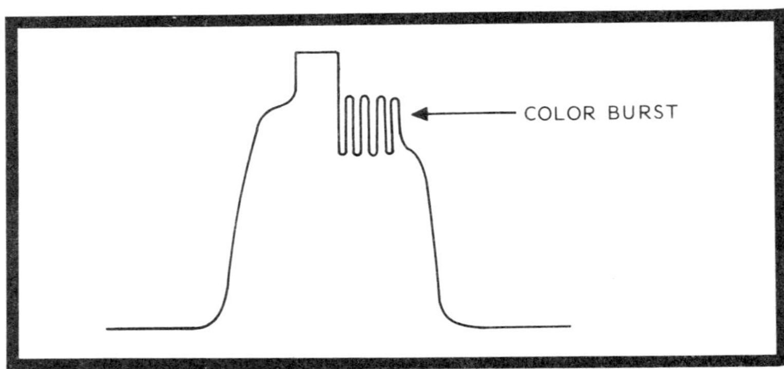

Fig. 16-1. Color sync signal on back porch of horizontal sync pulse.

If the burst amplifier stops working there will be no color sync (and sometimes no color at all). But if the color burst amplifier works all the time rather than just during the horizontal pulse, the color lock will be nebulous and colors will change with picture content.

A burst amplifier (Fig. 16-3) is triggered into conduction by a pulse from the horizontal output transformer, meaning that it acts only as an amplifier during that time. The color signal from the chroma or video amplifier is also fed into the input and since the color burst, which is the color sync signal, occurs at the same time as the horizontal pulse, it is amplified during that interval. The burst amplifier does not conduct during the trace time and so the color signals other than the burst can have no effect on the lock-in of the 3.58-MHz color oscillator.

In this circuit there is no DC bias applied to the transistor; thus, without input the transistor would be cut off and so would not amplify. However, a horizontal pulse applied to the base through R1, C1, R2, R4, turns the transistor on by biasing it positive during the pulse interval. This pulse causes a surge of voltage across R5 which charges up C5 and holds it at about 4 volts in this case. This greatly reverse-biases the transistor and holds it reverse-biased between horizontal pulses, so that even a strong color signal cannot inadvertently cause the burst amplifier to conduct during trace time.

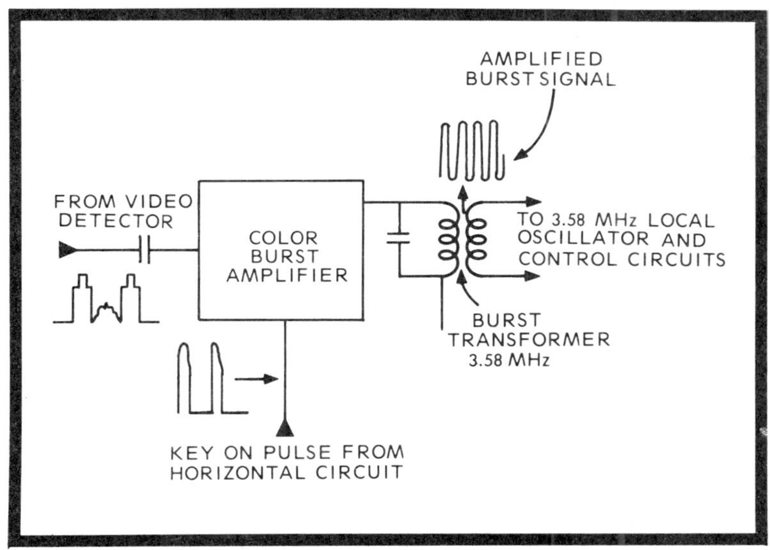

Fig. 16-2. Burst amplifier block diagram.

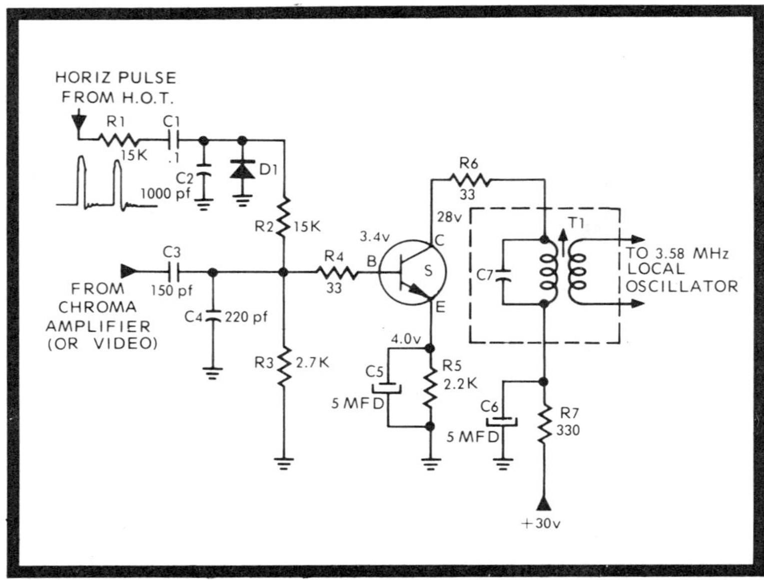

Fig. 16-3. Burst amplifier circuit for color TV set.

During the horizontal pulse time, when the transistor is biased on, the burst signal through C3 is amplified by the transistor circuit and a large, continuously-ringing burst signal output is obtained from T1. The burst signal output, in turn, is used to lock the local 3.58-MHz oscillator in phase with the transmitter signal.

The resistors and capacitors in series with the horizontal pulse provide just the right amount of phase delay for the circuit to operate properly. Diode D1 "damps" the horizontal signal, preventing any negative pulse from reaching the transistor base and causing possible base-emitter "zenering" or breakdown.

Capacitors C3 and C4 act as a voltage divider to reduce slightly the input from the color amplifier circuits.

Resistors R4 and R6 are simply small isolation and protective resistors that also tend to prevent parasitic oscillations in the circuit due to the pulse input.

Troubleshooting the Circuit

When a burst amplifier is not working correctly, one of two things normally occur. Either there will be no color lock at all, or the color lock will vary depending on the color in the picture. The first is caused when the amplifier is not working at all, the second occurs when the burst amplifier works continuously rather than being triggered on.

You can check for a horizontal pulse input with a scope but you can also check by measuring the DC voltage at the emitter. If the DC voltage is low, it means that the transistor either has no pulse input, the transistor is defective, or else capacitor C5 is open. The emitter voltage is developed because of the charge developed on C5 by the triggering action of the horizontal pulse.

T1 must be tuned properly in order for the burst circuit to feed sufficient signal to the 3.58-MHz oscillator to cause lock-in. If C6 should open, the 330 ohm resistor (R7) becomes part of the collector load and so the circuit of T1 no longer has as much signal voltage across it. Always be suspicious of small electrolytic capacitors in any circuit, and secondly be suspicious of diodes. Check electrolytics by shunting them temporarily with a known good capacitor. Check diodes with an ohmmeter or by replacement.

Trouble Symptoms

Collector Voltage Low: May be caused by a shorted C5 or a change to a lower value resistance by R5. Also check supply voltage. Check R7 for change to higher value. Check C6 for leakage. Transistor defective.
Emitter Voltage Low: No horizontal pulse input. Transistor defective. C5 shorted or leaky. Low supply voltage. C5 open.
No 3.58-MHz Output from T1 or Output Weak: No input from color amplifiers to base of burst amplifier. No pulse input. Check diode D1 for short. Transistor defective. C5 open. C6 open. No supply voltage. R7 changed to higher value. T1 defective—check to see if it will peak when tuned—if it peaks but only at the extreme travel of its tuning slug, transformer probably needs to be replaced, but first check to be sure that C6 is OK.

To check for color input, check with a wideband scope, low capacitance probe, and with a color bar generator connected to the antenna terminals of the set. Remember also that the pulse from the horizontal output transformer may blank the color input signal so temporarily remove the pulse signal before checking for a color input signal. In this circuit you can short out the pulse by shorting across D1. Perhaps the safest way to remove the pulse temporarily, though, is to open the pulse circuit at some convenient terminal point.

COLOR TINT OR HUE CONTROL CIRCUITS

The actual color of any picture on a color set depends on its relationship in time to a reference signal sent out by the color transmitter. If this relationship is changed, the hue or tint will change. Since a number of things make slight phase changes both impossible to prevent or predict, every color set has a control for changing the phase relationships slightly so as to produce a picture with hues pleasing to the eye.

The standard for setting hue by eye is the color of human flesh because we know what colors to expect. (We cannot set by the color of the draperies, for example, since we have no idea what color they are supposed to be unless someone in the studio happens to mention it.) This setting of the hue by the color of human flesh is called "getting the fleshtones correct." There will be changes in the fleshtone color when you switch from station to station and the hue or tint control is used to compensate. (Recently, several manufacturers have developed "automatic hue controls" which tend to broaden out the range of fleshtone acceptability by slightly reducing the amount of green in the color picture. It is the greenish fleshtone that is most unacceptable to the color viewer, generally.)

There are two ways that the color phase reference can be shifted, either by shifting the color oscillator phase in reference to the color burst, or shifting the color sidebands in the chroma amplifiers in reference to the color burst.

Because all color depends on phase reference, any mistuning in burst amplifier circuits, color oscillator circuits, or chroma (color) amplifier circuits can cause serious hue shift that cannot be compensated for by adjusting the hue or tint control.

Component failures in these circuits can also cause hue changes or even complete loss of one or more colors.

TINT CONTROL CIRCUIT THAT SHIFTS OSCILLATOR PHASE

The burst amplifier and phase detector circuit are as described elsewhere in this book. The addition in Fig. 16-4 is C1, L1 and R1. C1 is connected to one side of the secondary of T1 and if connected directly to ground would be across one half of the secondary, thus reducing its resonant frequency. When the resonant frequency of a tuned circuit changes, it will, of necessity, represent a phase change to the signal it is passing.

If the phase of the burst signal going to the phase detector is changed, the phase detector will correct the oscillator phase to correspond and so the oscillator will "slow down" or "speed up" as the case may be. In actual operation, R1 is adjusted to the midpoint and then T1 is adjusted until fleshtones are true. Now R1 when rotated in one direction will shift the colors toward green and when rotated the opposite way the colors will be shifted toward red.

L1 is used in this circuit mainly to compensate for the capacity of the shielded wire which connects the tint control to the phase detector circuit. The long wire is generally necessary so the control can be mounted on the front panel of the set, and an unshielded wire could radiate the 3.58-MHz burst signal into other circuits and cause interference.

Troubleshooting the Circuit

If the tint control will shift the colors but will not shift them far enough to produce good fleshtones, the trouble may be that the tuning of T1 is incorrect. Center tint control R1 and then adjust T1 to get good fleshtones, or better still, use a color bar generator and set the 4th color bar for a magenta color. (Magenta is a purplish color, the 2nd bar should be orange, the 3rd bar should be red.)

If the control will not produce a color shift, check for an open L1, a broken lead to the control, or an open control. C1 could be open but this would be rare unless there was some physical damage.

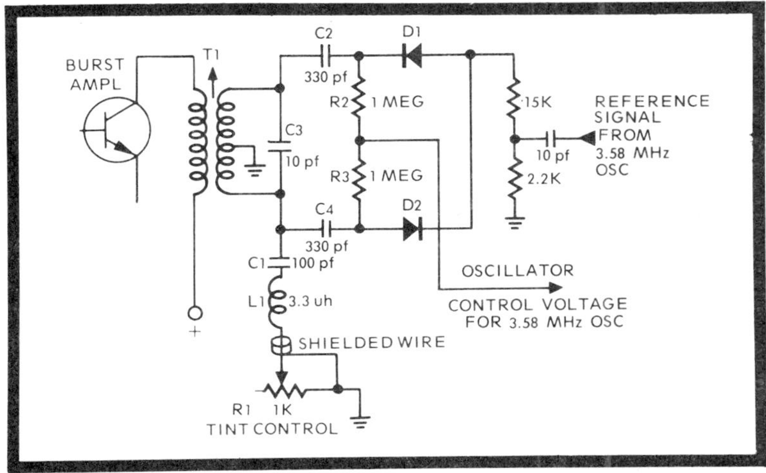

Fig. 16-4. Tint control which varies phase of burst signal to oscillator phase detector.

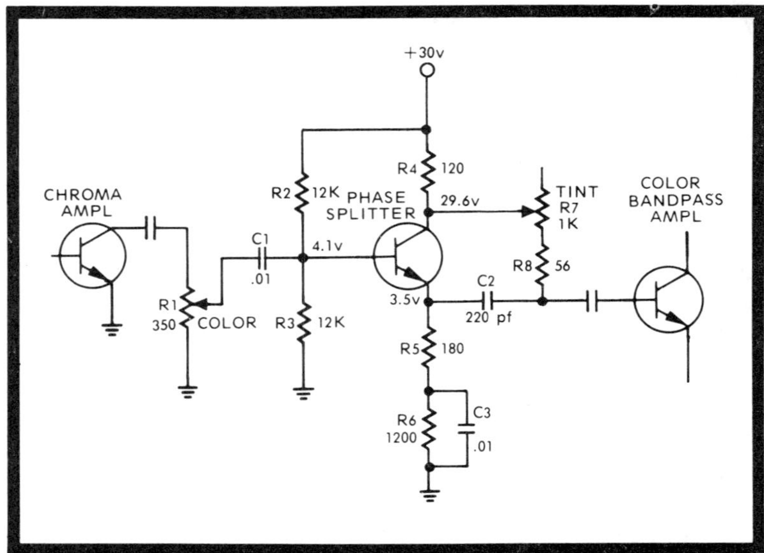

Fig. 16-5. Phase splitter tint control.

If the phase detector is not operating correctly, this would cause a complete loss of color lock, or the color lock would be critical. If the color is floating through the picture, making vertical objects appear to have candy stripes, the color is not in sync. In this case, ground out the phase detector control voltage and then adjust the color oscillator until the color floats but very slowly or even stops momentarily, then remove the control voltage short and see if the color locks tightly. If it does lock tightly, the phase detector is okay, if not there is some problem in the phase detector. See color phase detector circuits elsewhere in this book.

PHASE SPLITTER TINT CONTROL CIRCUIT

Many color sets change the tint of the picture by shifting the phase of the 3.58-MHz color oscillator. Other sets do not juggle the oscillator phase but shift the phase of the color sidebands instead. Since tint is relative and is entirely dependent upon the phase difference (or lack of it) between the local color oscillator and the color sidebands, the shifting of either the oscillator or the sidebands changes the tint of the color picture.

In Fig. 16-5 the designer has taken advantage of the 180-degree phase shift between the emitter and collector in a base-fed transistor amplifier. The color sidebands are fed through C1 from the COLOR control to the base of the phase splitter. The emitter circuit will "follow" the base and so have identical phase with the input, but the collector will have exactly opposite phase from the input. The output to the color bandpass amplifier is the result of the mixing of the emitter and collector outputs. With the TINT control at the upper limit, most of the output is directly from the emitter and so in phase with the input to the splitter. However, as the TINT control arm is moved downward, more and more of the collector output is routed to the color bandpass amplifier. This has the effect of changing the sideband phase because of the mixing of the two out-of-phase signals.

The emitter and collector each have small resistive loads, R4 and R5. The 1200 ohm resistor in the emitter circuit, R6, has no effect on the phase shift since it is bypassed by C3. The purpose of R6 is simply to limit the current flow through the transistor by providing DC bias.

R2 and R3 are the base bias network.

The 56-ohm resistor, R8, in series with the TINT control, prevents a complete or nearly complete loss of amplification as would occur if all of the collector output was fed into the emitter output circuit.

Troubleshooting the Circuit

The most common trouble with this circuit is a defective transistor. If the emitter voltage is above 25 volts, the transistor is almost surely shorted. If the emitter voltage is high but less than 15 volts, it may be that R3 is open. If the emitter voltage is zero, the transistor may be open or R2 may be open.

If the collector voltage is less than 25 volts, check for a changed value of R4 since even with a shorted transistor the total current that could flow, assuming R5 and R6 are normal, would be about 20 ma which would only cause a 2.44-volt drop across R4.

If the DC voltages on the transistor are normal but the TINT control action is almost nonexistent, check to see if C3 is open. You can check C3 by temporarily bridging another ceramic capacitor of about the same size across it—if the TINT control action returns to normal, replace C3.

Another cause of no tint control action could be an open 220-pf capacitor (C2) from the emitter output, or R7 itself could be open.

COLOR (CHROMA) OSCILLATORS

Every color TV set must reinsert a 3.58-MHz signal which is synchronized with the color subcarrier at the color TV transmitter. Remember that the color subcarrier is suppressed at the transmitter and only the color modulation is sent. But for the TV set to demodulate the color and make sense of the color sidebands, there must be a 3.58 MHz carrier exactly in step with the subcarrier suppressed by the transmitter (the subcarrier is suppressed because it would cause interference to the black and white picture and would require extra power for transmission).

The color oscillator must be extremely stable and for this reason there is almost always a crystal for control and to hold the oscillator very close to the correct frequency. The color oscillator is then locked exactly into phase by a comparison with a 3.58 MHz burst pulse which is sent out on the back porch of the horizontal sync signal (see discussion on burst amplifiers).

The color oscillator may be synchronized exactly by one of two or more methods. The most popular is the phase detector method, which develops an error DC voltage to either slightly speed up or slow down the color oscillator to bring it exactly in sync as required. The other method is the "brute force" method which uses the amplified burst signal to literally force the crystal oscillator to lock with it.

The color oscillator output is used to alternately turn off and on the color demodulators so that the demodulators respond to either the in-phase or quadrature-phase color signal (quadrature means 90 degrees out of phase). In order to put three colors on a single subcarrier, the 90 degree modulation is used, since a signal 90 degrees out of phase with another has no effect even though both are in the same circuit. The third color is a combination of the 180 degrees out-of-phase signals of the in-phase and quadrature signals and makes possible the recovery of three colors from the color information modulated on a single carrier.

3.58 MHz CRYSTAL OSCILLATOR

Fig. 16-6 shows a free-running oscillator, crystal-controlled. Feedback to keep the circuit oscillating is through the secondary of burst transformer T1. The exact frequency of the oscillator can be varied slightly by adjustment of C3. The 3.58-MHz oscillator in a color set reinserts the 3.58 MHz color carrier that is suppressed in the transmitter. In order for the

3.58-MHz local oscillator to lock in phase with the transmitter, a burst signal of about 8 cycles of 3.58 MHz is sent out on the "back porch" of the horizontal sync signal. It is this signal that is amplified by the burst amplifier, and the output of the burst amplifier "brute forces" the oscillator circuit to lock in step.

Solid-state 3.58-MHz oscillators are generally followed and isolated by a buffer amplifier before the signal is applied to the synchronous color detectors.

C1 in this circuit is a neutralizing capacitor which feeds an out-of-phase signal from the burst amplifier to the base of the oscillator. This out-of-phase signal cancels the effect of the burst signal being fed to the base through the capacity of the crystal holder, so that the output of the crystal oscillator is the result only of the crystal oscillations and not a result of a direct feedthrough from the burst amplifier.

Troubleshooting the Circuit

The output of a crystal oscillator can be checked using a wideband oscilloscope with a low capacitance probe to reduce loading on the circuit. The output from the circuit should be a sine wave which should increase considerably in amplitude

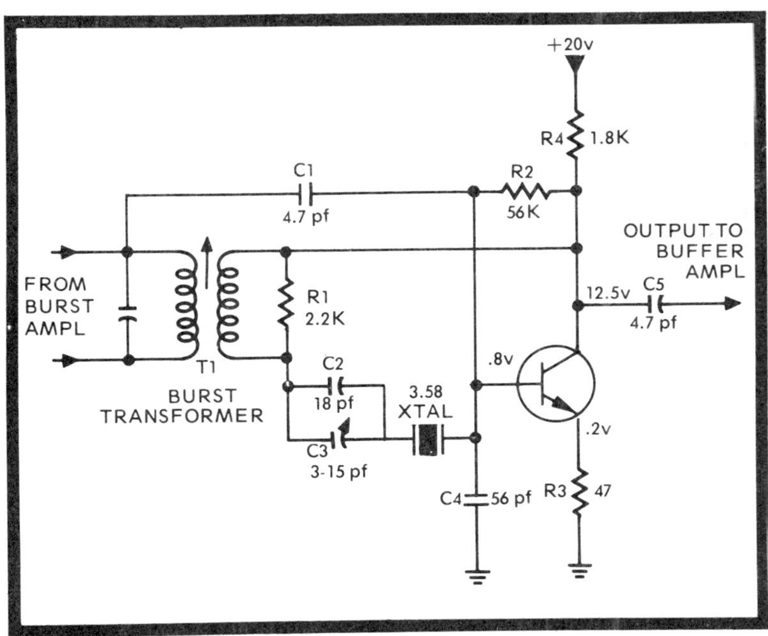

Fig. 16-6. 3.58 MHz crystal oscillator.

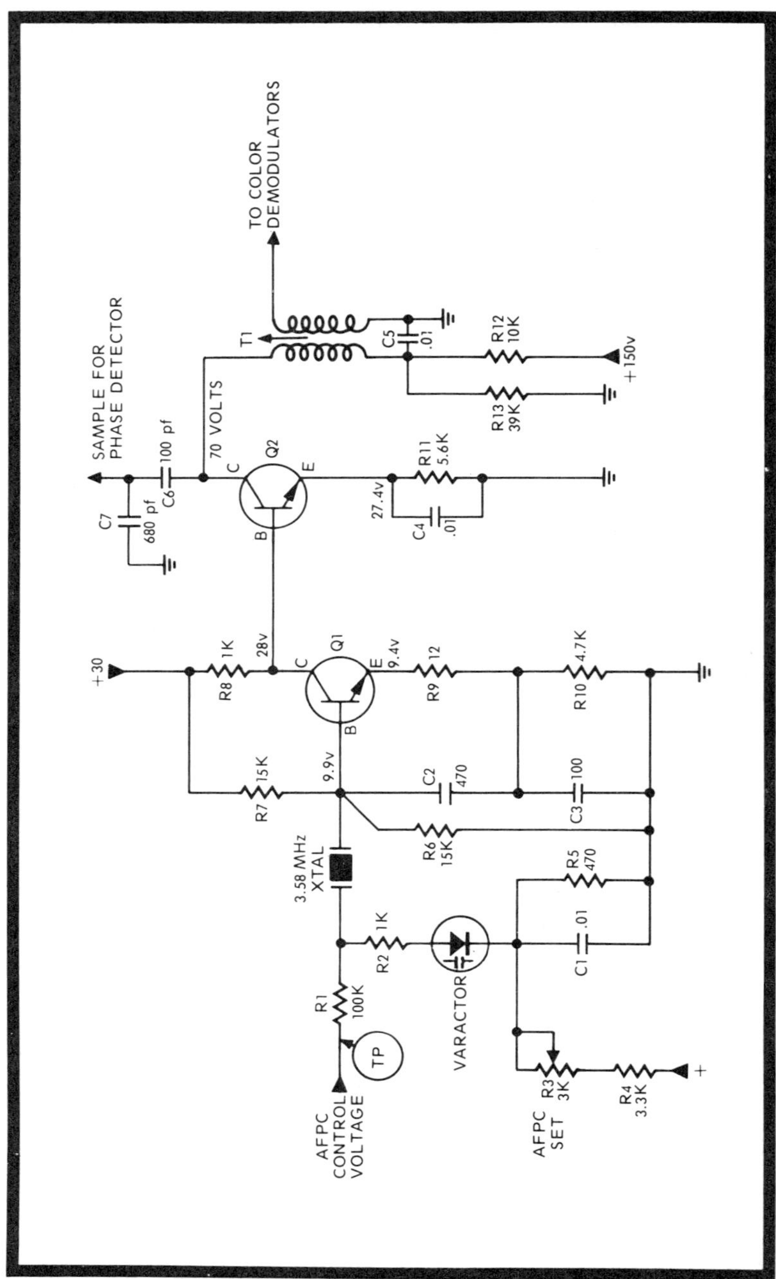

Fig. 16-7. 3.58 MHz color oscillator and buffer.

when a color signal is tuned in. In other words, when a burst signal is applied, the output of the oscillator is increased. Because of this increase in signal level, the DC voltages on the transistor will change also—collector voltage will rise and emitter voltage will drop.

To tune C3, tune in a color signal, then disable the burst amplifier by placing a short jumper between the base and emitter of the burst amplifier transistor. Now adjust C3 until the color bars on the screen "float" by slowly. Remove the burst amplifier jumper and color should lock in. T1 should be adjusted for maximum output at the collector of the crystal oscillator. If T1 must be readjusted, again adjust C3 as indicated and check for good color lock. T1 need only be adjusted if color lock is critical, or drops out easily when the fine tuning of the TV set is adjusted.

Trouble Symptoms

No Output: Check the collector voltage. If collector voltage is 20 volts (same as supply voltage) either the transistor is defective or the 56K bias resistor is open, or in a rare case, emitter resistor R3 might be open. If collector voltage is low, the circuit likely is not oscillating. This might be caused by a defective crystal or by an open secondary on T1, or by an open or short in C4.
Oscillator Output Does Not Change With Burst Signal Input: The most probable cause is incorrect tuning of T1, or a defect in T1. Can also be caused by a defect in the burst amplifier or its associated circuits. If color bars cannot be made to "float" then it could be caused by a defective 3.58 MHz crystal.

Special Note: Be sure to replace the crystal in this circuit with the correct type. Not just any 3.58-MHz crystal, though designed for use in a color oscillator, will perform correctly in this circuit. However, almost any 3.58-MHz crystal designed for a transistor circuit using "brute force" locking (no phase detector) can be used as a substitute. As a general rule, if the color bars can be made to "float" slowly by, with the burst signal removed, the crystal will be a suitable replacement. As always, though, you should check for "clean" color lock and absence of spurious color squiggles which may vary with the tuning of T1.

3.58 MHz OSCILLATOR AND BUFFER STAGE

This crystal oscillator in Fig. 16-7 is a transistor version of the Clapp oscillator. In effect the crystal, which acts in a circuit in much the same way as a series resonant circuit would, is across C2 and C3. Feedback is sustained by a small signal across C3 and R10 which is fed to the base through C2.

The actual oscillator frequency is dependent largely upon the crystal but is also affected to a limited degree by the capacity in the circuit. Because the capacity of the circuit does change the frequency slightly, adding or subtracting capacity can be used to lower or raise the frequency slightly for exact control necessary in a color TV set.

This circuit uses a varactor to control the frequency. A varactor is simply a reverse-biased diode which has been specially made to have a relatively linear change in capacity with a change in reverse DC bias. (All diodes have this capacity effect, but only specially-processed diodes are usable in this kind of circuit.) The DC bias for the varactor is supplied by the AFPC (automatic frequency and phase control) detector.

When the oscillator signal tends to lower in frequency, the AFPC detector output goes negative which provides more reverse bias for the diode and less capacity in series with the crystal.

The varactor is held reverse-biased by a positive voltage on its cathode fed through the AFPC set control, R3. R3 establishes the amount of reverse bias to set the circuit to 3.58 MHz when the AFPC detector output voltage is at zero.

C1 has no effect on the tuned circuit since it is large when compared with the capacity of the varactor; its purpose is to provide an AC signal ground return for the varactor while still allowing the DC voltage to be applied to the varactor cathode.

R6 and R7 are base bias resistors for Q1 and since Q2 is direct-coupled to Q1, they also determine the fixed current through Q2, the buffer amplifier.

The buffer amplifier is essential to prevent the tuned load in its output from affecting the oscillator frequency in any way, as it might if T1 were connected in the collector of Q1. The buffer amplifier also provides some amplification and furnishes a sine wave output signal to be fed to the color demodulators and also back through C6 to the AFPC phase detector so that the output can be compared with the incoming color sync (burst) signal.

Troubleshooting the Circuit

If the color oscillator frequency appears to be off frequency as evidenced by color stripes in the picture (barber pole effect) one of the first steps is to eliminate the AFPC circuit as the possible trouble. This can normally be done simply by shorting out the AFPC detector output to ground (at TP in this circuit). With zero voltage from the detector circuit, you should now be able to adjust the AFPC SET control so that the color bars float slowly through the picture. This is sometimes called "zero beating" the oscillator. If the oscillator can be set to the correct frequency, then the trouble is in the phase detector (AFPC) circuit.

If the AFPC SET cannot be adjusted for zero beat, the trouble is in the oscillator itself. This could be a defective 3.58 MHz crystal, a defective varactor, an open C1, or shorted C1 (check the DC voltage across C1, if it is zero C1 must be shorted). It can also be a defective transistor, defective bias resistor or emitter resistor, as well as change in value of C2 or C3. (The last are rarely the trouble.)

If a scope shows output at the collector of Q1 but no output at the collector of Q2, check for a shorted transistor Q2, especially if R11 shows signs of overheating. Check also for B+ on Q2. Lack of B+ is often caused by an open 10K resistor, R12, or an open T1 primary. If the collector voltage on Q2 is zero, and R12 is overheating or burnt, check for a shorted C5. If Q2 is open, emitter voltage will be zero if the open is from emitter to base, but not if from collector to base. Check the transistor in the circuit, using an ohmmeter, by measuring between base and collector and then reversing the ohmmeter leads. One reading should be high, the other low.

This same is also true if you measure between base and emitter. Between collector and emitter, the reading should not be low regardless of which direction the ohmmeter leads are connected.

Q1 can also be checked with an ohmmeter and most transistor defects can be determined with go no-go accuracy; however there are a few transistor defects that prevent the transistor from working normally in the circuit but will not show up when an ohmmeter check is made, and often not show up when a more sophisticated transistor test or tester is used.

Few testing methods excel those that check the actual performance of the transistor in the circuit where it is used. The only problem with a performance test is in knowing what to expect as output from the circuit—what kind of waveform, how much amplitude, frequency of operation, etc. This is why it is a good idea when you are checking any new circuit that you jot down the performance characteristics right on the schematic if possible so you can compare the performance with the same kind of circuit when it gives trouble.

COLOR PHASE DETECTOR

A color phase detector, or some brute force means of color lock, is needed in a color TV set. The reason is that only the color sidebands are sent out and not the 3.58-MHz color subcarrier because it would cause considerable interference, while the sidebands without a carrier tend to cancel out so far as interference is concerned. At the receiver, however, in order to detect the color, an oscillator signal must be reinserted at the demodulators and that oscillator signal must be exactly in step with the one at the transmitter. To accomplish this, a color burst signal is sent out along with the sync signal. The color burst signal is about 8 cycles of the 3.58 MHz transmitter signal.

The 3.58-MHz oscillator in the receiver is locked in step with this color burst signal generally in one of two ways, either by direct "brute force" drive of the oscillator by the amplified burst signal, or by use of a phase detector to determine whether the oscillator is running above or below the burst frequency and to correct the oscillator by a changing DC voltage so that the burst and oscillator signals exactly correspond, not only as to frequency but as to phase. (When an oscillator is more than 1 cycle off-frequency, it is called a frequency change. However, an oscillator can be running at the correct frequency but not in phase, just as two cars can be going around a race track at the same speed but one lagging always the same distance behind the other. This is a phase difference.)

How can a phase detector determine that there is a difference in frequency and how can it supply the necessary correction voltage? Fig. 16-8 shows how. In the upper drawing, A, the burst signal is fed from the secondary of the burst transformer. Since the two sides of an untuned transformer are always out of phase by 180 degrees, the two signals on either side develop a negative charge on the upper diode and a positive charge on the lower diode. Since these two charges are equal and opposite, they cancel out at the center tap of R1 and R2 and so the correction voltage is zero with a burst signal input only.

Now if we insert a sample of the oscillator frequency at the center of the two diodes and that oscillator frequency is such that at a specific time when the burst signal is maximum the oscillator frequency is a zero voltage, then the output from the detector still is zero.

Now let us take a condition when the oscillator starts to speed up. If that happens, the sample sine wave from the oscillator arrives a little early. This places an additional positive voltage at the junction of the diodes, and diode D1 will now have less forward bias so it will conduct less, but diode D2 with the more positive voltage on its anode conducts more and so there is no longer a balance at the center tap of the two resistors but a more positive voltage which when fed to the oscillator decreases the speed of the oscillator to again bring the correction voltage to near zero.

Depending upon the oscillator circuit, it may take a positive voltage to slow down the oscillator or it may take a negative voltage to do so. The designer sets up his phase detector circuit to deliver the polarity needed for a particular application.

Fig. 16-9 shows an actual circuit used in a color TV set. The burst amplifier feeds burst transformer T1, which splits the phase of the signal and feeds it equally through C1 and C2 to diodes D1 and D2. R1 and R2 are 1 megohm matched resistors. The sample signal from the oscillator is fed to the center of the two diodes. Capacitors C5 and C6 provide a capacity "bleeder" to drop the amplitude of the signal to the desired level. L1 provides a high impedance to the 3.58 MHz signal but a low-resistance DC path to ground for the diodes.

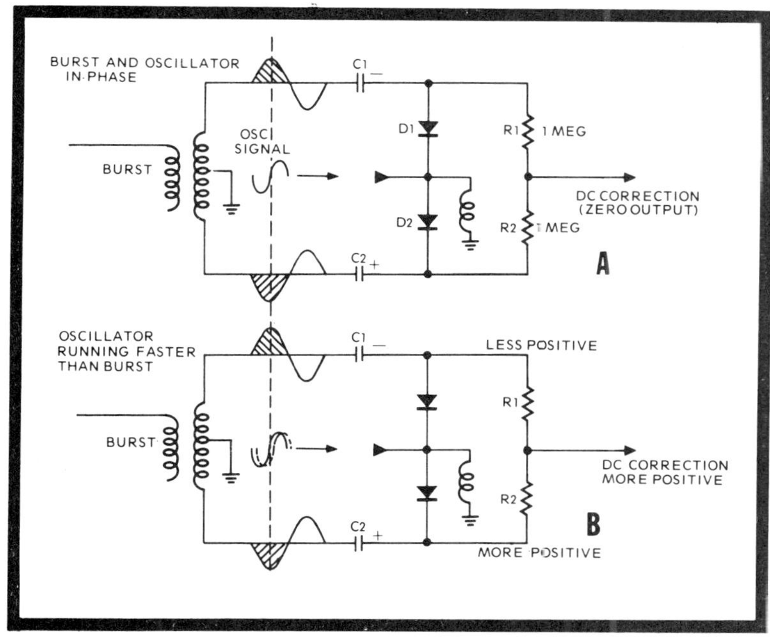

Fig. 16-8. Operation of phase detector.

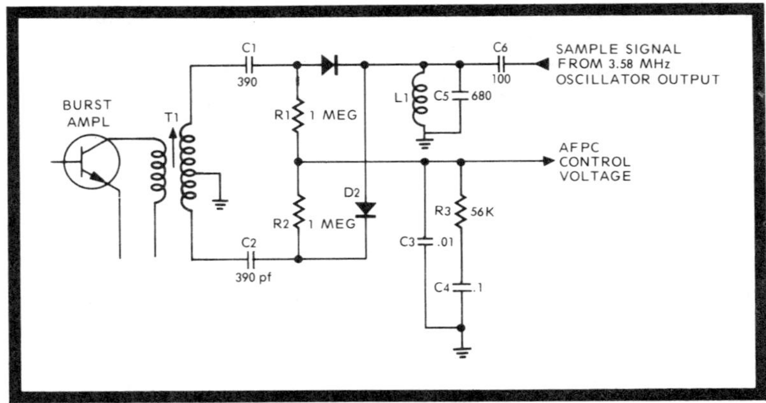

Fig. 16-9. AFPC phase detector for color TV.

The capacitor C3 and the RC network R3-C4 form an anti-hunt network and 3.58 MHz bypass. C3 bypasses the 3.58 MHz oscillator signal so that it will have no affect on the control.

R3 and C4 provide a time constant filter circuit, along with C3, so that the correction will not be "too quick." If the correction is too quick there could be jittery or shimmery color, or color with tiny, jagged ripples in it. Any correction that occurs is slowed enough by the RC circuit that it has no noticeable effect on small portions of the color picture.

Troubleshooting the Circuit

A phase detector is normally a "work horse" and gives little trouble in use except from imbalance, and imbalance is most often caused by defective diodes. If the diodes do not have similar conduction characteristics, one will conduct more than the other and the DC output will tilt in that direction. Of course, the same will happen if C1 or C2 opens or becomes leaky, or if the secondary of T1 opens on one side. Also, DC will be greater in one direction if either R1 or R2 should increase drastically in value. (Seldom will a carbon resistor go lower than its normal value unless it is subjected to heavy current flow, and in this circuit it is next to impossible for this to happen.)

Another thing that can upset a phase detector is a radical change in the feedback sample, such as could occur if C6 opened. Another trouble in this circuit is an open L1, which would eliminate the DC return path for the diodes.

A good quick check for balance is to measure the output AFPC control voltage. If it is zero, the circuit is balanced (or completely inoperative). If the output voltage is not zero, short across L1 to eliminate the feedback signal and see if the voltage output goes to zero. If it does, the circuit is balanced and the trouble is the oscillator circuit is not running at the correct frequency, or there is a defective component in the feedback circuit. (Almost any phase detector will have perhaps a few tenths of a volt rather than zero, and this should not concern the technician. In some phase detector circuits, there is actually a DC bias on the control voltage line.)

To check the diodes with an ohmmeter, it probably is best to disconnect one end of both diodes and then measure both the forward resistance and the back resistance (by reversing the leads of your ohmmeter). The forward resistance of the diodes is not critical so long as it is the same or nearly the same for both. The back resistance is not critical either if it is above 200K or so and if the two diodes have similar back resistances.

The value of resistors R1 and R2 is not overly critical but matching is again important. For example, two resistors each measuring 770K within 1 or 2 percent of each other would be much more satisfactory than if one resistor were 1 meg and the other 1.1 meg (10 percent difference).

COLOR DEMODULATORS

Color demodulators recapture color signals by reproducing the original carrier frequency in exact frequency and phase to that which is suppressed at the transmitter. A color demodulator is sometimes called a synchronous detector. It switches off and on 3.58 million times a second so as to react only to the portion of the signal which it is pertinent for it to detect.

The X and Z demodulation system in Fig. 16-10 operates on an approximate 90-degree phase angle (or somewhat wider angle if the designer wishes to have a wider range of fleshtones in the picture and sacrifice some of the other colors slightly). Some sets have a switch that will switch to a wider or narrower phase angle so the TV user can select the position he prefers.

In the X and Z system, the output of the demodulators is just two colors, red and blue, but green is really hiding in these two outputs—by taking the proper portions of the red and blue signals and inverting both and mixing them together, green results. This matrixing of green is done in the color difference amplifiers.

The other general type of color demodulation recaptures all three colors in the detection process rather than in the

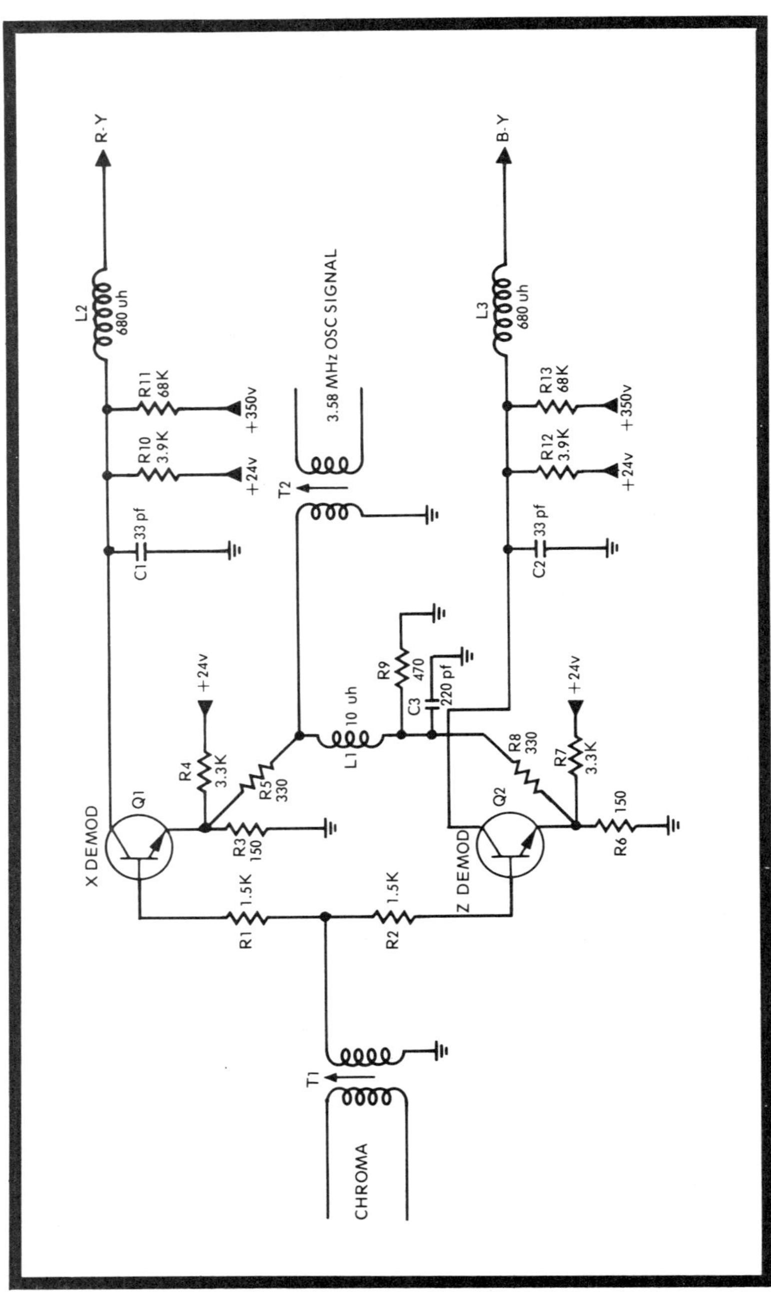

Fig. 16-10. Color demodulator for X and Z system.

difference amplifiers, but again this is done by reversing the phase of either the 3.58-MHz oscillator or phase of the chroma signal and then picking off the right amplitude to make the green signal. Again, green is the result of reversing the phase of the red and blue signals and then mixing the two inverted signals in proper amplitude, thereby establishing the proper phase angle to reproduce green.

It is difficult to separate phase and amplitude in actual practice when you get down to the nitty-gritty. If two signals, 90 degrees out of phase and of the same amplitude, are mixed, the resultant is a 45 degrees phase angle. If two signals, let us call them red and blue, are 90 degrees out of phase, but of equal amplitude, the resultant will be a magenta signal which results when we mix equal amounts of red and blue light. If we mix in more red than blue, the resultant phase angle will shift in the red direction and the color will be more red than blue. Conversely, if the blue signal is the larger, the resultant will be more blue than red. If the blue signal is missing and only a red signal is sent, the resultant will be red and there is no phase angle involved.

The idea of phase then is not really too important so long as you understand that this is just another way we talk about mixing. Mix signals of equal strengths and you get another signal that is a resultant of the two. A color picture tube responds to amplitude of signals—change in voltage between the grid and cathode. If the red and blue guns have equal-amplitude signals, the output will be neither red nor blue but half way between, a mixture, a magenta color. Expressed in degrees we could say that magenta is 45 degrees away from red, and 45 degrees away from blue but in reality so far as the eye can see it is just an equal mix of red and blue. Red and blue, 90 degrees apart, are said to be in quadrature.

A color demodulator operates because a large 3.58-MHz signal is fed into the circuit, alternately cutting off or turning on transistors or diodes so that they conduct only on the positive or negative excursion of the 3.58-MHz signal.

By inserting the chroma sideband signals so they also can add or subtract to the bias WHEN AND ONLY WHEN that particular part of the circuit is turned on by the 3.58-MHz signal, the color sidebands removed from the carrier at the transmitter remodulate a locally-generated carrier that has been locked in by a reference sync pulse sent out by the transmitter.

Sending out only the sidebands results in practically no interference to the black and white signal nor to the sound and requires little power at the transmitter, but to take full advantage of this carrier suppression, the demodulator must re-establish the condition at the transmitter before the 3.58-MHz subcarrier was removed, and it does, in the manner just discussed.

X AND Z DEMODULATOR FOR COLOR SET

The two transistors in Fig. 16-10 are biased somewhat beyond cutoff by the voltage divider circuits R3, R4 and R6, R7. Since these are NPN transistors they require a negative voltage on the emitter (or positive on the base) to cause them to conduct. Without a 3.58 MHz signal, the transistors do not conduct. When the 3.58 MHz signal is present, however, the transistors turn on during the negative excursion of the signal. Q1 conducts before Q2 because of the phase delay (due to L1 and C3) of about 90 degrees. In other words, Q1 conducts and then a quarter of a cycle later, Q2 conducts.

The chroma (color) sidebands are fed equally into the bases of both transistors. When Q1 is conducting, the color sideband amplitude at that time determines the output at the collector of Q1. A quarter of a cycle later, when Q2 conducts, its output is determined by the sideband amplitude at that specific time. If the amplitude is the same for the chroma sidebands at both times then both the X and the Z demodulator will put out virtually identical voltage changes and both the red and the blue guns of the color tube will turn on accordingly. If the amplitude is high there will be a bright magenta on the screen and if the amplitude is low, the bar will still be magenta but much weaker. A high-amplitude signal produces a highly saturated color and a low amplitude produces low saturation. The hue is determined by the amplitudes of the two signals at specific times (phase relationship). This is why it is sometimes said that the amplitude of the color signals produces the saturation (color brightness) and the phase of the color signals produces the hue (the color frequency in the visible spectrum).

To establish a voltage change slow enough that the color tube phosphors can respond, C1 and C2 are charged by the voltage changes but they are small enough so that the DC voltage change is as fast as possible. Another way you can consider C1 and C2 is that they bypass the 3.58 MHz switching signal, in concert with the action of L2 and L3, respectively.

This circuit uses two separate B+ sources, one from the 24-volt line and the other from a 350-volt line. The higher voltage source increases the collector voltage on the transistors and allows them to make a wider voltage excursion.

Sometimes a circuit is used in this demodulator to widen the phase angle between the two demodulators. The simple way to do this is to provide a switch to bypass another small capacitor, perhaps around 100 pf across the 220 pf capacitor, C3. This might increase the phase angle in this circuit from around 90 degrees to 120 degrees or so. Increasing the phase angle gives a wider latitude on fleshtones, and it is off-color fleshtones that result in most complaints from set owners, who are especially annoyed with having to readjust the tint control each time they change channels.

Widening the demodulation angle does make all the colors a bit more reddish, but usually this is not noticeable since there is no reference that can be used between the original and the picture on the color set. Fleshtones, however, are a reference and so are objectionable if either reddish or greenish.

Troubleshooting the Circuit

As far as DC voltages are concerned, the Q1 and Q2 transistor voltages should be almost identical. If there is a significant difference in the DC voltages on the transistors, then one of the circuits is not operating correctly. If you do not have a list of the correct voltages, the color symptoms should clue you in on which circuit is defective. If there is no red in the picture then the X demodulator is defective, no blue indicates the Z demodulator is defective. (Don't forget, of course, that these same troubles can be caused elsewhere than in the demodulator—perhaps in the color difference amplifiers, or biases on the color tube, in the color CRT itself.)

The phase delay circuit (L1, C3, R9) almost never gives trouble but a quick ohmmeter check of L1 is wise if the trouble seems obscure. Even C3 could be leaky or shorted, or open, but this is rare.

For bias problems, resistors can be at fault. If a resistor is burnt, it will usually have less than normal resistance unless it's burned virtually in two. Any burnt resistor almost surely has a cause. That cause may still be present. Of course, it may be from some previous repair (sometimes a technician, for example, may install a new transistor without inspecting the circuit parts, and so a burned resistor could have been caused by a previous fault already corrected but this is not too likely).

Lack of signal from either the chroma circuit or the 3.58-MHz oscillator circuit, will result in no output from the demodulator, and depending upon other circuitry, the color screen may go green or possibly some other color.

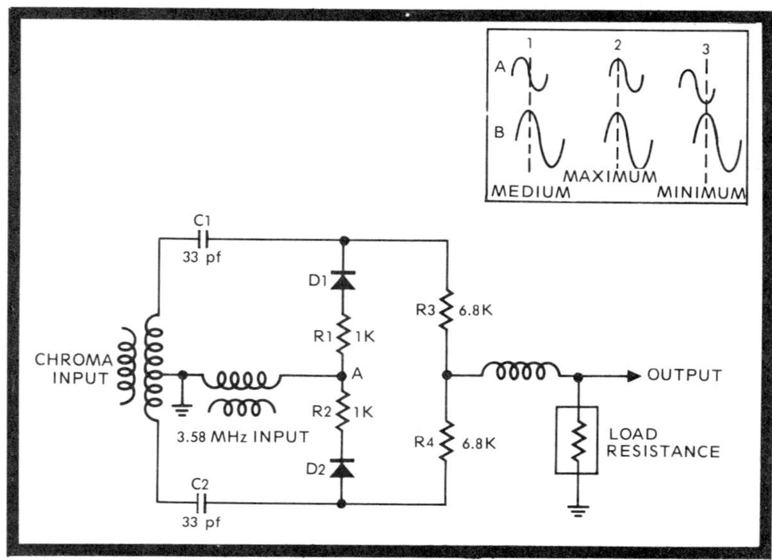

Fig. 16-11. Diode demodulator for a single color.

An oscilloscope is the best instrument for checking the input signals at T1 and T2. A color bar generator connected to the antenna terminals usually makes tracing color sidebands (chroma) much easier. It also lets you look at the output of the collectors of the demodulators and make a sensible diagnosis of a color problem in the demodulator circuit.

DIODE COLOR DEMODULATORS

A more and more common practice is to use diode color demodulators rather than transistors and usually one pair of diodes for each of the three primary colors, red, green and blue. Fig. 16-11 is a simplified schematic of a so-called diode synchronous detector. To understand it, assume that there is zero chroma input, but there is the normal steady input from the 3.58 MHz oscillator. The oscillator signal is going positive and negative at point A. When positive at point A, the diode charges C1 and a + voltage is developed across R3; however, on the next half-cycle, point A is negative and capacitor C2 charges through D2, placing a negative voltage across R4. The voltages across R3 and R4, being equal, will cancel, and so there will be no voltage developed at the output.

There is no output from the demodulator if a chroma signal was inserted that was exactly in phase with the oscillator signal, since such a signal would also add and subtract in step with the oscillator signal. But if the chroma input is out of phase with the oscillator signal, it will add its voltage to the oscillator voltage more on one cycle than another. In turn, this will cause one of the diodes to conduct more vigorously than the other, and if that diode is D1, the output voltage will go positive in direct proportion to the amplitude of the chroma signal.

To obtain a three-color output, a demodulator circuit must compare the chroma with the 3.58 MHz locked-in oscillator at three different times. The simplest way to do this is to use three separate diode demodulators similar to Fig. 16-11 with one important difference. Either the phase (time of arrival) of the chroma sidebands must be delayed so they arrive at different times within the 3.58 MHz cycle, or the 3.58 MHz signal itself can be fed to the demodulator at three different times in the cycle.

In reality, the demodulators simply sample the chroma sideband signals at three different times and compare them to the 3.58 MHz oscillator signal at these three different times.

The inset in Fig. 16-11 shows how two sine waves when compared at different times in the cycle produce different outputs. In "1," the "A" signal is going through zero while the "B" signal is maximum, which means the resultant signal would be a medium amplitude. In "2," both signals are reaching maximum at the same time, so the output will be maximum (positive polarity). In "3," still with the same size signals, the resultant output is low since the "A" signal is maximum negative while the "B" signal is maximum positive. In a simplified manner, this analysis shows how the same signals compared at different times result in different output levels. In a very real sense this is the way color works. At one instant the demodulator is checking the "red" signal and developing an output, in the next instant another demodulator is checking the "blue" signal and developing an output, and finally the "green" is checked and develops an output.

The demodulators are so fixed that they operate and develop output only on their respective signals developing either zero or negative output during the remaining portion of the 3.58 MHz cycle. This is totally a function of design as already explained, and problems in any of the circuits are nearly always the result of some "DC" component failure, that is, a diode shorts or opens or becomes excessively leaky, a coil opens, a resistor opens or changes value, a capacitor opens or becomes leaky, a transformer winding opens or is

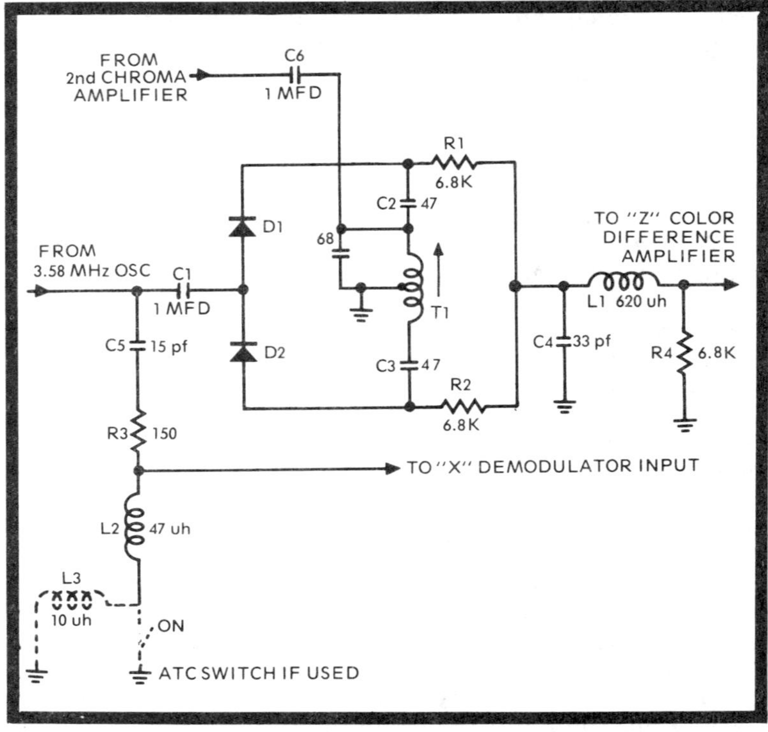

Fig. 16-12. Another diode synchronous detector (color TV set).

damaged so that its inductance changes drastically. The phase shifts in the circuit generally involve no more than two or three small components which almost never give trouble if not physically damaged.

ANOTHER DIODE SYNCHRONOUS DETECTOR

When a color signal is transmitted, the R-Y, G-Y, B-Y signals have a definite phase relationship, that is, one follows the other in a regular order. These color signals are used to modulate a 3.58-MHz color subcarrier which is suppressed before transmission.

In the receiver it is necessary to reinsert the 3.58-MHz color subcarrier so that the color difference signals can be demodulated in the same phase relationship as they were transmitted. In some receivers only the R-Y and B-Y signals are demodulated and the G-Y signal is derived in the color difference amplifiers by a proper combining and phase inversion of the R-Y and B-Y signals. In other receivers, a separate demodulator circuit is used for all three colors rather than just two.

If only the R-Y and B-Y signals are demodulated, it is common to call the R-Y an "X" demodulator and the B-Y a "Z" demodulator.

The circuit shown in Fig. 16-12 can be used with slight modifications as a color demodulator for any one of the color signals. This one shows a "Z" output. Note that the signal is fed directly into the demodulator from the 3.58 MHz chroma oscillator. (The input to the "X" demodulator is through C5, R3, L2, a phase delay network of about 90 degrees or ¼ cycle otherwise the "X" demodulator is the same as the one shown.)

In this circuit, the chroma sidebands are fed into T1 which feeds them out of phase to D1 and D2. The 3.58 MHz oscillator signal fed to the center of D1 and D2 alternately causes one diode or the other to conduct, depending upon the amplitude and the phase of the chroma signals. The resultant output of the demodulator is a series of pulses having amplitude variations corresponding to the B-Y sent by the transmitter.

L1 and C4 filter out the 3.58-MHz "switching" pulses so that only the B-Y amplitude modulation appears at the input of the "Z" color difference amplifier.

The "X" demodulator works in the same manner except that because of the delay in the 3.58 MHz oscillator signal due to the delay network (C5, R3, L2), the diodes switch off and on at a slightly different time than the "Z" demodulator and so the "X" (R-Y) output "looks" at the color signal from a different angle and therefore has an output corresponding to "red."

The delay angle between "X" and "Z" is normally around 90 degrees, although in some cases the angle will be less to compensate for interaction in the color difference amplifiers when green (G-Y) is derived. If there is no interaction, the phase angle may be increased to 105 degrees or more to provide a "wider" fleshtone range. Some sets use a switch that changes the phase angle to as much as 150 degrees or so in some cases. Although this makes a considerable difference in screen colors, it does provide a more "reddish" picture and the variation in skin tones from one station to another is less noticeable. These switches are often called "automatic tint control" (ATC) although they more nearly correspond to a "tone" control of the type you are familiar with in radio or TV audio amplifiers.

In this circuit, the ATC switch inserts a 10 uh coil when switched on, thus increasing the delay. In similar circuits the

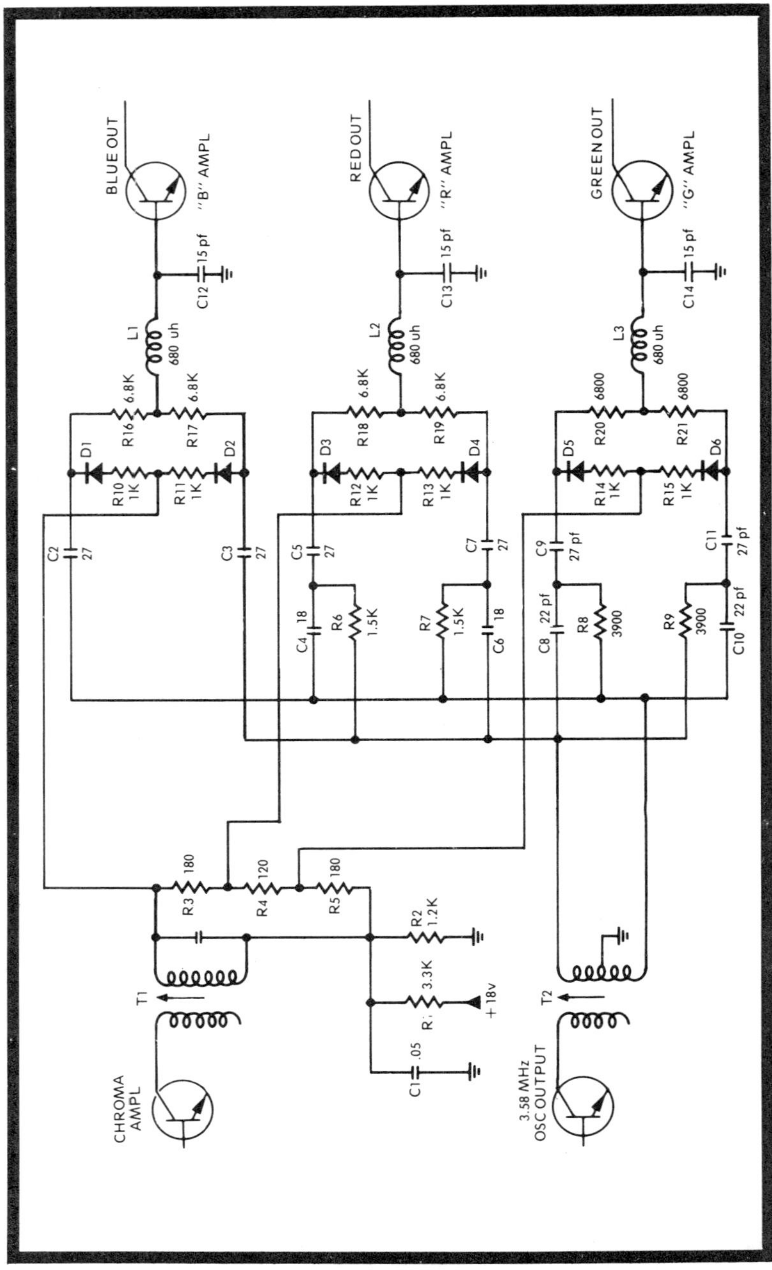

Fig. 16-13. Complete diode color demodulator.

ATC switch may insert or remove a small capacitor in the delay circuit to accomplish the same thing.

Troubleshooting the Circuit

Because all except really sophisticated test equipment will load this circuit during testing so that it cannot operate properly, in most cases the best troubleshooting procedure when you suspect trouble in this circuit is to remove the power to the circuit and test individual components with an ohmmeter as far as practical. Check the diodes to see that they are not shorted or open or do not have serious leakage. If possible to do easily, remove one lead of each diode from the circuit and then measure the front and back resistances of each. If these resistances are not similar, replace both diodes with a matched set of the same type as the original. Diodes used in this type of circuit are nearly always germanium types because of better linearity with weaker signal input, as compared to silicon types.

Often, electrolytic capacitors are used in circuits of this type for coupling as they are here (C1 and C6), and the most common trouble with these capacitors is an open. Try shunting a capacitor of similar size (note polarity) across each capacitor to see whether or not circuit operation is restored.

A good scope can be used to check the coupling capacitors. There should be virtually the same amount of signal on one side of the capacitor as on the other.

An open coil can be found with an ohmmeter, and it is always a good idea to check for an open coil when operation of the circuit seems erratic. In almost every case, it is not necessary to remove the coil from the circuit since the normal resistance is quite low compared to the shunt paths around it.

COMPLETE DIODE COLOR DEMODULATOR

Fig. 16-13 a complete demodulator circuit as used in one model of color TV set. All diode demodulators are similar, with most having certain circuit refinements or modifications to fit a particular criteria for the designer.

The chroma signal is fed from T1 to each of the demodulators. The resistive network of R3, R4 and R5 across T1 secondary establishes the proper amplitude of signal required by each demodulator. Different amounts of signal output are required because of the original imbalance at the transmitter necessary to provide good color tracking.

The full-amplitude sidebands are fed to the blue demodulator, about 70 percent as much to the red demodulator and about 30 percent as much to the green demodulator.

The 3.58-MHz oscillator signal is fed from T2 directly to the blue demodulator (C3, C2), but it is phase shifted by about 100 degrees by C4, R6 and C6, R7 (just over a quarter cycle) before it goes to the red demodulator. The oscillator signal to the green demod is flipped over 180 degrees by connecting the demodulator across transformer T2 in the opposite direction, and then the necessary phase shift to produce green is accomplished by C8, R8 and C10, R9.

Bias for each of the amplifier transistors is provided through T1 by bias resistors R1 and R2.

L1, L2, L3 and capacitors C12, C13 and C14 are filter circuits to eliminate the 3.58 MHz switching voltage and prevent it from reaching the color amplifiers.

Troubleshooting the Circuit

See discussion concerning Fig. 16-11.

COLOR KILLERS

Color killers are used on most color sets to kill any color amplifier noise during a black and white broadcast. The color killer generally prevents the amplification of any color hash by biasing the one or more color amplifiers to cutoff or saturation. Sometimes the killer voltage is applied to the color demodulators, but much more often it goes to the color amplifiers (also called chroma amplifiers and color IF amplifiers).

Almost all killer circuits have some method of adjustment which alters the bias on the killer circuit so that it will respond accurately and readily as it should for either a black and white or color picture. Setting the adjustment is easy, using a black and white picture being broadcast. Simply turn the killer control until you see colored hash in the picture then back off the control until the colored hash JUST disappears.

In the past several years it has been hard to find a black and white picture being broadcast so the killer is usually adjusted so that the color intensity JUST begins to drop and then all channels are checked to see that the color is all right.

In weak signal areas, or places where there is a tendency to have different strength of color signals, technicians often turn the killer adjustment "full on," making sure that the killer will not be the cause of intermittent color, and taking a chance that the customer will watch such few black and white pictures that he won't complain about a little color "snow."

COLOR KILLER CIRCUIT

When the color burst signal is present and a negative voltage output from the killer detector is fed to the base of Q1 (Fig. 16-14), this transistor will conduct. This places a positive voltage on Q2 and it conducts, producing a positive voltage at its emitter. This positive voltage is coupled through a 3.3K resistor to the base of the NPN bandpass amplifier, which now can amplify the color signals fed through the 470-pf capacitor to its base.

But, if a black and white picture is being sent, there is no color burst and the bias on the killer amplifier goes positive (due to the fixed bias provided through the killer detector circuit) and so Q1 is cut off. With Q1 cut off, the only bias available for Q2 is a negative bias through R4. Since Q2 is an NPN transistor, Q2 is cut off and so in turn is the bandpass amplifier Q3. With the bandpass amplifier cut off there is no chance for colored "snow" or noise during a black and white picture.

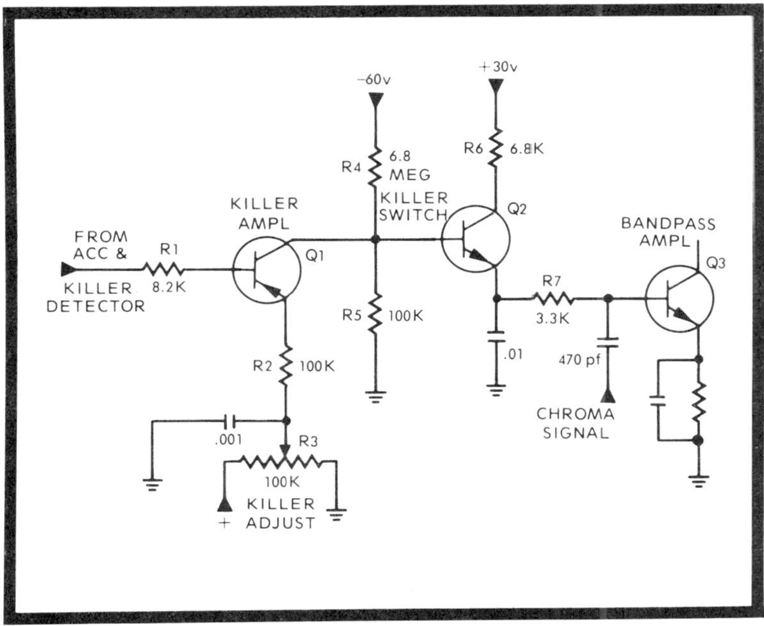

Fig. 16-14. Color killer circuit.

Troubleshooting the Circuit

A color killer circuit is redundant during a color broadcast, that is, it is not needed. **But the color killer can be the cause of no color when color is being broadcast.** For example, suppose Q1 were to open. This is the same as cutting off the amplifier and so Q2 and Q3 would also be cut off, and there would be no color output from the set even though the killer detector is functioning normally.

Another reason that the killer might kill color is for the **Killer Adjust** to be set incorrectly.

If Q2 should open, this will also stop the color, regardless of whether or not the killer detector or the killer amplifier is working.

In this circuit, unlike some killer circuits, you cannot just ground out the killer voltage to turn on the bandpass amplifier. In this case, a bias voltage must be supplied. So if you suspect the killer is causing a loss of the color signal, connect a jumper from the collector of Q2 to the emitter. This will apply the positive bias necessary (assuming that R6 is okay) to the bandpass amplifier; if the color returns, the trouble is in the killer circuit or in the killer phase detector.

Check out the transistors. Check the adjustment. Check to make sure the resistors in the circuit are near their marked values. Check to see if the bias on the killer amplifier goes negative when a color signal is received, then check at the collector to see if it goes positive when the signal is received, etc.

COLOR KILLER USING TWO TRANSISTORS

The circuit in Fig. 16-15 uses two transistors, one of which is called an ACC (automatic chroma control) amplifier. During a black and white transmission, transistor Q1 conducts to saturation because of a positive bias supplied through a fixed bias circuit in the ACC and killer phase detector. Saturation of Q1 applies a saturation bias to Q2, and the collector voltage on Q2 is nearly zero, depending upon the setting of the killer adjustment only slightly. This means there is no positive bias voltage for Q3 and so it is cut off and there will be no colored "snow" or noise output during a black and white transmission since Q3 is the 3rd Chroma Amplifier.

When a burst signal is received, the killer and ACC detector bias goes in a negative direction, not enough to completely cut off Q1 but sufficient to drop the positive bias on Q2 enough so that it will stop conducting (assuming that the killer adjustment is properly set). With Q2 not conducting, the voltage on its collector rises considerably (more positive) and this voltage is then used as bias to the base of Q3 and it is made to conduct and amplify the color signal.

The reason that Q1 is not completely cut off is that it supplies more or less positive bias to the 1st Chroma amplifier, depending on the strength of the burst signal, and so provides automatic chroma control.

Troubleshooting the Circuit

This circuit will stop color on a color broadcast if either Q1 or Q2 should short between collector and emitter, or if the ACC and Killer phase detector were not working.

If turning the killer adjust did not produce color, a quick check to see if there is killer trouble would be to connect a 100K resistor from the junction of R6 and R7 back to the +23 volts. This would bias the 3rd Chroma Amplifier into conduction even though there was trouble in the killer circuit—if color returns when this is done, you can be sure the trouble is in the killer circuit.

Critical adjustment of the killer circuit might be caused by an open 2 mfd capacitor at the collector of the color killer. Normally, if possible, a killer is adjusted on a black and white picture. Turn up the killer until you see colored "snow" in the picture, then back off the killer adjustment until the snow just disappears. If a black and white picture is not being transmitted, set the color killer by adjusting it, if possible, until the color is removed, then turn the killer back until the color is just at maximum gain and no farther, then check all the active channels in your area to make sure the color is seen on all channels.

With almost all programs in color now, many technicians will leave the color killer so that there is no chance of it killing the color, especially if the set is being used in a weak signal area, or with an antenna system that has a tendency to reduce the color on some channels.

AUTOMATIC CHROMA CONTROL (ACC) AND KILLER DETECTOR

This circuit (Fig. 16-16) is exactly the same as the phase detector described earlier and the burst takeoff is from the same transformer, but with a very significant difference. This phase detector circuit has the 3.58 MHz signal deliberately fed into it out of phase (by 90 degrees approx.). This means that

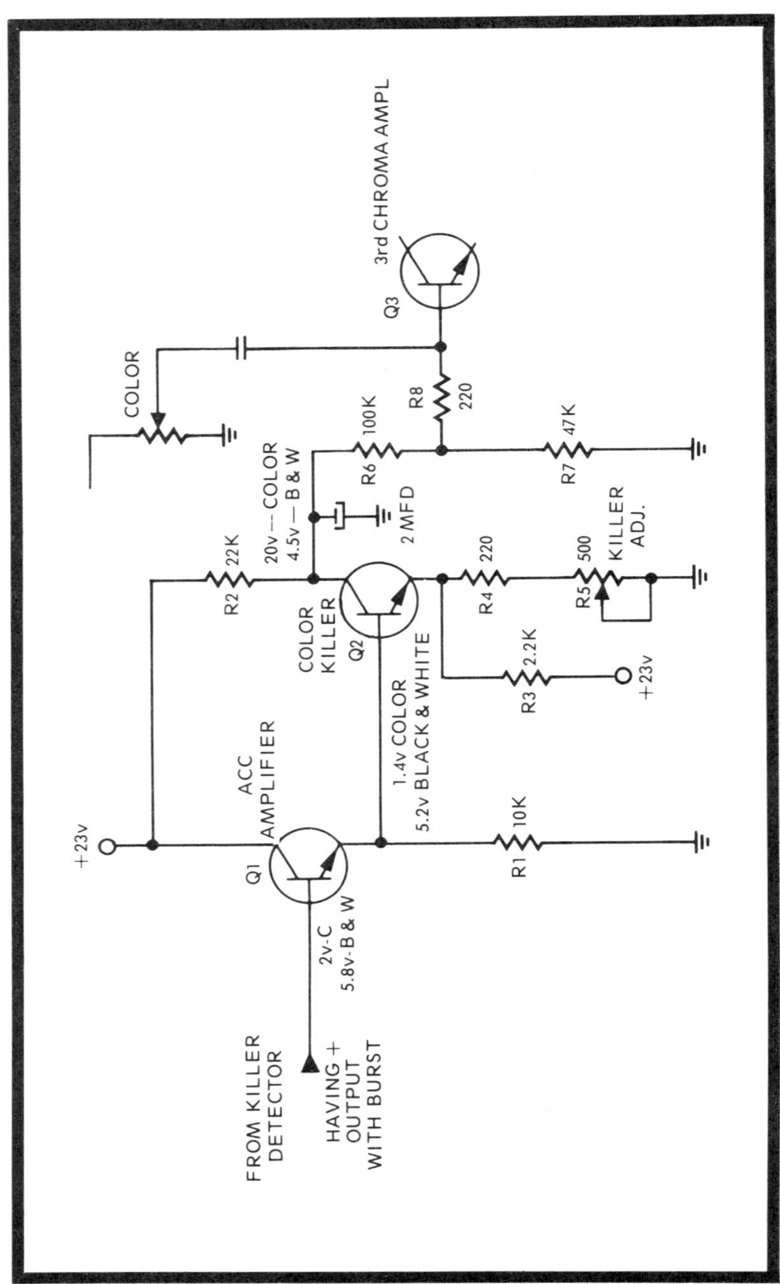

Fig. 16-15. Another color killer circuit.

the detector is always trying to "correct" for the difference in phase, and it is so connected here that this produces a negative output voltage. But why this? With this connection the negative voltage amplitude depends upon the amplitude of burst signal. With no burst signal, for example, the output from the detector is zero voltage, since the input from the 3.58 MHz oscillator alone develops equal and opposite voltages across the diodes, and these voltages cancel at the junction of R1 and R2. With a burst signal present, as when a color signal is being sent, the output becomes negative in exact relation to the amplitude of the burst signal; in other words, if the color burst is strong, the negative output voltage is higher than if the color burst is weak.

This "AGC" action of the detector provides an automatic biasing method for the chroma amplifiers in a color set and so controls the gain, keeping the color content of the picture fairly constant over a wide range of color signals. Note that this voltage is not dependent so much on the total signal strength but upon the **color** strength so that there is compensation for weak color even though the signal strength might be high, and compensation for too much color even though the signal strength might be less strong.

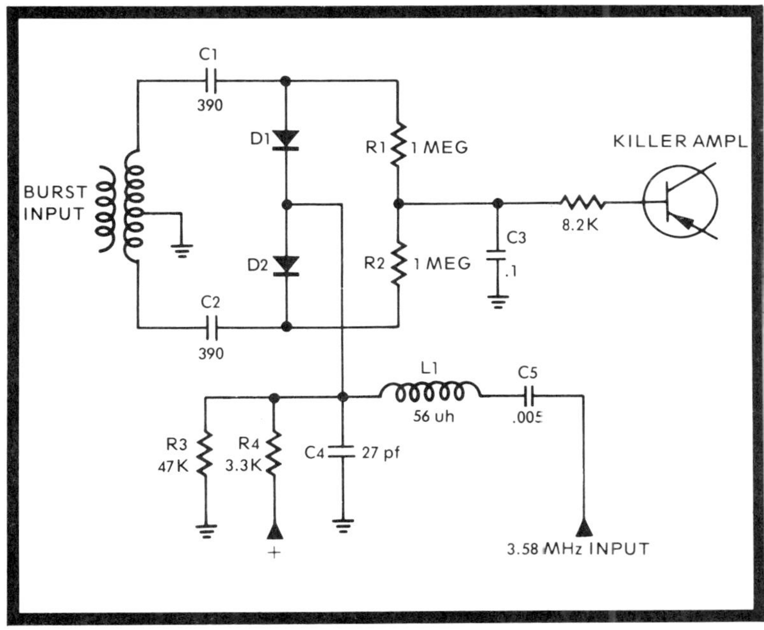

Fig. 16-16. ACC and killer detector circuit.

Another use of this detector is to automatically bias the color amplifiers on when a color signal is received. Without a color signal, there is no burst and so no output from this detector. With no output, the killer amplifier has no negative voltage and since it is a PNP transistor, it will be at cutoff. To make sure that the transistor is cut off, a small positive voltage is added through the bleeder R3 and R4 to the center tap of the diodes; this voltage, in turn, is applied through D2 and R2 to the killer amplifier base.

Troubleshooting the Circuit

The same troubleshooting procedures apply for this circuit as for the AFPC detector discussed before (Figs. 16-8 and 16-9), with the exception perhaps of the phase shifting network, L1 and C4. This network shifts the color oscillator signal approximately 90 degrees and so is necessary to the proper operation of this circuit. If, for example, C4 should open (highly unlikely), the negative output from the detector will be lowered. If L1 should open, there will be no signal to the diodes and so zero output voltage (positive because of the fixed bias) from the detector. Thus, with L1 open there would be no color on the set due to the killer action.

AUDIO AMPLIFIERS

Transistors were first used in large numbers in audio circuits. It would be virtually impossible to cover all the numerous variations of circuits that resulted, but I have tried to cover at least one of every popular, basic type.

Early transistorized audio circuits were mostly transformer-coupled from stage to stage, later there were more RC-coupled circuits, and later still, direct-coupling for two or more transistors became popular. Direct coupling not only may require fewer parts, but probably more important, frequency response is greatly improved at low frequencies.

As in all solid-state circuits, the DC supply voltage "hot" connection may be to either the emitter or the collector. For example, Fig. 17-1 shows two audio amplifiers that are identical, except that the one on the left is designed for a DC supply with the positive voltage "hot," and the other with "hot" negative. Note that the voltages shown are measured to ground; however, note also that if the voltages are read between the other terminals and the emitter they are the same for both circuits, in other words, the base-emitter bias is 0.65 volt in each circuit and the collector-to-emitter voltage is 3.95 volts. The drop across the 100-ohm emitter resistor is the same in each case, 0.15 volt.

The electrolytic coupling capacitor to the base circuit has reversed polarity as shown here because it is assumed that the other end of the capacitor returns to ground. This is not always true, however, and capacitor polarity must be determined by which side is most positive or negative.

AUDIO DRIVER NO. 1

The audio driver shown in Fig. 17-2 uses an NPN silicon transistor. Silicon transistors, because they have less leakage than germanium, do not always have a bleeder bias network as this one does (R1 and R2); instead such a circuit may have only R2, which will then be about 10 times larger (270K for example).

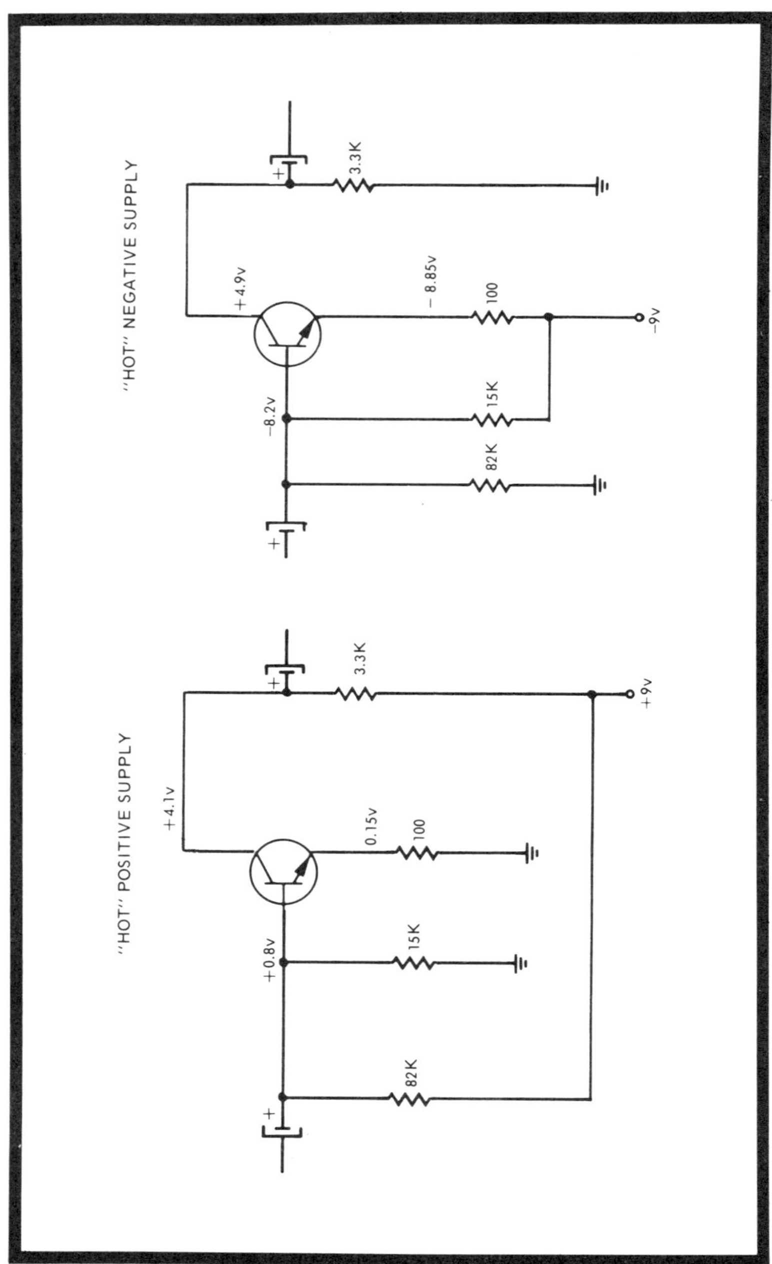

Fig. 17-1. Two identical audio amplifiers with reversed power supplies.

The 33-ohm emitter resistor is not absolutely essential in a silicon transistor circuit but is used here to provide some inverse feedback which results in the stage response being a bit more linear. If it were being used for protective bias, such as it might be with a germanium transistor, it would have a larger value and would be bypassed with an electrolytic capacitor.

The 2.7K resistor across the transformer is another design feature to "flatten" or broaden the circuit, that is, to make it respond more equally well for a wider range of audio frequencies, particularly in the bass regions. Without the 2.7K resistor, overall gain would increase, especially for medium to high audio frequencies.

The driver transformer here has a dual secondary. This is necessary where two NPNs or PNPs are used in a "stacked" push-pull circuit (to be discussed later), so that bias can be applied individually to the base of each transistor.

Troubleshooting the Circuit

If trouble is suspected in the driver stage, there are several ways to find out for sure. One method is to apply an audio tone at the input and use an oscilloscope to compare magnitudes of the input and output signals. (Be sure the input signal is inserted through a capacitor and that it does not overload the amplifier.) There should be from 3 to 20 times as much signal amplitude at the output as at the input and the output signal should be an exact replica of the input except for

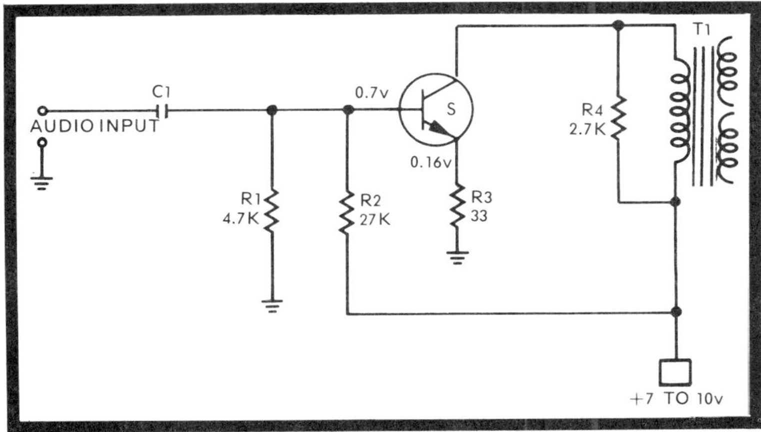

Fig. 17-2. Driver stage for transformer-coupled push-pull audio output stage.

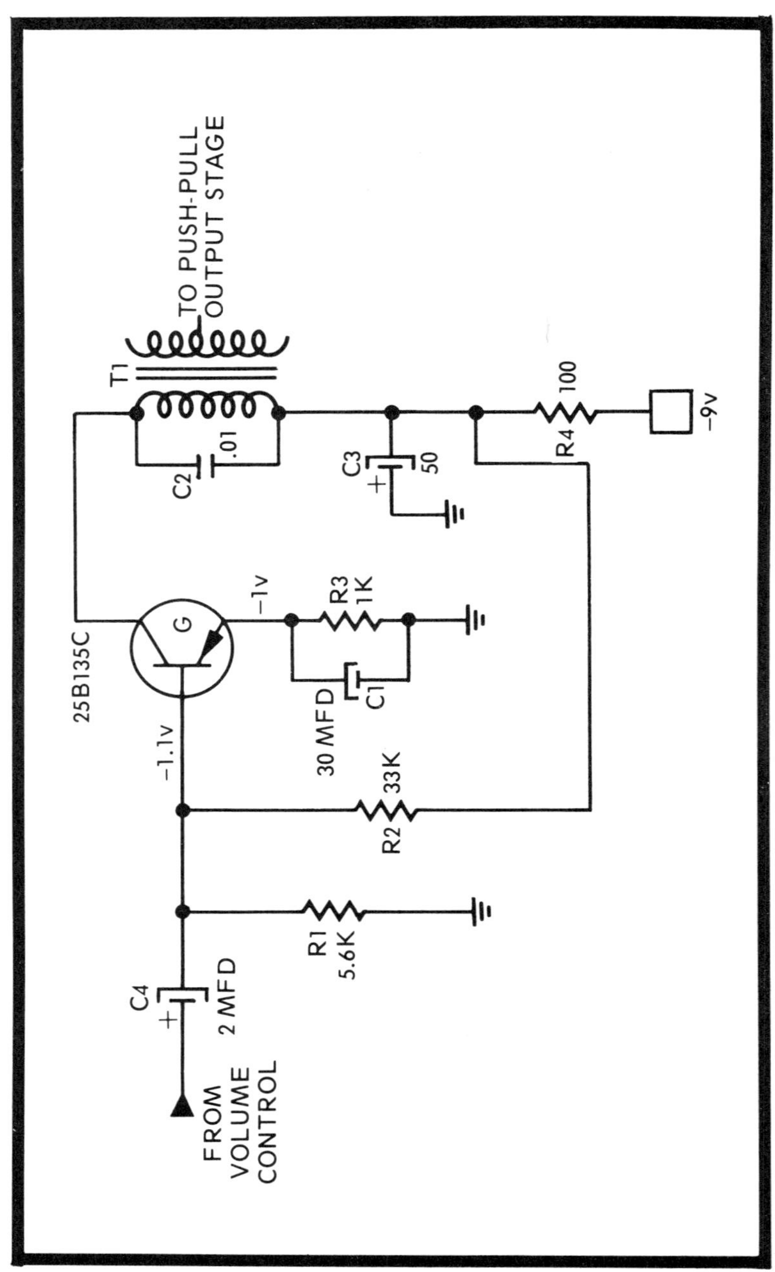

Fig. 17-3. Driver stage for push-pull transformer-coupled audio amplifier.

amplitude. If the output signal is flat-topped or flat-bottomed, reduce the input signal to see whether the amplifier is overloaded. If the output signal is either too small or is distorted, the next step is to measure voltages.

In this circuit the emitter drop is 0.16 volt across 33 ohms, which figures out to about 5 ma of current flow in the driver stage. This may seem a bit high—but generally, better linearity is possible for the output audio if the driver current is higher. Other driver stages, especially in portable radios, may draw no more than 1 to 2 ma.

If emitter voltage is rather high, the transistor is likely shorted. If low, the transistor is open, or the bias voltage is incorrect.

If distortion is the problem and DC voltages seem to be near normal, don't overlook the transformer as a source of trouble. The most practical way to be sure about a transformer is to disconnect all but one lead from each winding, tack in a new transformer, and check the performance.

AUDIO DRIVER NO. 2

Fig. 17-3 shows an audio driver similar to millions in use in older portable radios using germanium transistors. It is quite similar to Fig. 17-2 but uses a PNP germanium transistor, a larger emitter resistor, and an electrolytic emitter bypass. Because high gain is important at audio frequencies in portables, the driver transformer does not have a resistor bypass. Instead, a 0.01 mfd capacitor is used across the transformer primary to reduce gain at higher frequencies without seriously affecting the lower frequencies. (A high frequency bypass tends to improve the stability of the circuit as well as to remove or reduce much of the "hissy' high-frequency noise.)

The output transformer has a center-tapped secondary which will be used to drive a push-pull amplifier, discussed later in this chapter.

Troubleshooting the Circuit

Again, an oscilloscope can be used for signal tracing, but sometimes it may be quicker to make an educated guess or two before going to the trouble to hook up the test equipment. If the problem is low gain, a very prevalent trouble is an open emitter capacitor, C1. Temporarily shunt a known good capacitor across C1 and see if the volume level increases greatly.

Depending upon circuit parameters, an open C3 can cause oscillation; usually, it will cause a loss of gain also. If C3 does

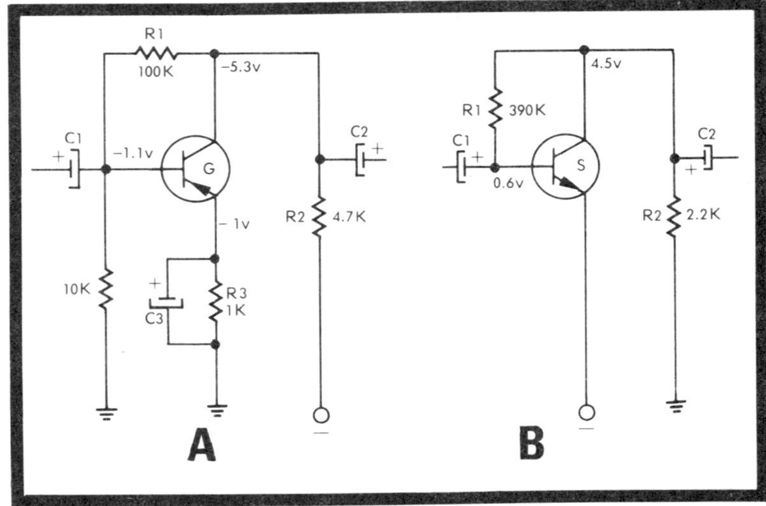

Fig. 17-4. Audio amplifier circuits using resistance-capacitance coupling.

cause oscillation, it will often be a low frequency "motor-boating."

To check the transistor, measure the voltage drop across the emitter resistor; if the voltage drop is near normal (-1v), then it's probable that both the transistor and the bias circuit are okay.

Excessive emitter voltage, with (usually) distortion of the signal, can be caused by a leaky input capacitor, C4. Disconnect one end of C4 and if the emitter voltage drops, C4 is leaky or shorted.

Excessive emitter voltage can also be caused by a leaky transistor, and leaky transistors are more apt to be a problem when the transistor is a germanium type.

If emitter voltage is low or zero, check the transistor terminal and the bias voltage.

For distortion when the DC voltages appear normal or nearly so, transformer T1 could be at fault. But before replacing T1, remove one lead of C2, the 0.01 uf capacitor across the transformer, and listen for improvement in the quality of the signal (not volume increases, it will seem to increase with C2 disconnected).

RESISTANCE-CAPACITANCE COUPLING

The two circuits of Fig. 17-4 are similar except that one is using a germanium transistor (A) and the other a silicon transistor (B). The important difference in these circuits, as compared with others, is the means of biasing. Instead of using a bleeder from the DC supply voltage, the bias resistor is connected to the collector. This serves two purposes:

(1) It tends to regulate the transistor bias, for if the transistor current increases for any reason, the drop across the collector voltage increases. This results in less collector voltage in respect to the emitter and so less available bias for the transistor and therefore a tendency for the transistor current to decrease.

(2) The other circuit response is that some of the output voltage is fed back out-of-phase into the input circuit at the base. This inverse feedback, although it reduces the overall gain of the circuit, nevertheless tends to flatten out the amplifier response so that it seems to have "higher fidelity."

The germanium circuit (A) uses a protective resistor for the emitter, although it hardly seems necessary, considering that the large collector resistor would limit the total transistor current to a safe level if the collector voltage is within reason. The silicon needs no emitter resistor and therefore needs no emitter bypass. Also, it doesn't need a bleeder resistor from the base, since inherent leakage in a silicon transistor is small and does not increase significantly even with reasonable increases in ambient temperature.

Troubleshooting the Circuit

Troubleshooting is essentially the same as already discussed for the driver circuit in Figs. 17-2 and 17-3. The voltage gain of a stage such as shown in Fig. 17-4 can be quite high although the loading by the stage following it often keeps the gain down to less than 10. However, a stage such as this, driving a tube, a field-effect transistor, or an emitter-follower bipolar transistor, can have gains of 150 or more.

A quick check for a loss in this circuit can be made by connecting an electrolytic capacitor from base to collector; if the gain does not change or if gain increases, it is a good indication that the amplifier circuit needs attention.

Remember that low gain in any amplifier circuit is very often caused by one or more open electrolytic capacitors, so a "quick and dirty" check is to shunt each of the capacitors temporarily with a known good capacitor. The actual size of the shunt test capacitor is not too critical, just make sure that the polarity is correct. You don't have to disconnect the original capacitor to shunt test it for an open circuit.

If the transistor or its bias is suspected, check the DC voltages. To find the current flow of the silicon transistor in

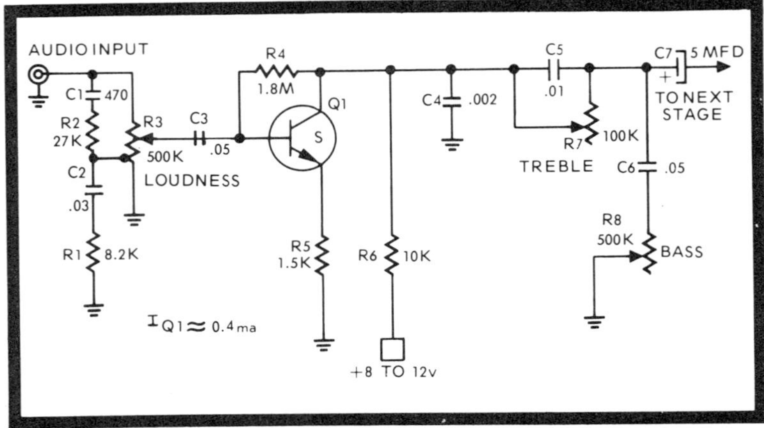

Fig. 17-5. Preamp stage to match high-impedance audio to transistor amplifier and to tone controls.

(B) you should check the voltage drop across the collector resistor.

AUDIO PREAMP STAGE

Fig. 17-5 shows a circuit that employs the basic amplifiers of Figs. 17-4(A) and (B). The 1.5K emitter resistor, R5, increases the input impedance but also reduces the gain. However, the designer was more interested in matching a high-impedance input than in gain (which he can easily obtain by adding an additional transistor later on). The circuit also has high-impedance output, and the tone controls use resistors and capacitors of about the same values as might be used in a tube circuit.

A bit of theory review may be helpful here in understanding the circuit. A "loudness" control differs from a "volume" control in that it is compensated to provide more bass amplification at low volume—this is because the human ear tends to lose its "sense of bass" as the volume is turned down. If properly compensated, a loudness control increases the apparent volume in direct relation to how the ear hears. Human ear characteristics are such that at low volumes an increase in volume appears to follow closely the increase in power output of an amplifier, but at higher volumes it takes 10 times increase in power to make a 2 times increase in apparent volume. This "taper" is built in to a properly designed loudness control. Most volume controls have resistance "taper" but the loudness control is also tone-compensated.

Troubleshooting the Circuit

Refer to preceding two circuits.

AUDIO AMPLIFIER, RC-COUPLED, WITH FILTERED BIAS

The circuit in Fig. 17-6 is much like those in Fig. 17-4 except that an additional resistor (R3) and an additional capacitor (C3) are used. The circuit still gives automatic regulation of the DC bias on the transistor, but it also prevents the audio feedback, which would reduce the gain. This is a circuit-designers choice, since he sometimes would want the inverse feedback to improve the frequency response; but if the designer has ample frequency response he may choose to have more gain, as in this circuit, and he can get added gain by "stripping" the audio from the bias circuit. Since C3 is "set off" by resistance from both the base and the collector, it won't bypass either the input or output signal but it will prevent any audio signal from the output going back to the input, or vice versa. (In the circuits of Fig. 17-4, enough audio will feed from base to collector so that with an open transistor the amplifier may still appear to work, though the user will recognize that the volume control has to be turned up more, and perhaps the sound will be just "not quite right.")

Troubleshooting the Circuit

If the DC voltages appear normal, it is a good indication that the transistor and the bias voltages, as well as the supply

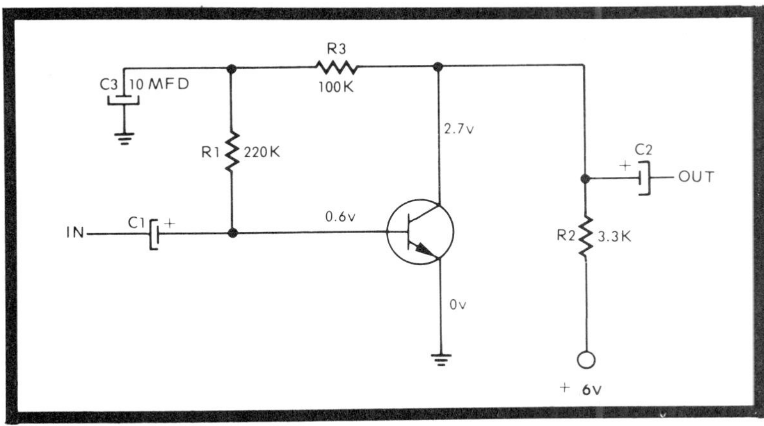

Fig. 17-6. RC-coupled audio amplifier with filtered bias.

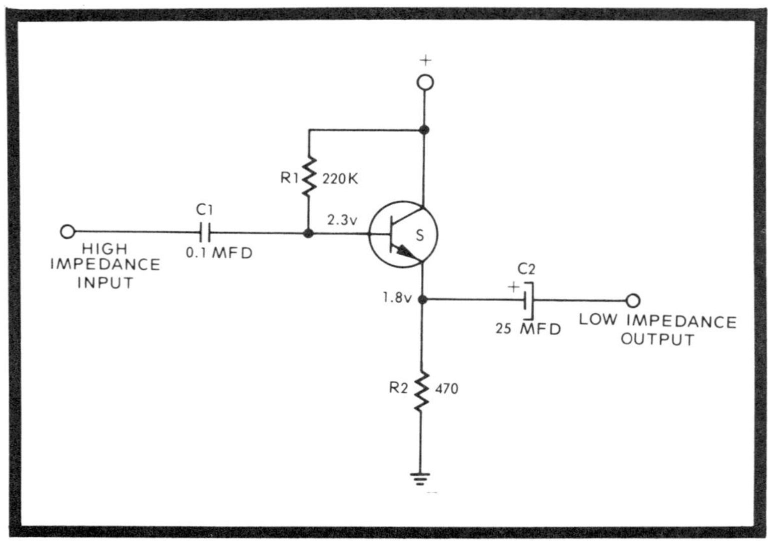

Fig. 17-7. Emitter-follower (common-collector).

voltages, are near normal. If C1 or C2 should open, the volume (gain) will be seriously reduced and will have a "tinny" or "faraway" sound. If C3 should open, the difference in output may not be noticeable unless you have another amplifier with which to compare, such as in a stereo phonograph. With C3 open, there will be some inverse feedback, and the gain will be lower, but just how much lower depends upon the size of R1 and R3 and also on how much original gain the transistor has.

If the transistor should short, the collector voltage will be zero or nearly zero, and the bias voltage will also be zero since the bias is supplied by the collector voltage.

If the transistor opens between collector and base, the collector voltage will be high but the bias voltage only slightly higher than normal, if at all. If the transistor opens between emitter and base, the collector voltage will be high and so will the bias voltage.

If the collector voltage is near zero, and the transistor checks okay, check for excessive bias voltage, which could be caused in some circuits by a leaky or shorted C1.

EMITTER-FOLLOWER AMPLIFIER

The emitter-follower (also called "common-collector") amplifier has no voltage gain, but it is an important circuit because it has power gain (Fig. 17-7). It is essentially a "transformer" amplifier that takes a high-voltage, low-current signal and transforms it into a high-current signal. It can be and is used as an earphone amplifier, and as a driver for a higher-powered speaker amplifier (described in next section). Because the input impedance is high, it hardly loads the previous circuit. Therefore, a voltage amplifier preceding this amplifier will pump out as much as 100 to 200 times gain.

Although there is no voltage gain, the voltage appearing across the emitter resistor will be about 95 percent of that on the base, but the emitter current change is high, let's say 2 ma, while the base current is very small, say 0.05 ma. Since DC power is E x I, a 1-volt signal on the base would mean input power of 0.05 mw while the output power is (2 x 1) equals 2 milliwatts.

Reduction of the value of R1 would result in additional output power with only slight additional loading on the input circuit. Because of R2, the emitter resistor, the transistor current will not become excessive (except with very low values of R1 and rather high collector voltage).

Troubleshooting the Circuit

There is little to go wrong as far as the bias or the transistor are concerned that won't show up immediately with an emitter voltage check. If the emitter voltage approaches the collector voltage, either the transistor is shorted or the bias resistor R1 is much too small. If the emitter voltage is low or zero, the transistor may be open, or the bias resistor open.

Weak output, with DC voltages normal, can be caused by either C1 or C2 being open. C2 is the first to suspect since it is an electrolytic.

You can use a scope to check for an open capacitor, but it may be easier simply to shunt the suspected capacitor with a known good capacitor. The actual size is not too important. For example, a 0.5-mfd paper capacitor can be used for a test and you won't have to worry about polarity; it won't work quite as well as the 25 mfd but it will work so much better that you will know immediately that C2 is open.

AUDIO DRIVER STAGE AND CLASS A POWER AMPLIFIER

Fig. 17-8 shows an early circuit that is infrequently used today in portable radios. A class A output stage draws high current continuously, as compared to a class B stage which

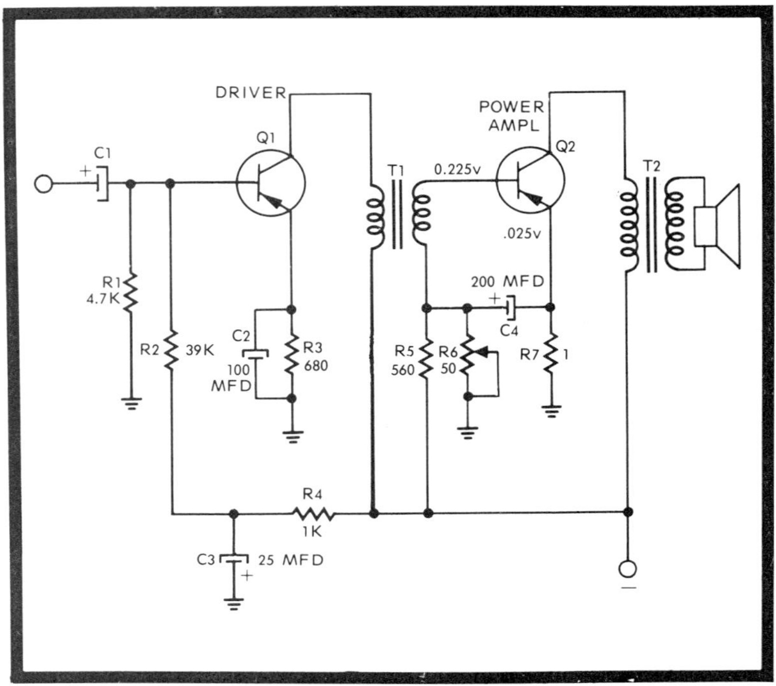

Fig. 17-8. Audio driver stage and class A power amplifier.

draws current in direct proportion to signal output. That is, a portable radio with class B draws little current when the volume is turned low, and draws heavy current only on strong peaks of signal even with the volume turned up high. This saves batteries. (In a 60 Hz powered circuit, class B reduces the amount of power supply filtering needed, because at high volume the hum is masked by the sound output and at low volume, the current from the power supply is small and so it takes small filters to filter out the hum.)

The driver circuit in Fig. 17-8 is very similar to those in Figs. 17-2 and 17-3. Matching transformer T1 has a higher-impedance primary to match the output of Q1 and a lower-impedance secondary to match the input of Q2.

The bias for Q2 is adjusted for a steady current of about 25 ma (for portable radios) by R6. Q2 is protected by the 1-ohm resistor in the emitter. C4 insures that the audio is coupled directly across between the base and emitter of Q2. T2 matches the output of Q2 to the low impedance of the speaker voice coil.

Troubleshooting the Circuit

The driver stage is serviced as described for Figs. 17-2 and 17-3. The output stage is carefully adjusted by R6 to have good fidelity at usable volume levels with the lowest possible steady current flow (again this is applicable to portable radios generally). A low current flow means less battery power used and also means that the output transistor will run cooler.

The output current can be determined by measuring the emitter resistor voltage.

If the 1-ohm resistor is burned open, the likely cause is a shorted output transistor. Always check the transistor before replacing the resistor.

If C4 should open, the output gain will be lowered considerably.

Distortion can be caused by shorted turns in either T1 or T2. Unless you have another exact circuit with which to compare, checking of these transformers is best done by tacking in a new transformer after removing from the circuit at least one lead of each winding. Shorted turns in a transformer produce a "mismatched" or "tinny" output sound which is hard to describe but which is usually fairly easy to recognize when you've heard it a few times.

PUSH-PULL AUDIO OUTPUT AMPLIFIERS

The circuits in Figs. 17-9 and 17-10 are representative of the two-transformer push-pull output circuits that formerly were extremely popular, but which are now being superseded by a number of other types.

The signal from the driver is applied 180 degrees out of phase to the individual bases of the output transistors. In the push-pull, each transistor works only half the time, and only a small amount of current is drawn from the battery when there is no audio signal input, because both transistors are at near zero bias except when a base is driven by an audio signal of the correct polarity.

The transistors must have a small amount of bias to prevent what is called "crossover" distortion. "Crossover" distortion occurs when the bias is insufficient, therefore the idling current is too low. At low volume, crossover distortion is very noticeable. With insufficient bias, high peak input signals will "blast" while nominal inputs will be hard to hear at all.

For germanium transistors it is a good idea to have some method of compensating for transistor current because of heat. As you recall, germanium transistor leakage between

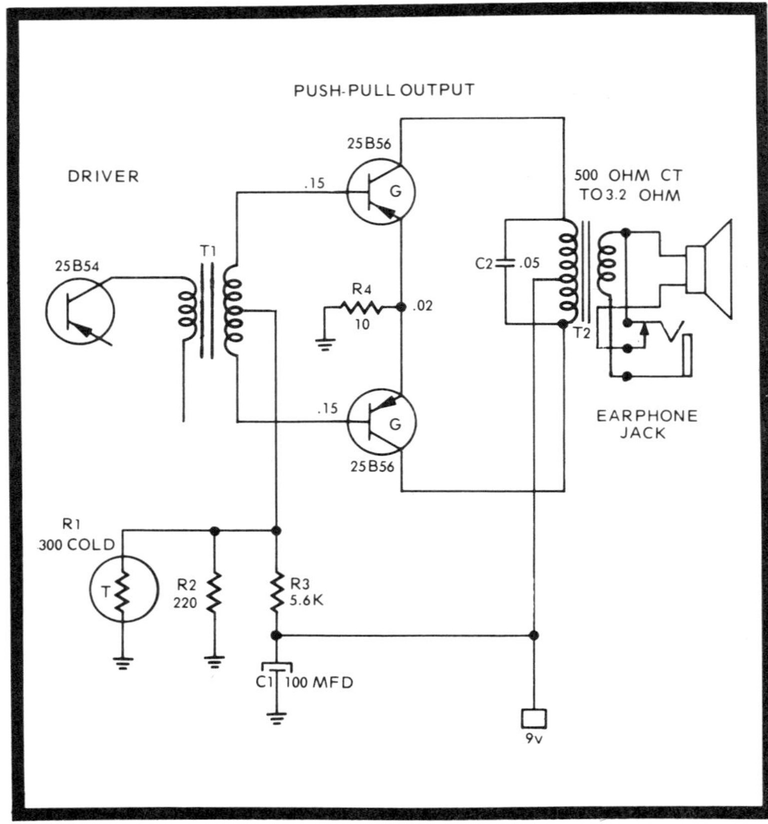

Fig. 17-9. Transformer-coupled push-pull output stage.

collector and base increases (resistance lowers) as the transistor heats up. As the resistance decreases, transistor current increases, causing more heat and still more leakage. Without protective circuits the transistors would "runaway" and destroy themselves.

Protection is provided in two ways in these circuits: A small current-limiting resistor is connected in series with the emitters, and a Thermistor, a resistor whose resistance decreases with heat, is used in the base bias circuit as a current shunt. The emitter resistor cannot provide complete protection as in other circuits because it must be small. A high resistance would mean excessive power loss in the output stages. (Batteries wouldn't last long enough.)

Fig. 17-9 shows a .05-mfd bypass capacitor (C2) across the primary of output transformer T2. C2 reduces the high "hissy" components of the audio signal which without this bypass would be amplified disproportionately to the low frequencies. Such disproportion is caused by the fact that miniature audio output transformers have very little iron.

The circuit in Fig. 17-10 is compensated to reduce high "hisses" by a small capacitor from collector to base of each of the output transistors (C2, C3). Returning the capacitor from collector to base makes it possible to use smaller value capacitors.

Overall negative feedback in Fig. 17-10 is from the voice coil through R3 to the base of the driver transistor. Negative (inverse) feedback tends not only to reduce the overall gain of the circuits but simultaneously provides a "flatter" overall frequency response.

Troubleshooting the Circuit

These circuits can have "trouble" and still seem to work normally. This can happen if the bias increases, where there's little apparent effect on the audio output signal but considerably more current drain from batteries in a portable radio. That's when your customer complains "the batteries in my portable radio run down too quickly."

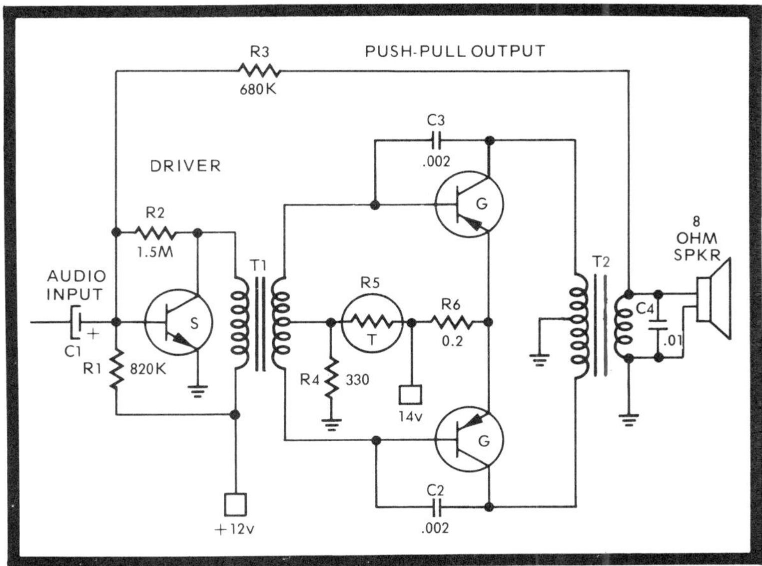

Fig. 17-10. Transformer-coupled push-pull output stage with negative feedback.

In a portable radio with a class B output stage similar to these, the idling current (no audio signal input) should be no more than 4 to 6 ma, and should always be as low as possible without causing distortion at low volume levels. Insufficient bias, which causes the idling current to be too low, produces "crossover" distortion which may not be noticeable at high volume but quite noticeable and annoying when volume is low.

Severe distortion at all volume levels is often caused by one of the push-pull output transistors being open. With one transistor open, only half the audio signal is heard, so distortion is severe. When replacing a transistor in the output stage you should closely match the original or replace both output transistors with a matched pair.

Other causes of severe distortion may be either an open secondary in T1 allowing only one transistor to be driven, or one side of the primary of T2 open. Distortion will also be high if output transistor current is low, and this can be caused by an emitter resistor which has increased considerably in ohmic value, or of course, by a low DC supply voltage.

Whistles in the output could be caused by an open electrolytic, or an open bypass capacitor. In a circuit such as in Fig. 17-10 if the output transformer is replaced, feedback resistor R3 might be connected to the incorrect side of the voice coil winding—if this is the problem, reverse the voice coil winding and put the opposite lead to ground.

STACKED PUSH-PULL AUDIO OUTPUT STAGE

It was inevitable that the transistor, by nature a low-impedance device, would be used for directly driving a low-impedance speaker. One of the first of these circuits is shown in Fig. 17-11. Two matched transistors are stacked, that is, they are in series across the power supply. The transistors are individually biased and this requires that the driver transformer have two secondaries. The transistors are fed out-of-phase audio just as in Figs. 17-9 and 17-10.

Since in a class B push-pull circuit only one transistor works at a time essentially, the fact that these two transistors are in series would seem to mean little if one is shut off when the other is turned on. However, because the speaker input is via a capacitor, the transistor that turns on either charges or discharges C2, and the charge-discharge pulsations of C2 move the speaker cone in and out. Let's see how the circuit works. When the audio signal goes negative on the base of Q1 this turns Q1 on and capacitor C2 charges through the speaker, whose cone moves in (or out, depending on how it is phased).

On the next audio half cycle, the base of Q2 goes negative, turning on Q2 (and the positive voltage on Q1 turns it off). Now capacitor C2 which was charged through Q1 is the collector supply voltage for Q2. With Q2 conducting, capacitor C2 discharges again through the speaker and the cone moves in the opposite direction. This push-pull action continues with each audio half cycle, charging and discharging C2 and moving the speaker cone in proportion to the amount of charge, which in turn depends on the amount of alternating conduction of Q1 and Q2.

This type of circuit, sometimes called an output transformerless amplifier, has excellent frequency response and has been used not only in many portable radios, but also in high-power, high-fidelity amplifiers.

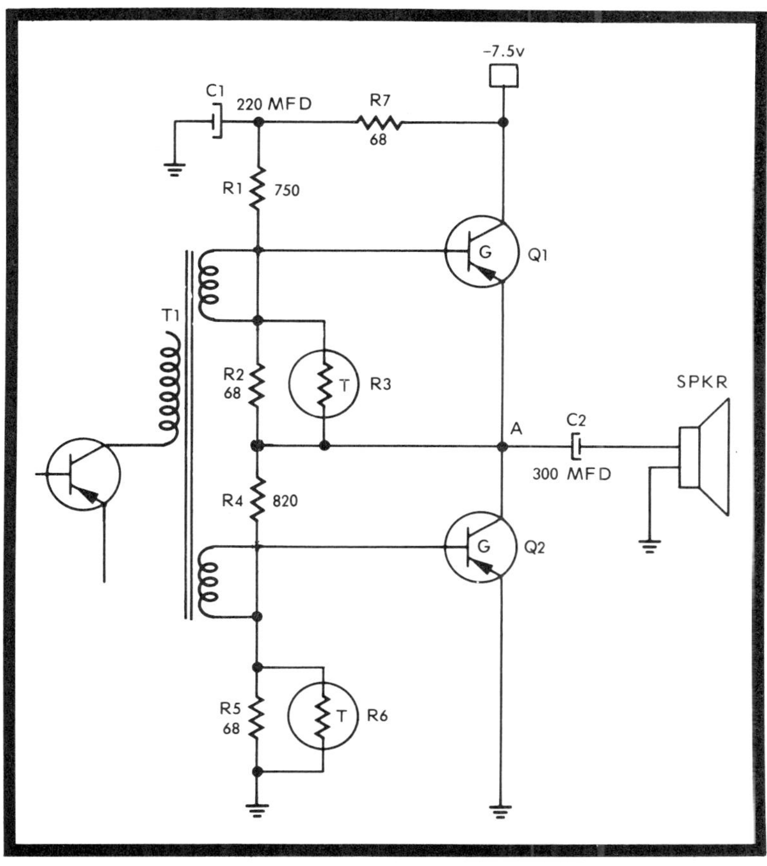

Fig. 17-11. Stacked push-pull audio output stage.

Not all circuits use the temperature compensation in the bias stages. Some sets use diodes or diode-connected transistors as temperature compensators rather than Thermistors.

This circuit, like other class B push-pull audio output stages, requires enough bias to provide an idling current when there is no audio input signal, otherwise there will be severe "crossover" distortion especially at low volume levels. (See discussion of "crossover" distortion, Push-Pull Audio Output Amplifiers, Figs. 17-9 and 17-10.)

Troubleshooting the Circuit

The same troubles may occur in this circuit as in any other push-pull circuit.

A shorted transistor will generally drop the audio volume to zero or nearly zero. If any sound is heard at all it will be only with the volume level high, and the sound will be severely distorted.

To check for a shorted transistor, measure the DC voltage at the collector-emitter junction (point A) of the two transistors. If the voltage at this point is the same as the supply voltage, obviously Q1 is shorted. If the voltage at this point is zero or nearly so, then Q2 is shorted. (The same symptoms as for a shorted transistor can also be caused by excessive bias on the corresponding transistor.)

If one of the transistors opens, the distortion will be severe, as it will be if the bias voltage on one of the transistors is incorrect.

Distortion in the output, which is most pronounced at low volume, can be caused by a poor speaker, but also by insufficient bias on either of the transistors. The idling current of this circuit for a portable radio may be as low as about 3 or 4 ma, and for a high-power circuit may be as high as 50 to 100 ma.

Extremely weak output may be caused if C2 opens, and the output may not appear so much distorted as "tinny."

If one of the transistors shorts or opens, it is best to replace both output transistors with a matched pair; however, it is possible with care to replace only the defective transistor and still have good performance. A good check, when replacing only one transistor, is to see whether the low-volume (crossover) distortion is minimal or zero. If not, replace both transistors or increase the bias slightly.

FIELD-EFFECT TRANSISTOR AMPLIFIER

Because the FET circuit is generally more noisy or "hissy" at audio frequencies, it hasn't been too popular. But the advantages of both high input and high output impedances make the FET so attractive we can expect to see it used more in audio in the future.

The junction field-effect transistor (JFET) circuit is basically simple (Fig. 17-12). The audio is applied to the gate. The source terminal is self-biased by a resistor, bypassed by an electrolytic to prevent loss of gain. The load resistor at the drain may not be quite as large as that normally used with tube circuits simply because the DC supply voltage is normally lower.

A practical JFET amplifier, as in one high fidelity amplifier (Fig. 17-13), uses a dual power supply, the negative side going to the source and the positive side to the drain. The gate is returned to ground through a potentiometer.

Troubleshooting the Circuit

As for other circuits, taking DC voltage readings is important, even vital, in diagnosing the troubles. A lack of source bias, for example, probably means that the JFET is open. Low gain might be caused by an open electrolytic in the source circuit.

Using an ohmmeter, you can rough-check a JFET without removing it from its circuit. Turn off the circuit power and

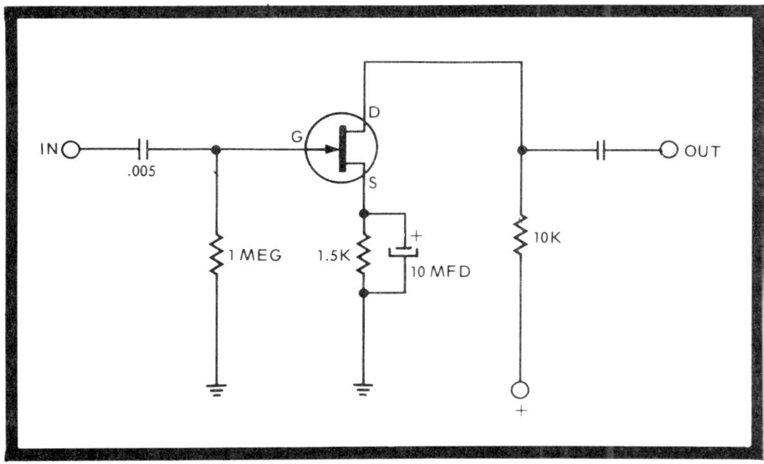

Fig. 17-12. JFET audio amplifier.

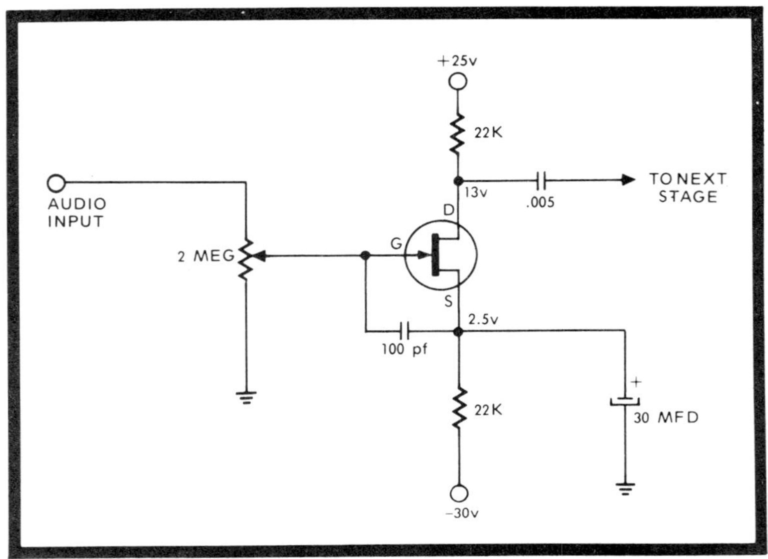

Fig. 17-13. JFET audio amplifier using dual power supply.

measure between the drain and source terminals. This should be a fairly low resistance but in any case should be the same with the ohmmeter leads reversed. Measuring between the gate and either the drain or source terminals should give "diode" action just as you would expect to read between the base and either the collector or emitter of a bipolar transistor, that is, the ohmmeter reading should be low in one direction of the ohmmeter test leads and high in the other direction. This occurs because the battery voltage of the ohmmeter either forward-biases or reverse-biases the junction, depending on which way the ohmmeter leads are connected across the junction. (There are special ohmmeters which have low enough test voltage so that they will not forward-bias a transistor. These are useful when checking components in the circuit because they prevent the "diode" action of the transistor from affecting the readings regardless of which way the leads are connected.)

DIRECT-COUPLED CIRCUITS

More and more as the solid-state art expands, direct coupling between two or more stages is found in almost every multiple-stage amplifier. Direct coupling of circuits did not really become popular until the development of silicon transistors. With silicon transistors, which have good thermal stability, direct-coupled circuits can be designed to have long term performance stability and without elaborate schemes for temperature compensation. Also, circuits that are direct-coupled nearly always have an overall degenerative feedback loop, so far as DC bias is concerned, so that any change in current in one stage is immediately compensated by a change of bias to that stage.

Fig. 17-14 shows an example of a self-compensating direct-coupled amplifier. Suppose for some reason the current through Q1 increases. This means more current flowing through R2 which in turn means more voltage drop across R2, making a less positive voltage (more negative) to the base of Q2. A less positive voltage on the base of Q2 results in less current through R4, which means there is a less positive emitter voltage on Q2. The bias for Q1 is taken through R1 from the emitter of Q2, so with the Q2 emitter going less positive, the base bias on Q1 also goes less positive; this reduces the amount of current in Q1, thereby compensating for the original increase in current through R2.

In this circuit, there is no audio degeneration since C2 bypasses the audio around the emitter resistor; thus, only the DC bias voltages are affected.

Troubleshooting the Circuit

The big problem with troubleshooting direct-coupled circuits is the cumulative effects just described. Attempts to isolate specific parts result in incorrect measurements of currents and voltages in all arms of the direct-coupled circuit even though the actual trouble is only in one small section of the circuit.

Checking direct-coupled circuits, then, is much, much easier if you understand what to expect from the circuit. For example, in Fig. 17-4, you should be able to predict what would happen to the voltages on Q2 if Q1 opened up. Let's take a look. With Q1 open there would be **reduced** current through R2, not zero current since the base of Q2 will draw more and more current as the Q2 base voltage tries to increase. This increase in base voltage on Q2 causes Q2 to have a considerable increase in current and may even result in the collector of Q2 dropping to zero or nearly so. At the same time the emitter voltage of Q2 will rise, trying to follow the base voltage. This means that the base bias voltage for Q1 will go, or try to go, more positive. If Q1 is open between collector and base, the bias voltage on Q1 will not get much above perhaps 0.7 volt,

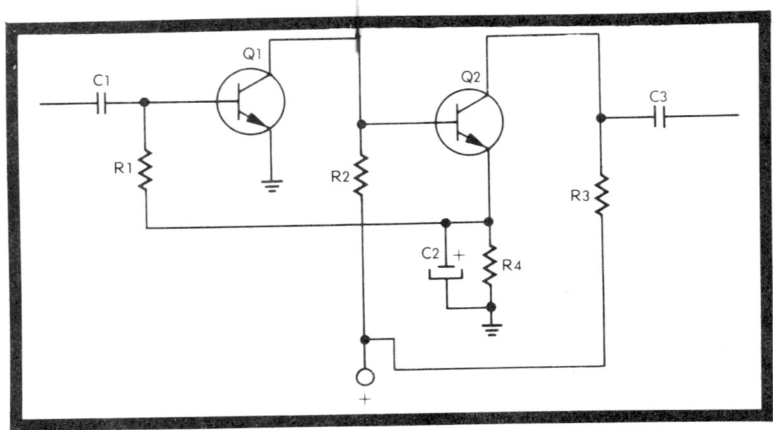

Fig. 17-14. Simple self-compensating direct-coupled circuit.

but if the open is between the emitter and base, the base bias will rise to equal the Q2 emitter voltage.

The secret, then, of checking direct-coupled circuits is to measure the voltages from the **base to emitter** and from **collector to emitter** of EACH circuit and record them. Now look at the schematic and determine what is wrong. In the above case you know that Q2 is likely not bad since the emitter is still following the increase in base voltage. This turns you back to Q1, which evidently must be defective. In this circuit you can quickly find out. Short between collector and emitter of Q1 and see if the emitter voltage of Q2 drops to zero.

TAPE HEAD PREAMPLIFIER

This circuit (Fig. 17-15) is a refinement of the basic circuit of Fig. 17-14. A 100-ohm resistor, R4, is placed in series with the Q2 emitter and is unbypassed. This is to provide the designer with a bit of inverse feedback to obtain the desired performance from the circuit. Another refinement is an unbypassed emitter resistor R2 for Q1. This resistor is an impedance so that a signal can be fed back from the Q2 collector to Q1. The feedback signal here is out of phase and it is used to provide some "low" peaking, that is, to provide an apparent increased bass output by reducing treble amplification more than the bass.

Resistor R9 in series with output capacitor C5 provides some isolation between the preamp and the next stage amplifier, which minimizes the effect on the preamp of changes in the next amplifier's input impedance.

Note the size of R3. This seems rather large for a transistor circuit operating at relatively low voltage, but this is one reason that transistors lend themselves so well to direct-coupled circuits. Such circuits will operate with good linearity at low collector voltages, and if the input voltage is low, as it is from a tape head, there is no danger of overloading the circuit and causing distortion, which at first glance might seem likely.

Troubleshooting the Circuit

The secret of fast troubleshooting on any direct-coupled circuit is in "knowing the circuit." If you can, AND YOU CAN, predict what will happen to the biases in the circuit if some part goes bad, you are a long way toward knowing what needs replacement when you make voltage measurements. For example, suppose the base bias for Q1 is zero, and the collector voltage is 12 volts. Can you tell from this much information what the trouble is? Let's see. With zero voltage on Q1, it is cut off. It seems logical that the collector voltage on Q1 should rise to 12 volts since there is no collector current. But wait, what about the base current for Q2? Wouldn't it drop the voltage through R3? Yes. This means then that Q2 base-to-emitter circuit must be open. It could be the transistor, but if not that, it could be R4 is open.

This is just one example of how you can find troubles in a direct-coupled circuit by DC voltage deductions. The deductions won't all be that easy, of course. Suppose that the base bias of Q1 reads nearly zero yet the voltage on the opposite side of R1 reads high, what could be the trouble? Well first we can deduce that without bias the collector voltage of Q1 will go positive and so the base bias of Q2 will go more positive, increasing the current through R5; and this increases the supply voltage for Q1. The trouble? Well R1 could be open or increased to a very high value. But what else? Capacitor C1 could be shorted. This would drop the base voltage nearly to zero because of the low resistance of the tape head, L1.

Direct-coupled circuits, more than any other kind, probably can be diagnosed best with a correct interpretation of the DC voltage readings. DON'T ATTEMPT TO READ VOLTAGES TO GROUND. Read bias from the base to emitter of each transistor. Read collector voltage of each transistor from collector to emitter. Determine current through any transistor by measuring the emitter voltage and dividing the emitter resistance into the voltage to determine the current.

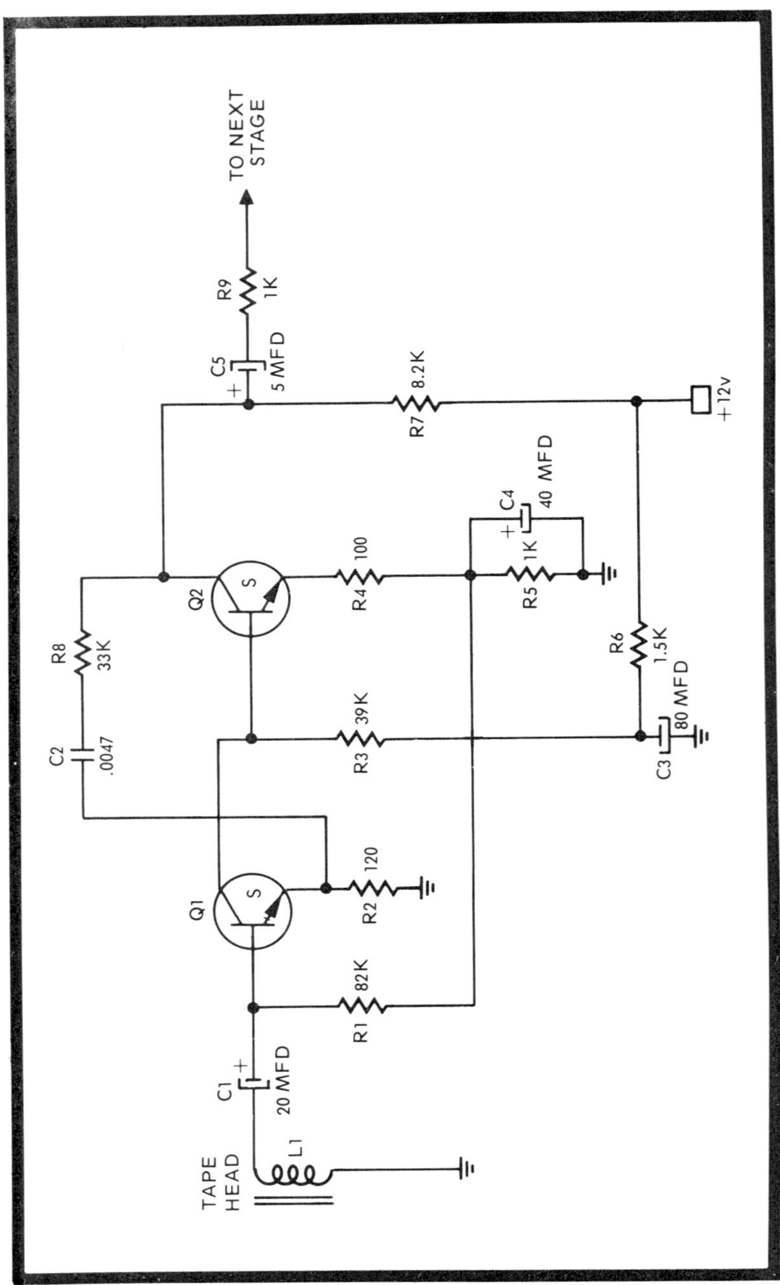

Fig. 17-15. Tape head preamplifier.

Remember that for each 1K of resistance there will be 1 ma of current flow for each volt measured. For example, for a 2K resistor with a 1 volt drop across it, the current through it is 0.5 ma. For a 500 ohm resistor, with a 1 volt drop across it, the current through it is 2 ma.

SINGLE-ENDED DIRECT-COUPLED OUTPUT STAGE

A circuit used quite frequently in small radios operating from line power supplies is shown in Fig. 17-16. Transistor Q2 is designed for use with high collector voltage.

The operation of the circuit is similar to the previous circuit in Fig. 17-15. Self compensation is provided by using the emitter of the second stage as the bias source for the first stage. In this circuit the emitter resistor of Q2 is not bypassed for audio, which means some audio is fed back along with the DC bias. Because this is a degenerative circuit, the audio fed back tends to flatten out the frequency response by producing more feedback for the portion of the frequency spectrum that is amplified most by the circuit. Additional inverse feedback is provided by R3, the unbypassed emitter resistor of Q1.

The "varistor" or voltage-dependent-resistor is sometimes used in this circuit to protect the output transistor. This resistor is virtually an open circuit until some specified voltage is reached, then its resistance drops rapidly—thus peak voltages which might break down the collector-to-base junction of the transistor are harmlessly shunted aside through the varistor.

Output transformer T1 matches the medium impedance of transistor Q2 to the low impedance of the speaker voice coil. C2 bypasses the high "hissy" frequencies, thereby improving the apparent tone quality of the circuit.

Troubleshooting the Circuit

A common trouble with this circuit is a shorted output transistor. If the transistor is shorted and a varistor is used, the varistor should also be replaced as a safety precaution. A shorted transistor will also burn up emitter resistor R5. If an output transistor is shorted and no varistor is used, a 15K 1 watt resistor across the primary of the output transformer may prevent a recurrence of the trouble, yet the 15K resistor is large enough that it will have little effect on the output signal volume for the circuit.

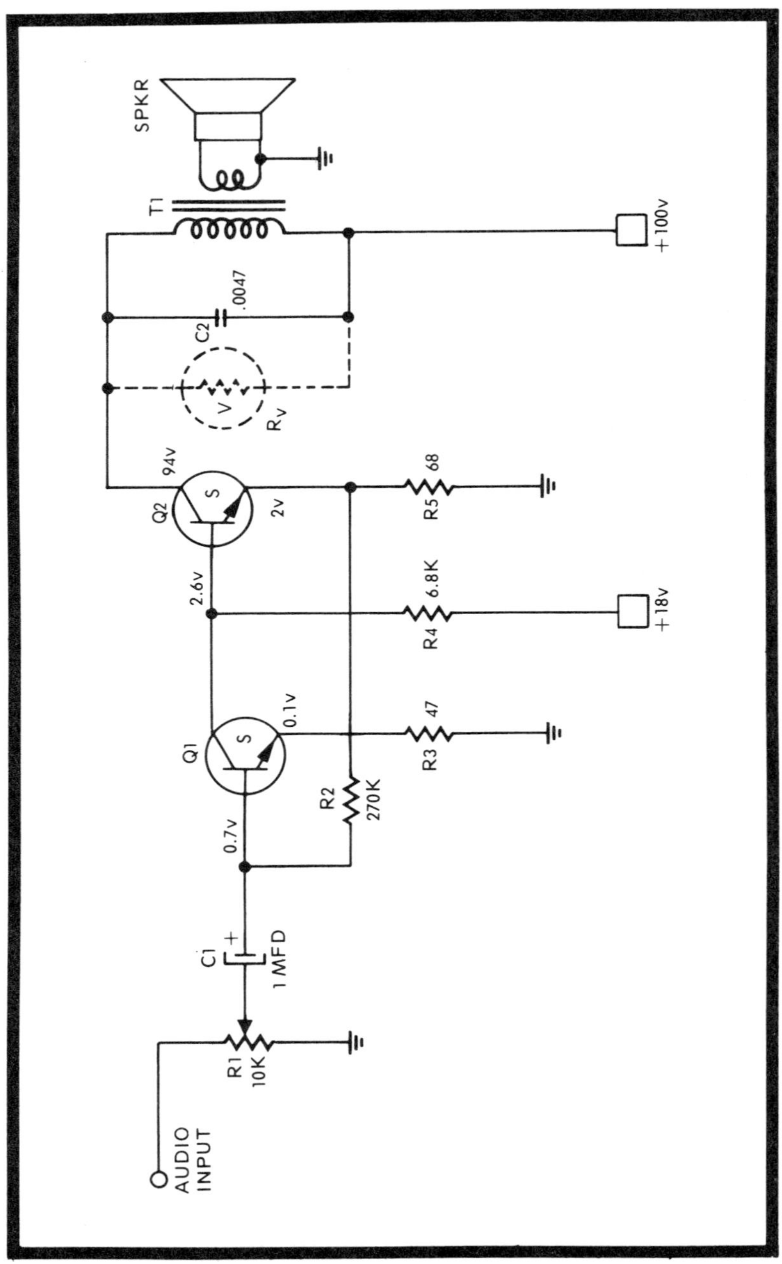

Fig. 17-16. Single-ended direct-coupled output stage using high-voltage output transistor.

If Q1 opens, Q2 will draw more current and its emitter voltage will be higher than normal. An open Q1 will of course mean no voltage drop across R3, its emitter resistor.

If this circuit has distortion at low volume it may be because of a leaky input capacitor, C1.

As with other direct-coupled circuits, carefully check the DC voltages for signs of trouble. Measure bias between the base and emitter of the transistors.

Be sure to replace the output transistor with the same high voltage type. Usually, Q1 can be replaced by any small-signal silicon NPN transistor. After replacing Q1, however, make sure that the emitter voltage of Q2 is within around 20 percent of normal. If the emitter voltage is lower than normal yet the power output of the radio or TV sounds okay, then the replacement is probably okay. If the emitter voltage is significantly higher, the output transistor may overheat, since it operates in class A, meaning the current is steady regardless of signal input.

EMITTER-DRIVEN DIRECT-COUPLED OUTPUT

Although the circuit in Fig. 17-17 uses two NPN transistors, the output transistor here is driven by the emitter of Q1, instead of by the collector as in Fig. 17-16.

This circuit has no self compensation but it has a "hard" bias circuit for each transistor, that is, a low resistance in the base circuit. The low resistance in the base tends to prevent any change in base voltage due to internal leakage. The 1K resistor, R3 in the collector of Q1, is essentially a current-limiting resistor to keep the current in Q1 at the design level.

The 1 meg resistor, R5, at junction of Q1 emitter and Q2 base, is there more for audio inverse feedback than for bias. The bias for the output stage is essentially provided by the emitter current of Q1. R7 is a protective resistor for Q2 and also provides some inverse feedback to flatten out the frequency response.

The 15K resistor, R6, at Q2 collector, is to help minimize peak pulse voltage that might damage the output transistor. C2 is the "tone control" capacitor which bypasses the high frequency hiss and thereby helps stabilize the circuit and hold down any tendency toward fringe oscillation.

Although Q1 has no gain as used in this circuit, it does have a high input impedance and provides a power gain to the output transistor so that this circuit or the one in Fig. 17-16 have roughly the same effective total power gain.

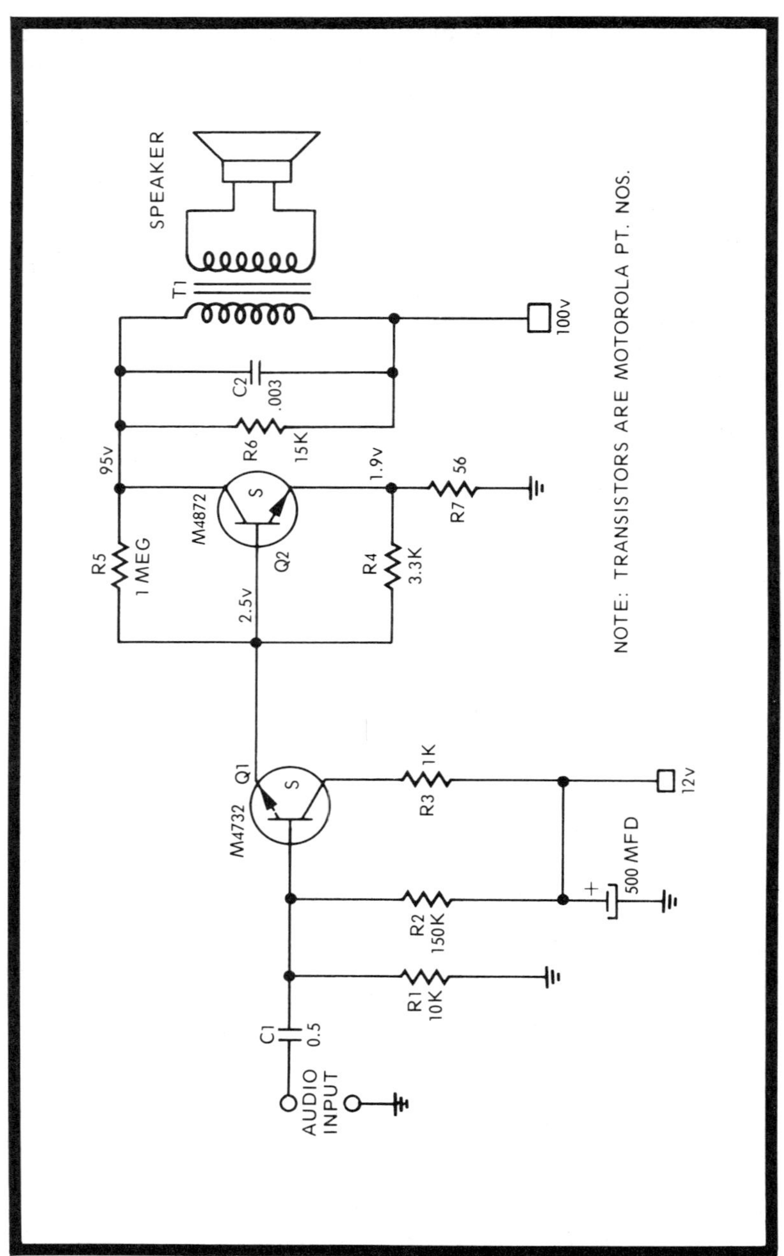

Fig. 17-17. Audio driver, and emitter-driver output using high collector voltage.

Troubleshooting the Circuit

This circuit, as other direct-coupled circuits, usually can best be checked by interpretation of DC voltages.

If Q1 opens there will be no bias on Q2 and so no current will flow in the output transistor.

If output transistor Q2 shorts, emitter resistor R7 will likely burn out also.

DIRECT-COUPLED THREE-STAGE AUDIO AMPLIFIER FOR AUTO RADIO

This circuit (Fig. 17-18) has three direct-coupled transistors; two silicon transistors, and a germanium power transistor output stage. As far as the first two transistors, Q1 and Q2, this is essentially the same circuit as the four preceding circuits. The first stage drives the second. In the collector of Q2 there is a 220 ohm resistor and a 47 ohm resistor, R6. The PNP germanium output transistor, Q3, is also connected across R6. Since the current flow is more negative on the top of the 47 ohm resistor (at the base), correct bias is provided for the PNP transistor, which requires a negative base bias.

A self-compensating portion of this circuit is from the collector of the output transistor Q3 back to the base of Q1. Two separate feedback circuits are used. R7 and R8 with C3 provide the DC bias compensation but have no effect on the audio. A separate audio compensating circuit is used (C4 and R9).

To follow the action of the self-compensating network, suppose the Q1 bias goes positive; this means that the base bias of Q2 goes negative, which in turn reduces the bias for Q3. With less bias on Q3 there will be a less positive voltage on the collector of Q3 which when fed back to the base of Q1 will compensate for the original higher positive bias.

The output transformer is a "tapped choke" or auto-transformer type. The output impedance of Q3 is only around 20 ohms, and sometimes the speaker can be connected directly between collector and ground with perhaps a choke shunting the speaker, as in the inset figure. The speaker choke has a low DC resistance but a high inductive reactance to audio, thus all or nearly all the audio is transferred to the speaker, but the low DC resistance path of the choke shunts much of the DC current. The lowered current flow in the voice coil eliminates or at least greatly minimizes the DC magnetization of the voice coil which would either hold the speaker cone outward or

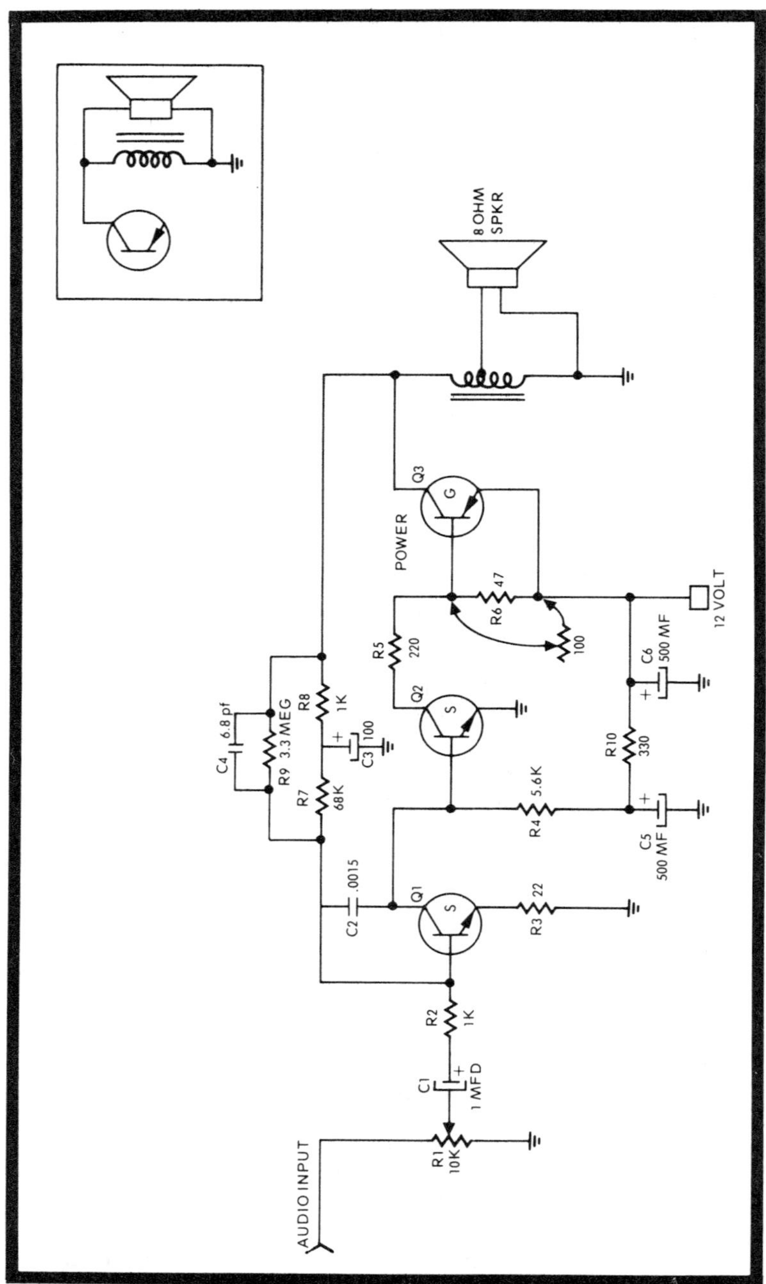

Fig. 17-18. Direct-coupled 3-stage audio amplifier, auto radio.

inward and thus permit less travel when reproducing audio. The choke also minimizes the "pop" when the set is turned on or off due to the sudden "biasing" of the speaker cone.

Troubleshooting the Circuit

The most common cause of trouble in this circuit is a shorted output transistor, Q3. When a new transistor is installed, a milliammeter should be connected in series with the collector to make sure that the current is not excessive. Many of these circuits operate normally with about 1 ampere (1000 ma) of collector current; however, in an automobile when the engine is running, the voltage to the radio may be around 14 volts or slightly higher and this overvoltage may cause the transistor current to rise too high.

A good method when installing a new output transistor is to shunt R6 with a 100 ohm potentiometer, as shown in the schematic. Make sure that the supply is 12v, then adjust R6 until the audio just starts to distort, then turn it back in the opposite direction until tone is clean at low volume. Measure the resistance of the pot (after removing it from the circuit) and shunt the 47 ohm resistor with this size resistor. This reduces the output current to a lower value without affecting the tone quality and pretty well assures that the radio will not have too much output transistor current even when the car's engine is running.

If placing the 100 ohm pot across the 47 ohm resistor causes distortion, then there is no need for a permanent shunt.

This method of adjusting output transistor current may also have to be used if either Q1 or Q2 is replaced with other than an exact replacement.

If you find that the output transistor current is already too low, shunt a 330 ohm resistor across R5 to increase the current rather than increasing the size of R6. If a 330 ohm resistor is not enough, use a 270 ohm and check again, etc.

COMPLEMENTARY SYMMETRY OUTPUT CIRCUIT

Two transistors, one an NPN and the other a PNP, which have similar characteristics except for polarity can be used in a transformerless audio output or driver circuit. The big advantage of this circuit is that as a push-pull stage it can be driven by a single-phase amplifier. This is because when the input audio signal is positive-going the NPN transistor draws current and when the audio signal is negative-going, the PNP transistor draws current.

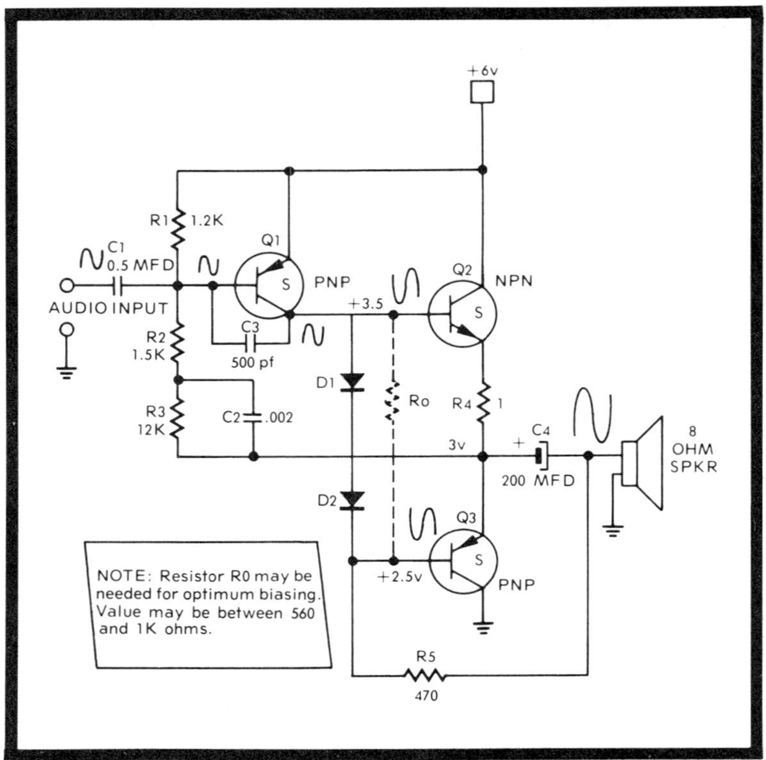

Fig. 17-19. Complementary symmetry output and driver.

In Fig. 17-19, diodes D1 and D2 provide a regulated source of bias, and because they are forward-biased, they have no effect on the audio signal. Collector current for Q1 is through the 470-ohm resistor, R5, and through the diodes. Instead of being tied to ground, R5 is tied to the "hot" side of the speaker voice coil. This results in some inverse feedback and helps to improve the frequency response of the circuit. (Sometimes the drop across the two silicon diodes may be slightly more than is required for optimum biasing of the two output transistors, and if so, a resistor may be placed across the diodes.) The output resistor Ro is selected to provide good fidelity with reasonably small idling current.

To see how the circuit works, let's follow an audio signal from the input. When the audio cycle goes negative, Q1 draws more current since it is a PNP transistor. This in turns means more current through R5, which means a more positive voltage on the bases of Q2 and Q3. Since Q2 is an NPN, a more positive voltage on its base will cause it to draw more current and to charge capacitor C4 through the speaker voice coil. The charging of the capacitor causes the voice coil to move either in or out. The more positive voltage on Q3 has cut it off since it is a PNP transistor.

On the positive half of the audio input signal, the collector voltage on Q1 goes negative, turning off Q2 but turning on the PNP, Q3. Now capacitor C4 discharges through Q3 and the speaker cone moves in the opposite direction.

Note that the DC bias for Q2 is about 0.5 volt positive with respect to its emitter, and the bias for Q3 is about 0.5 volt negative with respect to its emitter.

The bias for Q1 is supplied through an RC network, C2-R3 and R2. This is a bias compensating network as well as a circuit to reduce the high "hissy" frequencies by feeding back more high frequencies than lower frequencies by virtue of the size of C2. C3 from the collector to base of Q1 also affects the "tone" of the audio signal. Without the reduction of the high frequency signals, especially those near the upper limit of hearing, the wide frequency range of the circuit could easily cause instability and oscillations. These oscillations may be above the audio range but they will cause the audio signal to sound "raspy" because of the upsetting effect on the transistor bias.

Some early circuits of this general type were designed to use a silicon NPN transistor for Q2 and a germanium PNP for Q3, and they worked well. For such a circuit, only one diode was necessary.

Note that the diodes can be replaced with a resistor of the correct size (usually 100 ohms or less). But diodes provide some thermal compensation, because the hotter they become the lower their resistance, the result being lower bias on the output transistors and a reduction of output transistor current which would otherwise have a tendency to increase with higher ambient temperatures.

An 8-ohm speaker is shown, but many portable radios using a similar circuit may use speakers with impedances of 45 ohms or higher. An 8 ohm can be used to replace the 45-ohm speaker but volume will suffer slightly and current drain from the batteries, when used, will be somewhat higher as a rule.

Troubleshooting the Circuit

This circuit is similar to other direct-coupled circuits in that DC measurements when properly interpreted can isolate almost any trouble except an open capacitor.

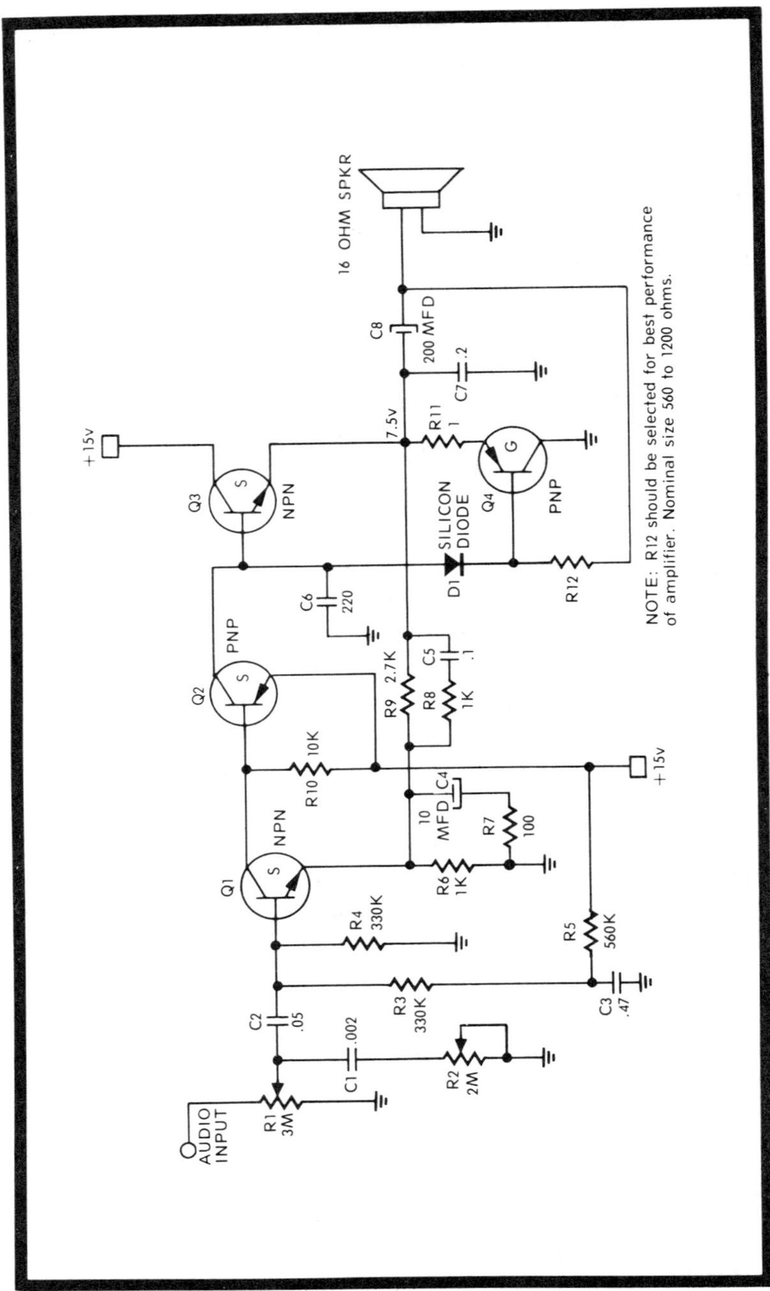

Fig. 17-20. Direct-coupled phono amplifier.

As an example, suppose Q3 shorts, what would happen? With Q3 shorted, the 3 volts at the emitter of Q3 would be zero, and the bias on Q1 would drop to zero. This would drop the collector current of Q1 to zero and the voltage at the collector would be zero measured to ground, which in turn means zero bias for Q2 and it would be cut off.

Suppose Q2 should short, what would happen? With Q2 shorted, the emitter of Q2 would be at 6 volts which in turn would apply a high positive bias to Q1 collector. Collector current of Q1 would increase, and the voltage on the bases of the output transistors would go more positive. Additional positive bias on Q3 would cut it off. This circuit then is self-protecting; should an output transistor short, the other transistor will be zero biased or even reverse-biased.

If one of the output transistors opens, the other transistor will receive no DC voltage and so it cannot work either.

If Q1 should short, the voltage on the bases of Q2 and Q3 will go highly positive. This will cut off Q3. It would at first seem to bias Q2 on heavily; but because Q3 is cut off, there is no DC path through which Q2 can conduct and so it is protected against any overbias condition. As a matter of fact, the emitter of Q2 will rise to 6 volts or nearly so because Q3 is open and because the Q2 base voltage will be near 6 volts.

DIRECT-COUPLED PHONO AMPLIFIER WITH COMPLEMENTARY SYMMETRY OUTPUT

Fig. 17-20 is a complete circuit using the principles discussed in the text for Fig. 17-18. This circuit uses one germanium transistor and one silicon transistor as the complementary pair in the output. The bias regulation is by one silicon diode D1. The value of R12 may vary depending upon the exact bias required and it should be selected to provide the best tone quality in the amplifier.

There are three direct-coupled stages and because of this the compensating bias fed back from the output stages is to the emitter of Q1 rather than to the base of Q2 as in the previous circuit. The bias for the first stage (Q1) is supplied by bleeder resistors R3, R4, and R5.

The input impedance of Q1 is quite high, as indicated by the small size of the input coupling capacitor C2 and by the size of volume control R1, 3 megohms.

To show how the bias compensation circuit works, suppose that for some reason the bias increases (goes more positive) on the base of Q1. Due to phase inversion, there will be a more negative voltage on the collector of Q1 and the base of Q2.

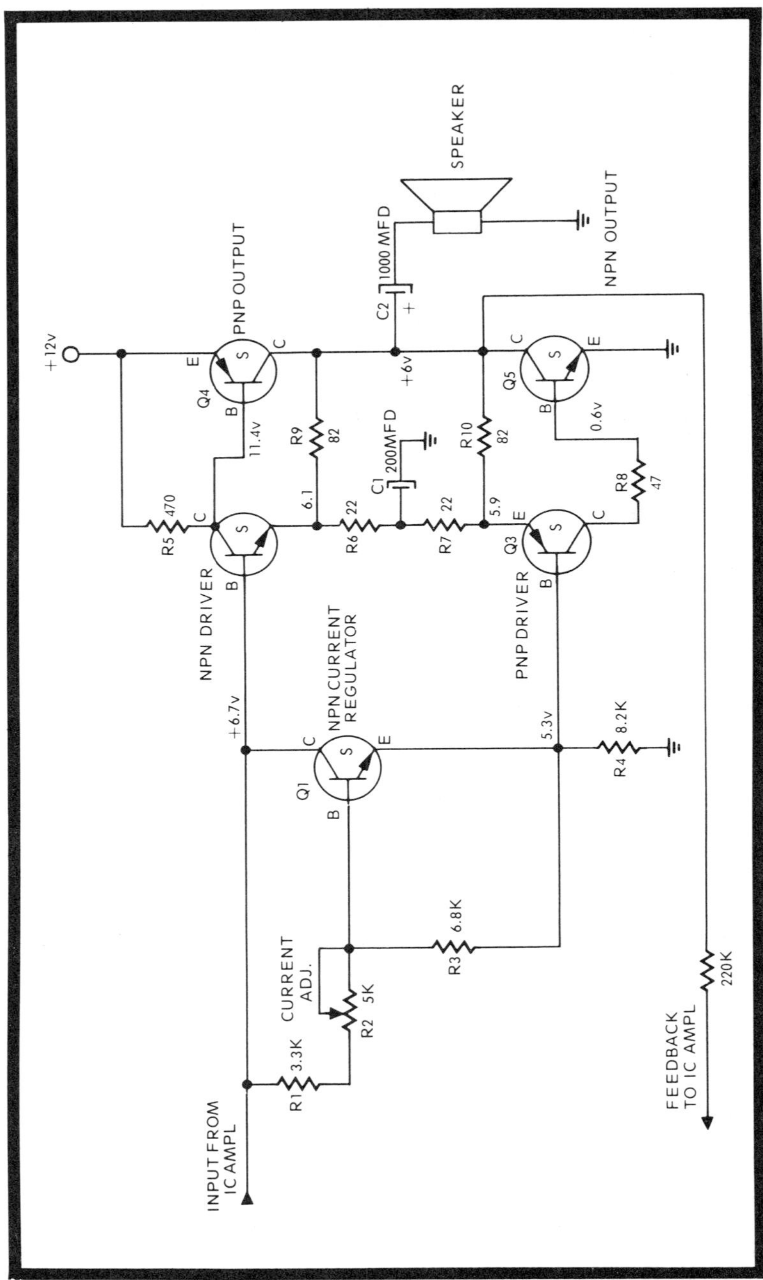

Fig. 17-21. Transformerless audio output amplifier used in auto radio.

More negative voltage on Q2 means a more positive voltage on its collector and on the bases of Q3 and Q4. A more positive voltage here reduces the current flow through Q4 and increases it through Q3. This means the voltage at the emitter of Q3 goes more positive (the emitter follows the base) and a more positive voltage is fed through R9 to the emitter of Q1. A more positive voltage on the emitter of Q1 reduces the amount of base bias on Q1 because a more positive emitter has the same effect as a more negative base, and this compensates for the original increase in bias. For example, if the original base voltage is 1.6 volts and the emitter is 1 volt, the base bias is 0.6 volts positive. If we hold the base voltage at 1.6 but increase the emitter voltage to 1.1, the base bias has now dropped to 0.5 volt. This is the same thing as holding the emitter voltage at 1 and reducing the base voltage to 1.5.

Troubleshooting the Circuit

Refer to discussion associated with Fig. 17-18.

TRANSFORMERLESS AUDIO OUTPUT AMPLIFIERS, HIGH-POWER, CURRENT-REGULATED

The circuit in Fig. 17-21, using silicon transistors, is in reality two complementary symmetry circuits using a PNP-NPN driver and a PNP-NPN output. Q1 (current regulator) is a forward-biased NPN transistor which establishes the bias difference for Q2 and Q3, the same as is done with a diode or resistors in other similar circuits. The advantage of using a transistor is that the equivalent resistance can be varied by a simple bleeder circuit in the base bias circuit. Adjusting R2 then establishes the bias for Q1 which in turn establishes the DIFFERENTIAL in bias for Q2 and Q3, which in turn, because of direct-coupling, establishes the bias for output transistors Q4 and Q5.

Q1 does not amplify any audio signal. It does provide some temperature compensation for the circuit since with more heat Q1 will tend to have slightly less resistance from collector to emitter and thus slightly reduce the bias for Q3 and Q5.

The speaker output capacitor (C2) is large as compared to previously described circuits of this type. This is because the speaker impedance is lower, as is the output impedance of the amplifier, so this means more current flow through the capacitor and results in the need for a 1000 mfd capacitor, especially to pass the low frequencies.

Troubleshooting the Circuit

The current adjustment control, R2, is adjusted so that the voltage at the collector junction of the output transistors is exactly half the power supply voltage. If the tone quality of the amplifier is okay with this adjustment then it is reasonable to assume that the amplifier circuit is normal.

If trouble does occur in the amplifier, only an open capacitor could cause a problem that would not be indicated by DC readings on the transistor terminals.

If C1 should open, the amplifier output would drop significantly due to the degeneration effect of Q2 on Q3 and vice versa. For example, without C1, when the voltage on the Q2 base went more positive, the Q2 emitter would follow and go more positive. This in turn would apply a more positive voltage to the PNP Q3 emitter, thus increasing its current also. In other words, the current through Q2 and Q3 would increase simultaneously, making the current through Q4 and Q5 increase at the same time, and the speaker output would be zero. This kind of circuit can only work if the output transistors operate on alternate half cycles of audio and give a push-pull effect to the voice coil of the speaker by charging and discharging C2 through the speaker.

If C2 opens, there will be little if any output. If it does not completely open there may be output but it will have a "tinny" sound totally lacking in bass notes.

A quick check for either C1 or C2 is to shunt a known good electrolytic across the suspected one, making sure that the polarity is correct. For a shunt check only, a 100 mfd capacitor with a rating of 10 volts or more is suitable. If either capacitor is open, a 100 mfd capacitor shunted across it will make a very significant improvement in the output signal.

If either of the output transistors (Q4 or Q5) should short (a fairly common occurrence for output transistors of some types especially) then the voltage at the positive side of C2 will be either near zero or near the source voltage. For example, if Q4 shorts, the voltage will be near 12 volts (assuming 12 volts as the source as shown here) and if Q5 shorts the voltage will be near zero.

What if Q2 should short? This would mean that the output transistor, Q4, would have high bias (only an 82 ohm resistor between collector and base) and so the voltage at the plus side of C2 would seem as if it should rise to nearly 12 volts. However, because of the short, the emitter voltage on Q3 would go more positive, increasing the current of the PNP transistor and increasing the current of Q5 so that both output transistors would be drawing more than normal current. Therefore, depending upon power supply current and the transistors themselves, a short of Q2 could result in damage to both output transistors. The same is true if Q3 should short.

QUASI-COMPLEMENTARY SYMMETRY OUTPUT

Fig. 17-22 uses two NPN output transistors, Q5 and Q6, driven by an NPN-PNP combination, Q3 and Q4. Q2 is a bias-set transistor with characteristics similar to the output transistors so that it automatically compensates for bias changes due to heat. Q1 is the predriver transistor.

Let's follow a signal from the base of Q1 to the speaker. For sake of explanation we will start with a negative-going signal. The negative-going signal is inverted by Q1 and becomes an amplified positive-going signal. The positive-going signal tends to turn off NPN transistor Q4, but it is also fed through the bias resistor (which is heavily forward-biased) to the base of Q3, increasing Q3 current. Q3 is an emitter follower, so the signal at the base of Q5 is also positive-going. Q5 is "turned on" and C4 charges through the transistor, R14 and the speaker, moving the speaker cone in one direction.

Going back to the input, when the input signal goes positive, the collector of Q1 goes negative as does the base of Q4. This negative-going signal is inverted by Q4 and becomes a positive-going signal on Q6. Now capacitor C4 is discharged through Q6 to ground and the speaker cone moves in the opposite direction.

The bias for Q1 obtained from the emitter-collector junction of Q5 and Q6 (positive side of C4) provides not only an inverse audio feedback but also a self-regulating DC bias.

The advantage of using a transistor (Q2) instead of a diode is that the bias can be manually adjusted easily to provide the correct idling current for the circuit. This particular circuit has an idling current of about 10 to 15 ma and the bias adjustment is set so that between 0.01 and 0.015 volt is dropped across the 1 ohm resistor R10.

Capacitors C2, C3, C5 and resistor R11 all help to shape the final output waveform and to compensate the circuit so that its output is essentially flat over the audio spectrum. Tone controls are provided in preamplifier circuits not shown.

Troubleshooting the Circuit

This circuit is DC-coupled and therefore its troubles can almost always be found best by taking DC voltage

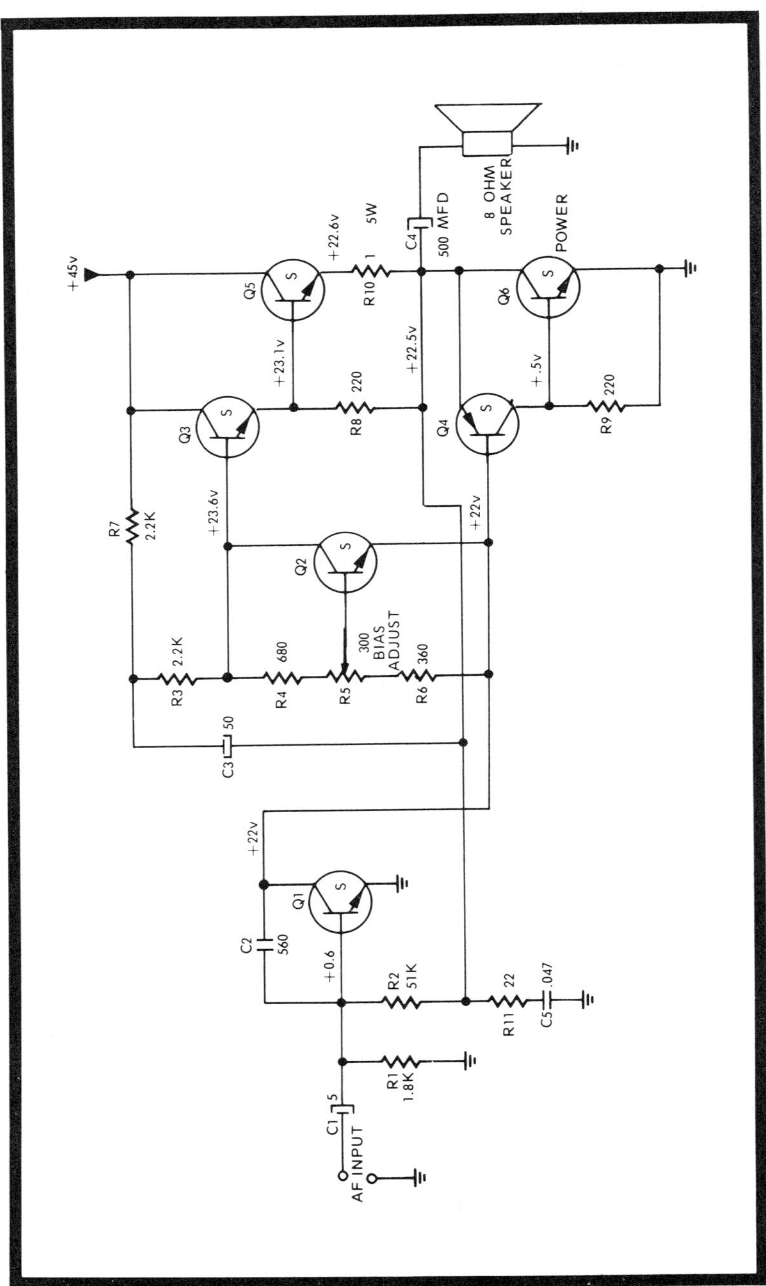

Fig. 17-22. Quasi-complementary symmetry output.

measurements. Only an open capacitor could cause a problem that would not be indicated by DC measurements, and only an open C4 would cause a serious reduction in volume. However if C2 should open, the circuit may have a tendency to squeal or oscillate especially when the tone control circuits are set for maximum treble in the preamplifiers.

To check for an open capacitor, shunt the suspected capacitor with a known good one, and if the capacitor is electrolytic, be sure to note polarity.

If the output circuit is dead, measure the voltage at the emitter-collector junction of the output transistors (positive side of C4) and see if it is close to **half** the source voltage measured at the collector of Q5. If the voltage is zero or nearly so, it could mean a shorted Q6, a shorted C4 (disconnect speaker to check for shorted C4, if voltage returns to normal C4 is shorted) or a shorted Q4. If the voltage is near the source voltage, it could mean a shorted Q5 or Q3 or both.

If the voltage is near zero at the collector of Q6 but nearly normal at the emitter of Q5, check R10, the 1 ohm resistor, for an open. If R10 is open, be sure to check the transistors for shorts.

If the bias adjustment (R5) will change the voltage across R10 from near zero to about 0.03 volt or slightly more, you can pretty well assume that Q2, Q3, Q4, Q5, and Q6 and the associated circuitry is normal (except of course for an open C4).

DC POWER SUPPLIES

DC power supplies that operate from the AC mains range from the simple half-wave rectifier to a complex amplifier-regulated unit sporting several transistors and one or more zener diodes. The complex units have somewhat better regulation, of course, but it is a truism that the more parts involved, the more service problems that are likely to occur.

The simple power supply does a very acceptable job so long as it feeds circuits which are little affected by slight changes in voltage, such as RF, IF, and AF amplifiers. Circuits which need more stable voltage include oscillators of all sorts, with higher frequency oscillators ordinarily being more voltage-sensitive than lower frequency ones. Even oscillators work acceptably from simple power supplies if the supply is not affected by some other varying load, and if input line voltage is fairly constant.

The filter capacitor values are chosen to provide whatever degree of filtering the designer feels is adequate. Low-current power supplies use the simplest filtering system, while higher-current supplies may use one or more sections of resistance-capacitance or inductance-capacitance filtering. Also, higher-current power supplies may use electronic filtering, a system where the gain of a transistor is used to amplify the filtering action of a capacitor; for example, a transistor with a gain of 20 can be connected in a circuit to make a 100 mfd capacitor have the same effect as a 2000 mfd capacitor.

There are many ways to regulate a DC power supply so that its output voltage will not be significantly affected even though the power line voltage or the DC current drawn from the power supply fluctuates considerably. The zener diode is the standard reference used for power supply regulation and often it is used alone as a regulator. The zener is a reverse-connected diode that "breaks down" at some specific voltage, determined at the time of manufacture. For example, a 6.3-volt zener will always have a 6.3-volt drop across it if connected properly in a circuit.

Fig. 18-1 shows a zener circuit. The half-wave power supply is filtered by an RC pi network (C1, C2, and R1). The 470-ohm resistor, R3, drops the voltage for the 6.3 volt source. The 10 ma required by the source would produce a 4.7-volt drop across R3 and without the zener the voltage would be about 11.3 volts. But with the zener, which conducts to maintain a 6.3-volt drop across its terminals, the voltage at the output is dropped to 6.3 volts because the zener current is slightly over 10 ma. If the load requirement should rise to, for example, 12 ma, the current through the zener drops by 2 ma, thereby maintaining the same 6.3 volt drop across itself. On the other hand, if the load current drops, the zener current increases to compensate and hold the voltage steady. The capacitor C3 across the zener is useful to bypass noise signals on the 6.3-volt line and prevent noise from being coupled to some other circuits which the line feeds. It also helps to eliminate any possible noise caused by the zener itself due to its regulatory activities.

A SIMPLE HALF-WAVE POWER SUPPLY

It is virtually impossible to make a simpler power supply than the one shown in Fig. 18-2. It has a step-down transformer, a single diode, and a single filter capacitor. This circuit or one very similar to it is used in thousands of

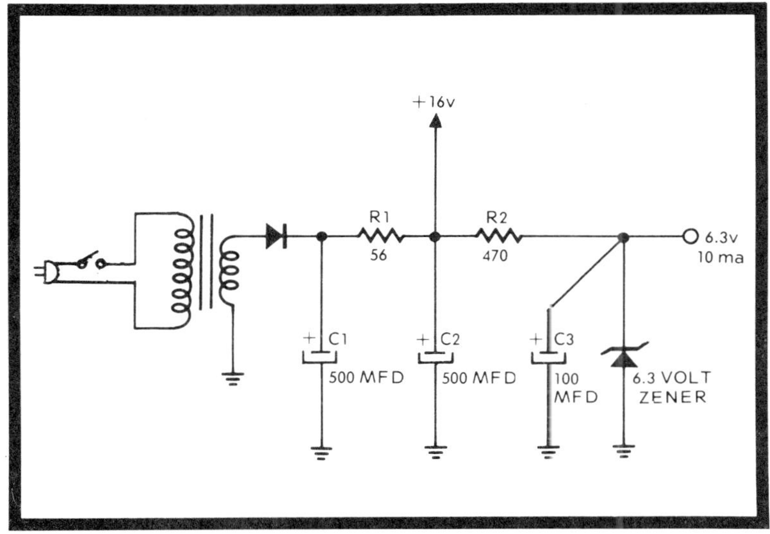

Fig. 18-1. Half-wave rectifier with zener diode control of 6.3v output.

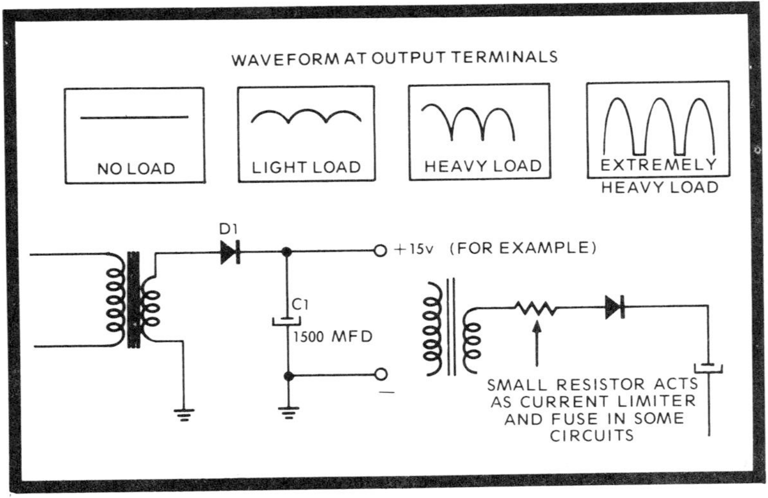

Fig. 18-2. A simple half-wave power supply.

phonograph amplifiers, especially small portable stereo phonographs.

For technicians familiar with tube power supplies, or power supplies for tube circuits rather, the use of a single filter capacitor is unthinkable because of hum. But most tube circuits worked class A, that is, current remained constant and quite high.

Hum in a power supply is a function directly related to the amount of current drawn from it. A power supply such as this one, with no load, has no hum. The capacitor charges up to the peak value and since there is no current drawn from it, it stays at that point and there is no hum (check with an oscilloscope if you doubt). Even with a little current, the hum is virtually nonexistent since the capacitor can supply the current with but slight discharge. But if a large amount of current is drawn, the filter capacitor voltage is discharged considerably before the next positive pulse from the rectifier comes along to charge it up again.

Audio amplifiers for transistors generally operate class B, which means that the amplifier current is dependent upon the amount of drive or volume. At low volume settings, the amplifier draws little current and so draws little current from the power supply, which means that the hum level is low even with simple filtering. At high volume levels, the amplifier and power supply current is high and hum is also high, but at high volume levels the hum is covered up or masked by the music and so is not objectionable at all. To repeat, at low volume settings where hum would be objectionable, the power supply current and hum level are low, and at high volume settings the hum is "swamped" by the signal itself.

Troubleshooting the Circuit

Troubleshooting such a circuit is usually quite easy. If the DC output voltage is low, and the amplifier it feeds has distortion or hum or both, place a known good electrolytic across C1 (watch the polarity), and see if the trouble is not cured.

If the diode should short, the low voltage of the circuit and the DC resistance of the transformer winding generally combine to prevent damage, although the transformer may get rather warm. If the designer feels there is a danger of fire, should D1 or C1 short, he will insert a small resistor in series with the diode and transformer winding, or sometimes between the diode and C1. The main purpose of a small resistor is to act as a fuse in case of trouble and burn in two, but it also acts as a current limiter when the power supply is first turned on. (When the circuit is "cold," the filter is discharged completely, and turning on the power supply causes a sudden rush of current from the diode to try and charge the capacitor. This sudden rush can overload the diode and burn it out. If the DC resistance of the transformer is not high enough to act as a limiter, then the resistor in series also performs this function as well as preventing fire.)

Almost any rectifier diode can be used here for a replacement so long as it has a current rating high enough for the device being powered. For most portable phonographs, a 100-ma rectifier is more than sufficient. However, a few high-powered portables require rectifiers with current ratings of 500 ma or more.

FULL-WAVE POWER SUPPLIES

The full-wave power supply output is about half as hard to filter into a smooth DC than the half-wave power supply output because the filter system receives a charge from the power line at twice the rate. In Fig. 18-3(A), first diode D1 conducts when the upper side of the secondary is positive and charges the filter capacitor, then on the next half cycle when diode D1 cannot conduct, the lower lead of the secondary is positive and diode D2 conducts and charges the capacitor. Because one diode conducts regardless of whether the AC alternation is

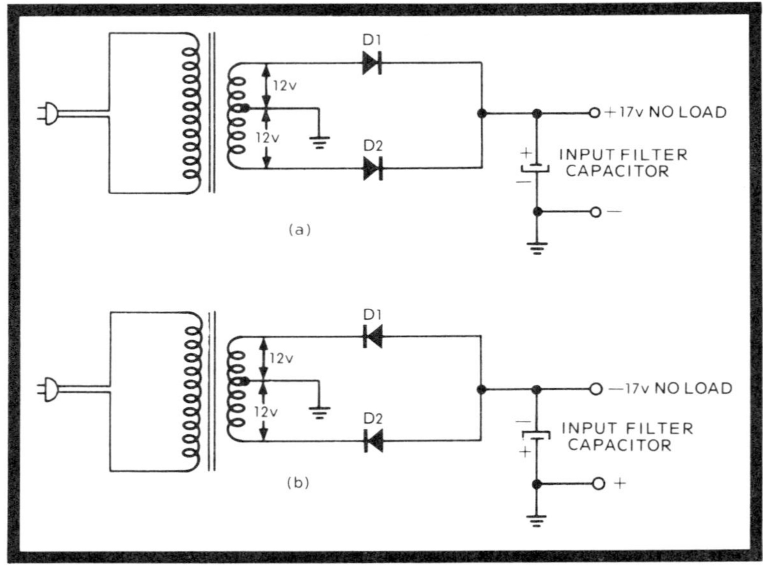

Fig. 18-3. Full-wave power supplies.

positive or negative, the conduction occurs at twice the frequency and so for a 60 Hz line frequency the ripple output is 120 Hz. (The circuit in Fig. 18-3(B) operates similarly, with the polarities reversed, of course.)

With no load, either the half-wave or the full-wave supply will have a DC voltage output equal to the AC input multiplied by 1.414 (the peak voltage is 1.414 times the rms measured voltage); thus with 12 volts AC input the output will be about 17 volts. Therefore, the voltage rating of the input filter capacitor must exceed this peak voltage, and in this circuit a capacitor rated at around 25 volts would likely be used. The size of the filter capacitor is entirely dependent upon the amount of hum that can be tolerated in the DC output. If current is low, the filter capacitor will also be fairly low in capacitance, and as a matter of fact, if current is low it is highly probable that a half-wave rectifier circuit will be used instead of the full-wave since the half-wave type is simpler and less expensive. The main advantage of full-wave rectification is decreased ripple and therefore smaller value filter capacitors may be used.

Troubleshooting the Circuit

If either of the diodes shorts, it will place an effective short circuit across the power transformer secondary and the transformer will burn up if it is not fused in either the primary or secondary circuit.

Sometimes a designer will use resistors in series with the diodes to act as fuses since if a short occurs the high current through the resistors will cause them to burn and open.

If the input filter capacitor opens, the DC voltage output will drop drastically. The output will also have high ripple or hum. If the input filter shorts, the DC voltage will of course drop to zero, but again the power transformer will burn up unless protected by some kind of fusing. Normally, a power transformer will not burn out unless subjected to some overload, so if a transformer burns, be sure to check the diodes and filter capacitors or other load which may have been the cause.

FULL-WAVE BRIDGE RECTIFIER

The full-wave bridge rectifier in Fig. 18-4 uses two more diodes than the conventional full-wave circuit, but does not require a center-tapped transformer secondary. In the conventional full-wave rectifier circuit, just discussed, to have a 17 volt (unloaded) output, the transformer must be a 24 volt AC transformer with a center tap which in effect makes two 12 volt AC windings in series. In the bridge, the transformer secondary need only be a single 12 volt winding.

The circuit works this way: When the upper lead on the secondary goes positive, the lower lead is going negative. This means that in "A," diodes D2 and D3 conduct, D2 making the ground negative and D3 making the output line positive. On the next half cycle, with the upper lead of the secondary negative and the lower lead positive, diode D1 conducts negative to ground, and D4 conducts positive to the output line. So in each case the output line is positive and the ground side is negative, and as in the conventional full-wave power supply, the output ripple is at 120 Hz for a 60-Hz power line input.

The DC output voltage without a load will be the same as the peak voltage in the AC wave, which as shown here, would be about 17 volts for a 12 volt AC input. See inset "C" in Fig. 18-4.

Inset "A" shows how a bridge rectifier is often drawn on schematics. Inset "B" is another way a bridge circuit may be drawn.

Troubleshooting the Circuit

As in the conventional full-wave circuit, the bridge will draw heavy current if any one of the diodes should short, and

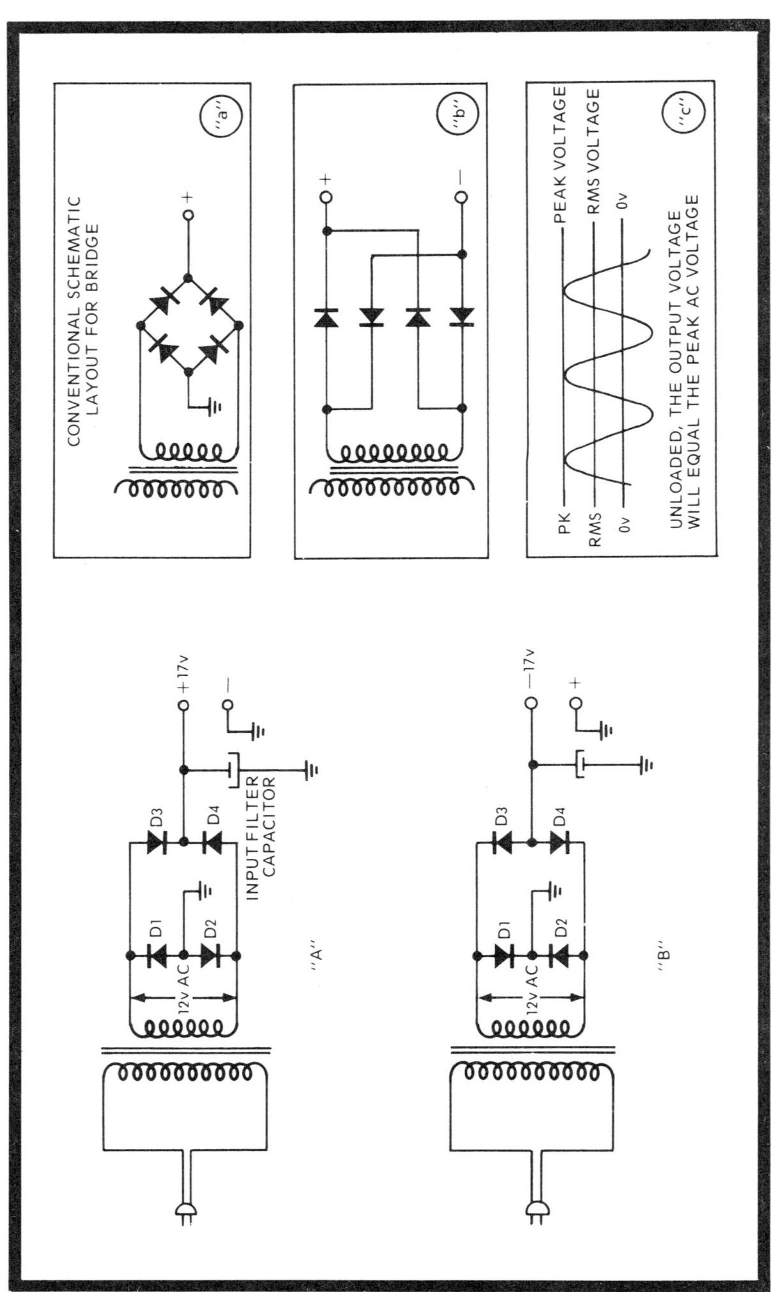

Fig. 18-4. Full-wave bridge rectifier.

unless some sort of fuse protection is provided, the transformer will likely be burned out.

An open diode will not cause the supply to stop working but will increase the hum output since the circuit will now operate at half-wave with the ripple frequency at only half speed.

An open input filter capacitor, as for any power supply circuit, will cause increased hum and lowered DC output voltage. A shorted filter capacitor, like a shorted diode, will damage the power transformer unless some method of fusing is used.

VOLTAGE DOUBLERS

It is possible to get twice (or even three or four times or more) voltage from a power supply by charging capacitors to the peak voltage and then rectifying the next cycle and adding this voltage to the previous one. The easiest way to understand this effect probably is by examining Fig. 18-5A. If D1 and C1 were eliminated and the negative side of C2 grounded, we

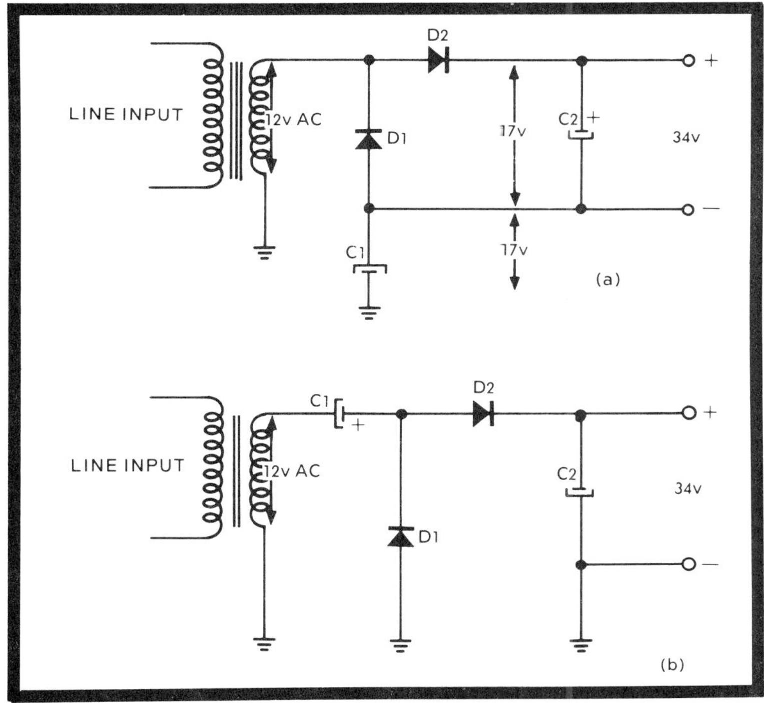

Fig. 18-5. Voltage doublers.

would have a simple half-wave rectifier with an unloaded output equal to the peak of the AC input, i.e., 17 volts in this particular circuit. By connecting D1 and C1 into the circuit, a negative 17 volts will be developed across C1. By adding the two supplies in series we have a +17 volts and a -17 volts or a total of 34 volts in all between points + and -.

The disadvantage of the circuit in (A) is that neither the negative side of the supply nor the positive side is grounded, in other words, the + and - points are floating above ground (which is useful in certain circuits). The circuit in (B) is one that does have one extremity (-) of the power supply grounded. In this circuit D1 charges C1 to 17 volts positive when the ground end of the transformer secondary is positive. On the next half cycle, when the upper side of the secondary is positive, diode D2 conducts in series with the +17 volts already on C1, developing another 17 volts which is added to the first 17 volts to make 34 volts across C2.

The doubler circuit is not often used in transistor circuits; usually the designer selects the transformer to match the voltage output he wants, because with transistors, higher current is often important and to have high current flow in a doubler, the capacitors must have high capacity. (But it certainly is feasible to use doublers if about twice as much voltage is needed than can be derived from a transformer that some manufacturer may be oversupplied with.)

Servicing the doubler is the same as for any other supply. The most common trouble is a defective capacitor or diode. If either C1 or C2 should short, the transformer will most likely be damaged unless it has some form of fuse protection. If capacitor C1 opens, the output will drop drastically. Often, capacitor C1 may be open when cold, but tend to start working when warmer. This can result in a high hum level and low output of whatever equipment is powered which tends to start working normally after several minutes of operation. The same symptom can happen if C2 should develop this open-cold trouble.

Tripler and quadrupler circuits are possible but their efficiency tends to drop in direct relation to their increased complexity, so rarely will you find a circuit of this type in a power supply circuit, although quite possibly in circuits where a high voltage, low current output is required from a solid-state circuit.

SIMPLE POWER-SUPPLY FILTERS

A single filter capacitor may be all that is needed if current drawn from the power supply is low, or if there is little or no amplification following the circuit which is supplied, such as to the output audio stages. However, any small ripple in the power supply that is fed to an earlier audio stage will be amplified by the stage and result in considerable hum in the output.

As shown in Fig. 18-6, a resistor (A) or choke (B) in series with the DC supply line and a second filter capacitor (called the output capacitor) provide additional smoothing, and most home entertainment units have at least one or more of this type circuit, and often a combination of both. The resistor method works well if the current through it is not so large that the voltage drop across the resistor reduces the supply voltage below that required. The filter choke method provides the best filtering for high current circuits since the impedance to 60 or 120 Hz can be made high while keeping the DC resistance, and therefore the DC voltage drop, low. For example, the impedance of a typical filter choke at 120 Hz might be 2000 or 3000 ohms and the DC resistance might be no more than 10 to 20 ohms.

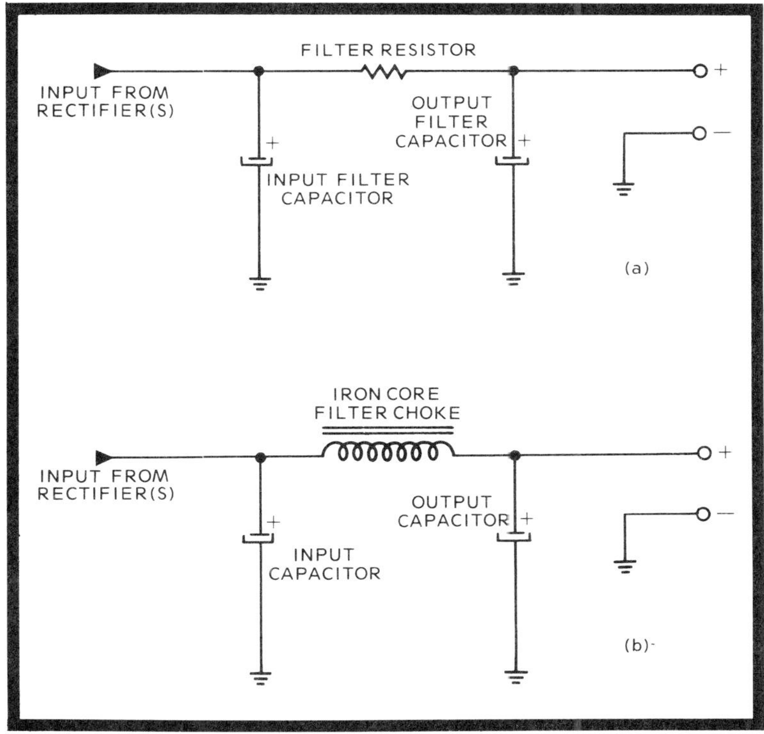

Fig. 18-6. Simple power-supply filters.

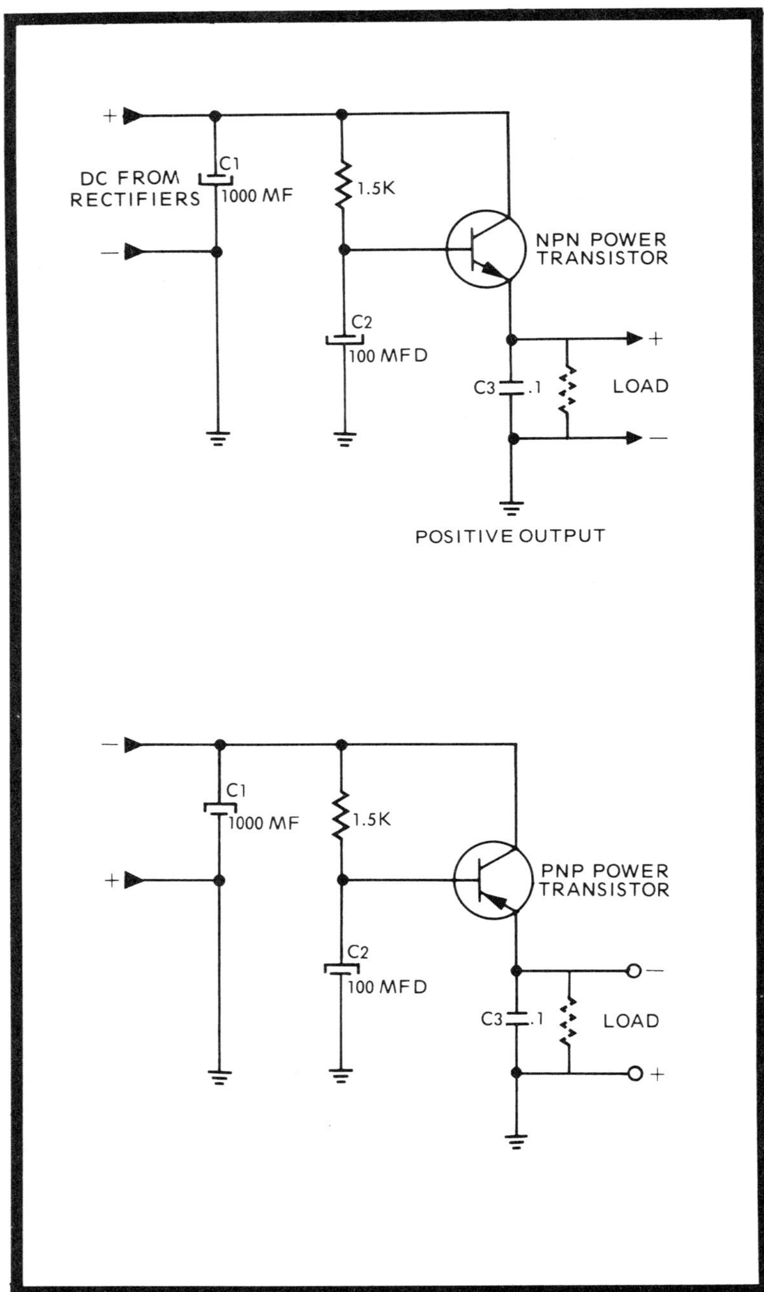

Fig. 18-7. Electronic filter (solid-state).

The size of the filter capacitors, the DC resistance and the impedance of the filter choke, or the size of filter resistor(s), is chosen to reduce the hum (or ripple) voltage to an acceptable low while still producing sufficient DC voltage to operate the powered circuit efficiently.

Troubleshooting the Circuit

The input filter capacitor, if it opens, reduces the DC voltage drastically but any other filter capacitor following the input capacitor has little if any effect on the DC voltage (unless it shorts).

If the filter resistor shows signs of overheating, the cause could be a shorted or leaky output filter capacitor and-or it could also be an excessive load.

Sometimes when the output filter capacitor shorts and a filter choke is used, the filter choke will overheat, developing shorted turns inside itself; this will reduce its inductive reactance drastically but still allow DC to pass normally. When the output filter capacitor is replaced and there is still hum in the circuit, temporarily replace the filter choke to see whether or not it is working properly, especially if the choke shows signs of overheating or smells of burnt wax or insulation.

ELECTRONIC FILTER CIRCUIT

With the advent of solid-state techniques, the need for a high-capacity filter circuit having fairly low series resistance inspired the electronic filter circuit. One of the simplest and yet quite effective ones is shown in Fig. 18-7. The idea here is that the filtered DC is applied through a resistor to the base of a power transistor with another small filter capacitor connected from the base to ground. The gain of the transistor amplifies the effect of the filter capacitor in the base circuit so that with a transistor beta of 50, a 100 mfd capacitor in the base becomes effectively a 5000 mfd capacitor in the emitter circuit.

This is how it works: If any ripple occurs on the load (emitter) of the transistor, a positive ripple reduces the transistor bias, which increases the transistor resistance and so the positive voltage reaching the emitter is reduced. On the other hand, if the voltage goes less positive on the emitter, the transistor conduction increases because of its increased bias and more voltage is available to the emitter from the collector circuit.

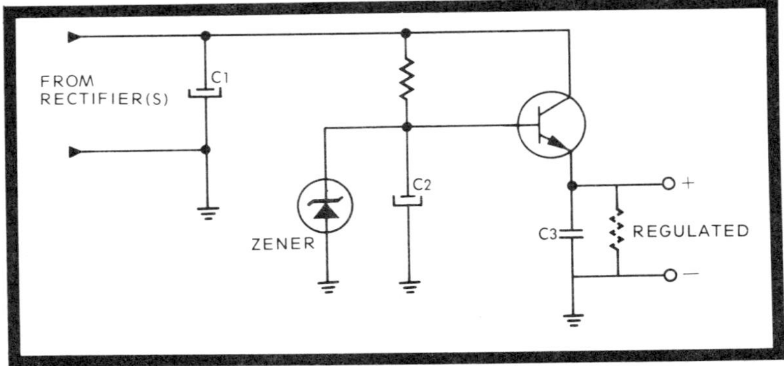

Fig 18-8. Regulated electronic filter.

The capacitor in the emitter circuit is not for filtering but to act as a bypass for high frequency signals which might be on the power supply line.

A similar circuit except with DC regulation is shown in Fig. 18-8. The difference here is the zener diode in the base circuit. This zener will hold the base at some fixed voltage and the action of the transistor will hold the emitter at this same voltage (minus the transistor bias of about 0.6 volt for silicon transistors).

Figs. 18-9 and 18-10 show similar circuits with variations. In Fig. 18-9, control in the base circuit makes the output voltage adjustable. The circuit in Fig. 18-10 uses two transistors in a Darlington circuit to provide additional gain and, consequently, improved filtering.

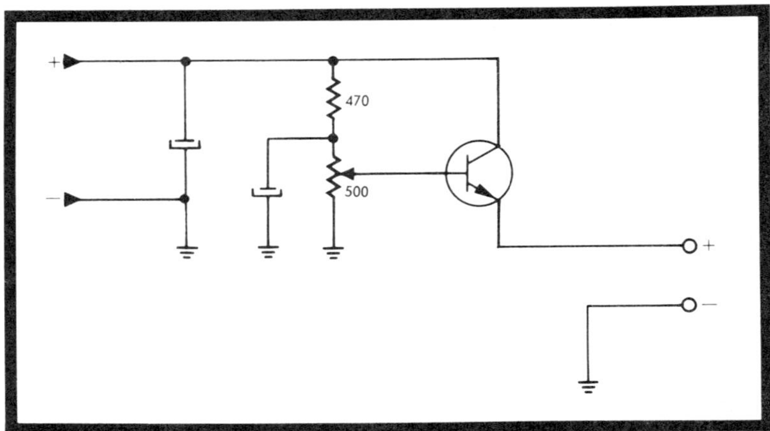

Fig. 18-9. Base control adjusts voltage output.

Troubleshooting the Circuit

The most common trouble here is either an open or shorted control transistor. If the transistor opens, the output voltage will be zero or nearly so. If the transistor shorts, the output voltage will be higher than normal and the collector and emitter voltage will be essentially the same.

Another cause for zero or nearly zero output voltage can be a changed value base resistor or a leaky base filter capacitor. Or where a zener diode is used, it may be shorted.

Low voltage can be caused by a heavy load on the emitter side, but in this case the transistor will likely become very much overheated and perhaps damaged, depending upon whether the power supply can furnish enough current through the rectifiers to destroy the transistor.

Excessive hum from this power supply can occur if the base capacitor opens, or if the transistor is shorted. Excessive ripple will also occur if C1 opens, and if this is the input filter capacitor (as it often will be), the output voltage will be low.

AN NPN-PNP ELECTRONIC FILTER CIRCUIT

The circuit in Fig. 18-11 is similar in many ways to those just described except that here a PNP power transistor is used to provide a positive output voltage. Q1 is the control transistor; it senses any change in the output voltage and in turn biases the output transistor, Q2. Suppose (for whatever reasons) the +30 volts tends to go a bit less positive; this applies increased bias to Q1 which in turn increases the

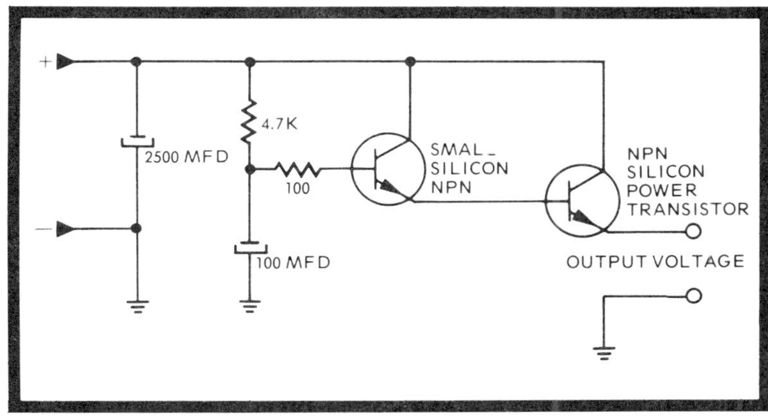

Fig. 18-10. Two-transistor Darlington circuit for additional gain and improved filtering.

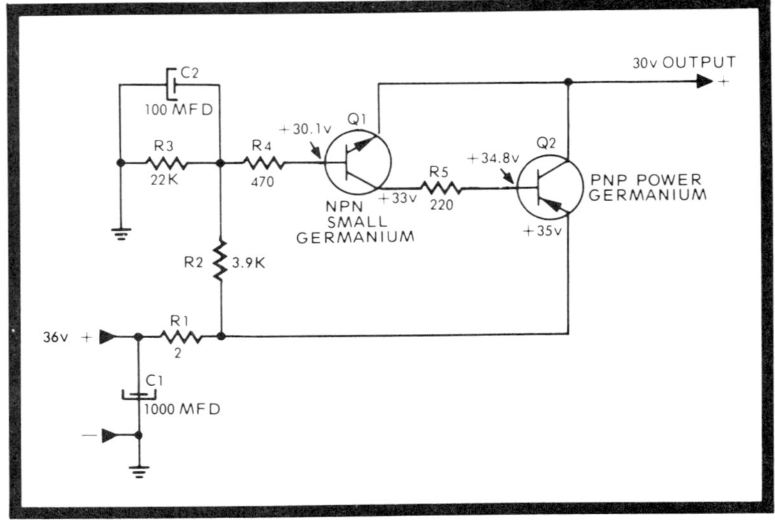

Fig. 18-11. NPN-PNP (germanium) electronic filter.

negative bias on Q2 and decreases its resistance. This decreased resistance allows additional current to flow to the +30 volt line and increases the positive voltage. Conversely, if the +30 volts increases, the circuit senses this and increases the resistance of Q2 and lowers the amount of voltage reaching the 30 volt line by increasing the voltage drop from the 36 volt source.

R1 is a series resistor which will limit current flow should a short occur in the output circuit. R4 and R5 are also current limiting resistors in case of circuit troubles. C1 is the input filter of the power supply. The effect of C2, the base filter capacitor, is amplified by the circuit so that it appears to the output circuit as several thousand microfarads.

Troubleshooting the Circuit

Trouble in this circuit will result in a significant change in the DC voltages around the circuit. Check the bias of the transistors between base and emitter. Check the total transistor voltage between collector and emitter. Under normal conditions, Q2 will have a drop across it of about 5 volts with the collector negative with respect to the emitter, assuming a transistor current of 500 ma which would cause a 1 volt drop across the 2 ohm resistor, R1. The voltage drop across Q1 will be around 3 volts in this circuit (with the collector more positive than the emitter since Q1 is an NPN transistor).

If Q1 should short there would be increased bias on Q2 (since now the collector of Q2 would be connected to its base through only a 220 ohm resistor) and the output voltage would increase. But filtering would decrease by a factor of around 100 times (depending upon the beta of Q1). If Q1 should open, there would be no bias on Q2 except whatever leakage Q2 has from collector to base. This would mean that the output voltage would drop considerably.

If Q2 should open, there would be little or no output voltage on the +30 volt line. If Q2 should short, the voltage output would increase to around 34 or 35 volts and hum would increase significantly, because of the lack of electronic filtering.

An open C2 will also cause an increase in output ripple but will not significantly affect the DC output on the +30 volt line. If C1 opens, the DC output voltage will drop drastically and ripple or hum will be severe, because it is the power supply input filter.

Check for open filter capacitors by shunting a known good capacitor across the suspected one, being careful to get polarities correct.

TAPE RECORDER OSCILLATORS

All except inexpensive "toy" recorders use a transistor oscillator to supply an "erase" voltage and also an "AC bias" to the recording head for tape recorders.

The erase voltage is necessary to clean the tape of any previous recording as a new recording is made. It is switched in automatically and to a separate erase head when the recorder switch is turned to "RECORD."

The AC bias is from the same oscillator but its level is considerably less than the amount used in erasing. The AC bias is applied to the RECORD head along with the audio voltage. This bias voltage "sets up" the tape so that the audio will be impressed at good fidelity. Without the bias voltage, the audio is distorted because of the nonlinearity that tape exhibits at low levels of magnetic fields. For example, at low levels, the tape might magnetize to a certain level with say 3 microamperes in the record head, but with 6 microamperes of head current, the magnetization level might be four times as much. By using an AC bias, various levels of audio signals will make a linear change in the total tape magnetization. To keep the AC bias from interfering with the audio, it must be at a frequency above the range of human hearing. Tape recorders use frequencies from around 40 kHz to 125 kHz or more. The higher frequencies generally are best but may also require more critical adjustment of level, and better head quality.

BIAS-ERASE OSCILLATOR NO. 1

Fig. 19-1 shows about as simple an oscillator as it is possible to design. Transformer T1 has a center-tapped primary which is fed at the center by the DC supply. The difference of phase between the upper and lower half is used to produce oscillation by feeding back a portion of the signal through C2 to the base of the transistor. C1 is the other part of a capacity "bleeder," and its value is chosen to provide the right amount of feedback to produce a sine-wave output.

The 39K resistor, R1, is the "turn on" bias for the transistor. It too is chosen for best waveform shape and stability.

The .01 mfd capacitor, C3, is a "tuning" capacitor which, along with the inductance of T1 and the load on T1, establishes the actual operating frequency, in this case about 45 kHz.

The output is usually fed directly to the erase head of the recorder. The output, fed generally through an RC network to the record head, is often adjustable so as to obtain the right amount of bias for least distortion and noise.

Troubleshooting the Circuit

Perhaps the best way to check the circuit would be with an oscilloscope, looking at the output waveform, which should be a sine wave. If it is a sine wave, this usually means that the circuit is working normally, since any serious defect will almost surely upset the waveform purity.

A voltmeter can be used also. Check the collector and the base voltages. If the voltages appear normal or nearly so, again check the base voltage and connect another .01 mfd capacitor across C3. If the transistor bias voltage changes, this is a good indication that the oscillator is working.

When a tape recorder seems to record but the playback is severely distorted, or if the previous recording on a tape is not

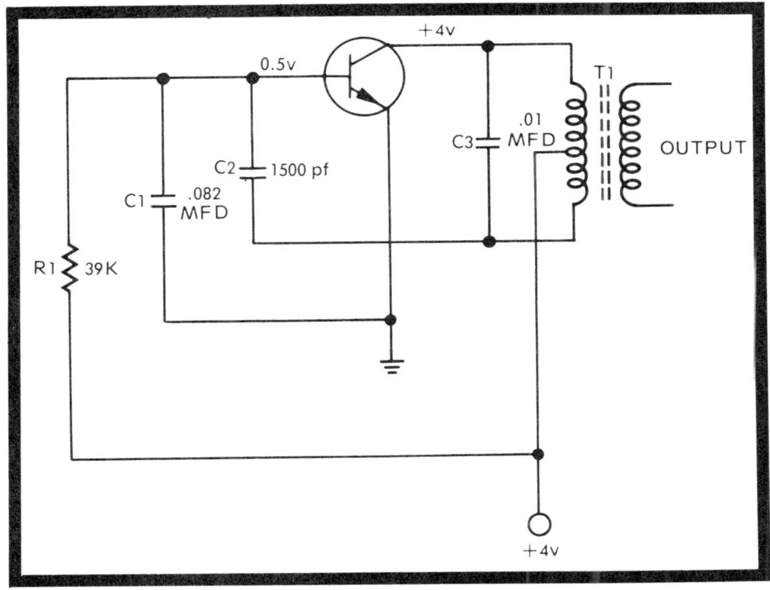

Fig. 19-1. Bias-erase oscillator 1.

erased, then the first place you will probably look is for trouble in the bias oscillator.

With an oscilloscope you can look at the signal going to the record head (with the recorder switched to RECORD). If you see changing audio only, then the bias oscillator is either not working or something is keeping the oscillator bias from reaching the record head. Normally, you should see a strong single-frequency sine wave, with only a "fuzziness" on the edges as you talk into the microphone, indicating that the AC bias is being "modulated" by the audio.

For DC checks, if the collector voltage is zero, check the DC supply voltage. If the supply voltage is normal, check transformer T1. If the supply voltage is zero, this could be because of a shorted oscillator transistor, assuming the remainder of the recorder seems to be working normally. (There is usually a resistor in the DC supply line going to the bias oscillator so a shorted oscillator transistor will have little effect on the remainder of the DC supply voltages.)

A lack of bias voltage, with the collector voltage normal, probably means an open 39K resistor R1, or it could mean a shorted C1 (rare).

Excessive bias, which could also cause lowered collector voltage, could be caused by leakage in C2. To determine if C2 is leaky, disconnect the base end and measure the voltage from this loose end to ground—it should be zero. Any DC voltage from the open lead of the capacitor to ground indicates leakage and the capacitor will have to be replaced. (Actually, it is quite hard to measure excessive bias when the emitter of a transistor is grounded, since the junction resistance of a transistor lowers as the voltage from base to emitter increases which tends to hold the voltage nearly the same but increasing the current flow. This is why the collector voltage reading might be more significant, and will be, if there is some resistance in the collector circuit back to the power supply so that the collector will make a significant voltage drop due to the high bias. If the collector voltage is low, and you remove one lead of C2 from the circuit, and the collector voltage increases significantly, replace C2.)

BIAS-ERASE OSCILLATOR NO. 2

The circuit in Fig. 19-2 is similar to the previous one, except that a bleeder bias circuit is used (this is a PNP germanium transistor), a protective emitter bias resistor is used, and a resistor in series (R4) with T1 and C1 is selected to provide the best waveform.

Another slight difference is that the secondary of the transformer is tuned instead of the primary (it really makes no difference since the impedances of both windings are reflected to one another through the mutual coupling of the two windings).

The output for the record head is taken through a small capacitor (C4) and usually there will be either a resistance or a trimmer capacity adjustment to provide the designer and technician with a means of adjusting the circuit for optimum voltage to the head.

The output for the erase head is taken from a tap on the tuned winding. This provides the higher-current source necessary so the erase head can do a "clean" job of freeing the tape of previously recorded material.

Troubleshooting the Circuit

Checking this circuit can be done in much the same way as described for circuit 1. Use an oscilloscope and check for good sine wave output. Lowered sine wave output can be caused by an open C2, although depending upon other circuit parameters, an open C2 may also cause a distortion of the waveform, but this is not too likely due to the small size of R2.

To check this circuit with a DC voltmeter, check the base bias and then short across the secondary of T1; the base bias

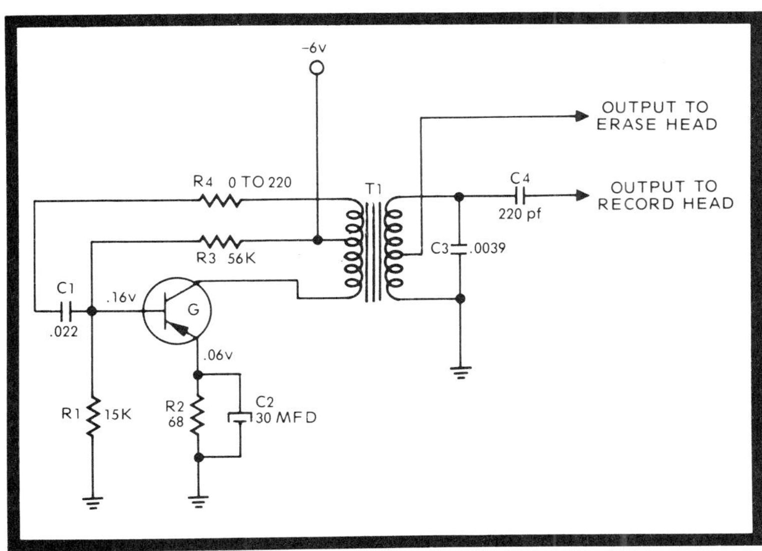

Fig. 19-2. Bias-erase oscillator 2.

should go up, indicating that the circuit has stopped oscillating. If there is no change in bias when T1 is shorted, the oscillator was not working in the first place.

If the oscillator frequency is high, very high, and seems to be erratic, check for an open C3. An open here, depending on the circuit, may cause oscillations to cease altogether. Because of the relatively low inductance of the heads, with C3 open, you may see a sine wave at the output of T1 but absolutely none reaching the heads, leading you to suspect trouble in the components between T1 and the head, rather than a too-high frequency.

Almost any audio germanium transistor can be used in this circuit as a replacement. Check after replacement, though, for a good clean waveform with a good shape. If it does not have such a waveshape, try changing R4. If this still does not get the right waveshape, you may want to juggle the size of R1, or try another replacement transistor.

PUSH PULL BIAS-ERASE OSCILLATOR

The push-pull circuit was an early favorite with transistor tape recorder designers. For reasons of economy probably, they have mostly been supplanted by the single-transistor oscillator, except in expensive recorders where the advantage of low harmonic distortion is considered worth the slightly higher expense of the push-pull type.

The feedback to the transistors is in the push-pull, of course, as well as the output. A center-tapped winding on T1 (Fig. 19-3), feeds a portion of the output signal back into the input to sustain the oscillations. Bias for the two transistors is supplied by the bleeder network, R2 and R3.

C1 and C2 both affect the output frequency of the oscillator, along with the inductance of the windings of T1.

The 10 ohm resistor, R1, in series with the two emitters, is a protective device. But more importantly here, it is also a stabilizing and wave-shaping device selected by the designer to get the desired output.

The decoupling circuit, used in most oscillators, is shown here (R5 and C4). The size of both R5 and C4 will vary considerably from design to design and depend to some extent on the value of the DC supply voltage as well as the desired voltage for the oscillator.

Note the 50K adjustment, R4, which is an initial factory adjustment to supply optimum AC bias to the record head. It should not have to be changed unless some major work is performed in the oscillator circuit, such as replacing T1, or the transistors, etc.

Troubleshooting the Circuit

Check the output with an oscilloscope. The output should be of the correct amplitude and should be a clean sine wave. The frequency of this oscillator is about 100 kHz but some push-pull oscillators will be higher in frequency than this, some lower. The exact frequency is often not as important as the right amplitude; any drastic change in frequency, however, will show up perhaps in serious audio distortion, which may be more noticeable at high frequencies and result in a sort of "muddy" sound.

In this circuit it is possible for the frequency to change drastically without perhaps affecting the waveshape seriously although it will likely affect the amplitude. This happens if either C1 (or C2) should open. If this happens, the other capacitor (C1 or C2) will continue to hold the circuit "tuned" but the output frequency will be considerably higher.

This push-pull circuit has a rather "hard" bias, that is, the small size of the bleeder resistors tends to hold the bias rather

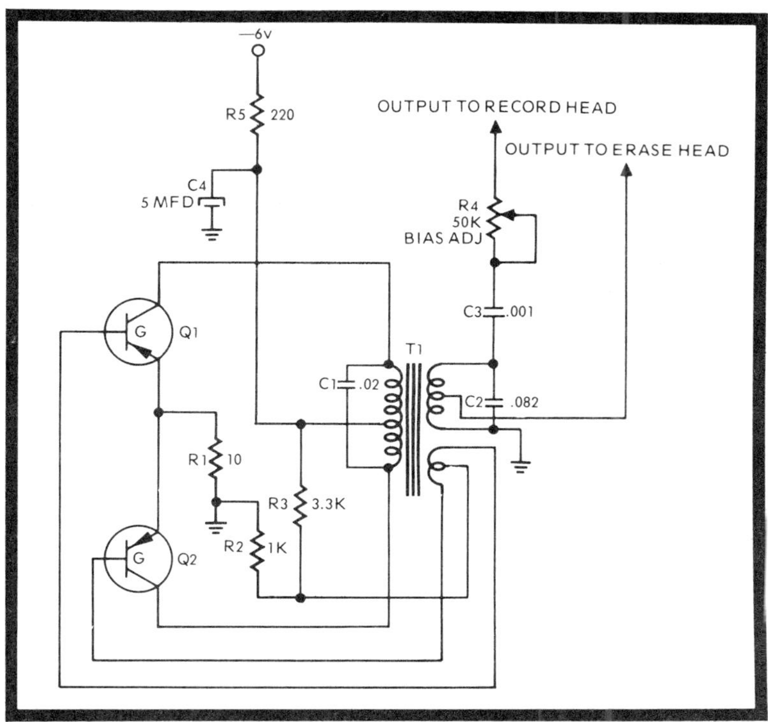

Fig. 19-3. Bias-erase oscillator 3 (push-pull).

constant whether or not the circuit is oscillating, making the reading of the DC bias not so significant a check as in the previous circuits, but still valid, if care is used. But the better method is to use the oscilloscope to find out if the circuit is working, and then use the DC voltmeter to find out which part may be defective.

You cannot check the transistors in this circuit with any degree of accuracy, as you can in many circuits, without disconnecting at least one, preferably both of the transistors, from the circuit. Because of the arrangement, and the low value of resistance of the collector and base coils on T1, if you try to read the diode action of Q1, for example, you would get the diode action even if Q1 were open because you are reading between the base and emitter of Q2 through the low resistance transformer windings.

Measuring the DC voltage at the emitter of Q1, of course, is also not conclusive because the emitter voltage is also the same for Q2.

One "quick and dirty" way you can check both transistors in-circuit to see if they are responding to bias is to measure the emitter voltage and then bring a heated soldering iron close to Q1 and see if the emitter voltage rises; if it does, then bring the iron close to Q2 and again check for an emitter voltage increase. Since these are germanium transistors, they are quite susceptible to heat change and the current through them increases markedly with additional ambient heat. Do not heat the transistor excessively or longer than for just a few moments, since you could possibly ruin the transistor due to the small size of R1. However, the small size of R2 also minimizes the effect of internal collector-to-base leakage by acting as a willing bleeder from base to ground.

A

B

C

G

H

I

J

K

L

M

N

T

V

X

Z